Introduction to
COMPLEX VARIABLES
AND APPLICATIONS

BY

RUEL V. CHURCHILL

Professor of Mathematics
University of Michigan

NEW YORK   TORONTO   LONDON

McGRAW-HILL BOOK COMPANY, INC.

1948

INTRODUCTION TO COMPLEX VARIABLES AND APPLICATIONS

XIII

THE MAPLE PRESS COMPANY, YORK, PA.

PREFACE

Theory of functions of a complex variable is a basic part of mathematical analysis. Its influence can be seen in almost every field of mathematics. In addition to its prominence in pure mathematics and its elegant logical structure, the theory represents one of the most powerful mathematical instruments of applied mathematicians, engineers, and physicists.

The first objective of this book is the presentation of a logical development of those parts of the classical theory which are most essential to the applications of the subject. Except for certain geometrical concepts that may be accepted as intuitively evident, the presentation here is intended to be rigorous and self-contained. The selection of the methods of proof and the arrangement of topics were made on the basis of simplicity and brevity, sometimes at some sacrifice of elegance. If the theory of residues and conformal mapping are to be emphasized in a one-semester course, the time that can be devoted to the earlier theory is limited and the development of that part must be fairly concise.

In addition to a substantial introduction to the theory, it is the second objective to give a brief introduction to the applications, including the uses of the residue theory and contour integrals in evaluating real integrals, and applications of conformal mapping to problems in potentials, steady temperatures, and flow of fluids. The applications of conformal mapping present one of the classical methods of solving boundary value problems in partial differential equations, restricted here to Laplace's equation with two independent variables. Thus the book serves as a companion volume to the author's books on "Fourier Series and Boundary Value Problems" and "Modern Operational Mathematics in Engineering," where the other two classical methods of solving linear boundary value problems are treated. In the second book further applications of complex variables are presented in connection with Laplace transforms.

The basic results are stated as theorems. Many examples and simple exercises are given to illustrate the theory and the applications. A short table of conformal transformations is presented in Appendix II. It is hoped that this novel feature will add to the usefulness of the book.

In the various stages of development, the first nine chapters have been used for several years at the University of Michigan as the text in a three-hour one-semester course. The classes are composed mainly of graduate students and seniors in physics, engineering, and mathematics. The students are expected to have completed the equivalent of one semester of advanced calculus.   Some of the simpler material is not covered in lecture form; the students are able to read many of the sections without difficulty. Portions of the last three chapters of the book can be included in a one-semester course.

The author is indebted to Profs. E. D. Rainville and W. Kaplan, both of whom used the manuscript as a textbook and made valuable suggestions.   Prof. Rainville's assistance in the writing of a portion of the manuscript is also gratefully acknowledged.   Prof. T. H. Hildebrandt read an early form of the manuscript and suggested numerous improvements.   The author wishes to acknowledge that assistance as well as Prof. Hildebrandt's cooperation in arranging for the continued use of the manuscript as a textbook.   The author is indebted to other colleagues and to the many students who have influenced the writing of the book, as well as to Betty Eastman for her able assistance with the typing of the manuscript.

RUEL V. CHURCHILL

ANN ARBOR, MICH.
October, 1948

TABLE OF CONTENTS

CHAPTER I

COMPLEX NUMBERS

1. Definition. A complex number z can be defined as an ordered pair of real numbers x, y that satisfies certain laws of operation. It is written in either of the two forms

$$z = x + iy \qquad \text{or} \qquad z = x + yi$$

where i is called the *imaginary unit*. As this notation suggests, when $y = 0$ the complex number z becomes the real number x; that is, complex numbers include all the real numbers,

$$x + 0i = x.$$

As a consequence, the laws of operation that are to be prescribed must reduce to laws of operations on real numbers when $y = 0$.

When $x = 0$ and $y = 1$, it is to be understood that z is the imaginary unit itself; that is,

$$0 + 1i = i.$$

The real multiples of i, $yi = 0 + yi$, are called *pure imaginary* numbers. When $y \neq 0$, the complex number $x + iy$ is often called an *imaginary number*.

The real numbers x and y are known as the *real* and *imaginary components* of the complex number z. They are also called the *real part* and the *coefficient of the imaginary part* of z. It is convenient at times to indicate real and imaginary components by the notation

$$\mathcal{R}(z) = x, \qquad \mathcal{I}(z) = y.$$

Two complex numbers

$$z_1 = x_1 + iy_1, \qquad z_2 = x_2 + iy_2$$

are equal if and only if their real components are equal and their imaginary components are equal:

$$z_1 = z_2 \qquad \text{implies} \qquad x_1 = x_2 \qquad \text{and} \qquad y_1 = y_2.$$

In particular, since $0 = 0 + 0i$, a complex number z is zero if and only if its real and imaginary components both vanish:

$$x + iy = 0 \qquad \text{implies} \qquad x = y = 0.$$

2. Fundamental Operations. Two further properties, the laws of addition and multiplication, are to be included in the definition of complex numbers. Let z_1 and z_2 be any two complex numbers,

$$z_1 = x_1 + iy_1, \qquad z_2 = x_2 + iy_2.$$

Their sum is the complex number whose real component is the sum of their real components and whose imaginary component is the sum of their imaginary components; that is,

$$(1) \qquad z_1 + z_2 = (x_1 + x_2) + i(y_1 + y_2).$$

The product of z_1 and z_2 is the complex number given by the formula

$$(2) \qquad z_1 z_2 = (x_1 x_2 - y_1 y_2) + i(x_1 y_2 + x_2 y_1).$$

When $z_1 = z_2 = i$, it follows that the product of the imaginary unit i by itself is -1; that is,

$$(3) \qquad i^2 = -1.$$

The law of multiplication (2) can be written down by simply expanding the product

$$(x_1 + iy_1)(x_2 + iy_2)$$

by the formal use of the operations on real numbers and replacing i^2 by -1. The definition (2) justifies this practical procedure.

We can define the operation of subtraction as the inverse of that of addition. Thus if the difference $z_1 - z_2$ is called z_3,

$$z_1 - z_2 = z_3,$$

then z_3 is the complex number that must be added to z_2 to produce z_1,

$$z_2 + z_3 = z_1.$$

In view of the definition (1) of addition, then

$$(x_2 + x_3) + i(y_2 + y_3) = x_1 + iy_1,$$

and consequently

$$x_2 + x_3 = x_1, \qquad y_2 + y_3 = y_1.$$

Solving for x_3 and y_3, we have the law of subtraction,

$$(4) \qquad z_3 = z_1 - z_2 = (x_1 - x_2) + i(y_1 - y_2).$$

We could of course prescribe this law at once; then it would appear as a consequence that subtraction is the inverse of addition.

Division is the inverse of the operation of multiplication; that is,

$$\frac{z_1}{z_2} = z_3 \qquad \text{implies} \qquad z_2 z_3 = z_1.$$

In view of the definition (2) of the product we can write

(5) $$(x_2x_3 - y_2y_3) + i(x_2y_3 + x_3y_2) = x_1 + iy_1.$$

Equating corresponding components in the two members of this equation, we get two simultaneous real equations in the unknowns x_3 and y_3. From their solution it follows that the law of division is

(6) $$\frac{z_1}{z_2} = \frac{x_1x_2 + y_1y_2}{x_2^2 + y_2^2} + i\frac{x_2y_1 - x_1y_2}{x_2^2 + y_2^2} \qquad (z_2 \neq 0).$$

It is useful to note that formula (6) is just the same as the result obtained by multiplying both the numerator and the denominator of the fraction

$$\frac{x_1 + iy_1}{x_2 + iy_2}$$

by $x_2 - iy_2$ and expanding the products by the usual laws for real numbers, then replacing i^2 by -1.

Division by zero is not defined.

As an example, the following reduction of a complex number to the form $x + iy$ employs the four fundamental operations:

$$\frac{(1+i)(-1+2i) + (2-i)}{2-3i} - 2i = \frac{(-3+i) + (2-i)}{2-3i} - 2i$$

$$= \frac{(-1)(2+3i)}{(2-3i)(2+3i)} - 2i = \frac{-2-3i}{4+9} - 2i$$

$$= -\tfrac{2}{13} - \tfrac{3}{13}i - 2i = -\tfrac{2}{13} - \tfrac{29}{13}i.$$

3. Laws of Algebra. It follows from the definition of a complex number laid down in the two preceding sections that these numbers satisfy the associative, commutative, and distributive laws of algebra.

The commutative laws of addition and multiplication for complex numbers,

(1) $$z_1 + z_2 = z_2 + z_1,$$
(2) $$z_1z_2 = z_2z_1,$$

follow from the definitions of these operations and from the fact that real numbers satisfy these commutative laws. For example,

$$z_1 + z_2 = (x_1 + x_2) + i(y_1 + y_2) = (x_2 + x_1) + i(y_2 + y_1) = z_2 + z_1.$$

The proof of law (2), as well as of the associative and distributive laws to follow, can be left as exercises.

The associative laws of addition and multiplication are

(3) $$z_1 + (z_2 + z_3) = (z_1 + z_2) + z_3,$$
(4) $$z_1(z_2z_3) = (z_1z_2)z_3.$$

The distributive law of multiplication with respect to addition is

(5) $$z_1(z_2 + z_3) = z_1z_2 + z_1z_3.$$

Another property that follows from our definition should be noted here. If the product of two complex numbers vanishes, then at least one of the factors must vanish. That is,

(6) $\qquad z_1z_2 = 0 \qquad$ implies $\qquad z_1 = 0 \qquad$ or $\qquad z_2 = 0.$

From the definition of the product it follows that if $z_1z_2 = 0$, then

(7) $\qquad x_1x_2 - y_1y_2 = 0 \qquad$ and $\qquad x_1y_2 + x_2y_1 = 0$

and therefore

$$(x_1x_2 - y_1y_2)^2 + (x_1y_2 + x_2y_1)^2 = 0.$$

This equation reduces to the equation

$$(x_1^2 + y_1^2)(x_2^2 + y_2^2) = 0$$

from which we must conclude that either $x_1 = y_1 = 0$ or $x_2 = y_2 = 0$, or both.

EXERCISES

In Exercises 1–8 reduce the number to the form $x + iy$.

1. $(3 + 2i) - (4 - i)$.   *Ans.* $-1 + 3i$.

2. $(2 - 3i)(-2 + i)$.   *Ans.* $-1 + 8i$.

3. $i(2 - 7i)$.

4. $\dfrac{1 + i}{2 - i}.$

5. $(1 - i)^4$.   *Ans.* -4.

6. $(3 + i)(3 - i)\left(\dfrac{2 + i}{10}\right)$.   *Ans.* $2 + i$.

7. $\dfrac{1 + 2i}{3 - 4i} + \dfrac{2 - i}{5i}.$ *Ans.* $-\dfrac{2}{5}.$

8. $\dfrac{2i}{(i - 1)(i - 2)(i - 3)}.$

9. Show that each of the two numbers $z = 1 \pm i$ satisfies the equation $z^2 - 2z + 2 = 0$.

10. Show that the numbers $z = (-1 \pm i\sqrt{2})/3$ satisfy the equation

$$3z^2 + 2z + 1 = 0.$$

11. Use the definition of the product of two complex numbers to prove that if k is a real number, then

$$kz = kx + iky.$$

Note the special case $k = -1$; thus to reverse the sign of z we reverse the sign of both x and y.

12. Prove that if $z_1 z_2 z_3 = 0$, then at least one of the three factors must be zero.

13. Establish the associative law of addition,

$$z_1 + (z_2 + z_3) = (z_1 + z_2) + z_3.$$

14. Establish the commutative law of multiplication,

$$z_1 z_2 = z_2 z_1.$$

15. Establish the associative law of multiplication,

$$z_1(z_2 z_3) = (z_1 z_2)z_3.$$

16. Establish the distributive law,

$$z_1(z_2 + z_3) = z_1 z_2 + z_1 z_3.$$

17. Prove that $z_1(z_2 + z_3 + z_4) = z_1 z_2 + z_1 z_3 + z_1 z_4.$

4. Geometric Representation. There is a one-to-one correspondence between ordered pairs of real numbers (x,y) and complex numbers $x + iy$. Corresponding to the ordered pair $(2,-3)$, or $x = 2$, $y = -3$, for instance, is the number $2 - 3i$, and conversely. It is natural to associate the complex number $x + iy$ with the point whose rectangular cartesian coordinates are (x,y) in the xy plane. To each point (x,y) corresponds a single complex number $z = x + iy$ and to each complex number z corresponds a definite point. When used for the purpose of representing complex numbers, the xy plane, together with the points representing the complex numbers being considered, is called the *Argand diagram*. The plane is also referred to simply as the complex plane or the z plane.

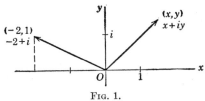

FIG. 1.

The number $-2 + i$, for instance, is represented by the point $(-2,1)$ (Fig. 1). The number $z = 0$ is represented by the origin O, real numbers by points on the x axis, and pure imaginary numbers by points on the y axis.

Again, the number z can be thought of as a vector from the origin to the point (x,y); also as any vector obtained by translating that vector in the plane. Thus the vector from the point $(2,1)$ to the point $(3,3)$, which has an x component of 1 and a y component of 2, represents the number $1 + 2i$. Both the vector representation and the point representation of complex numbers are very useful. Hereafter we shall often refer to the complex number z as the point z or as the vector z.

According to the definition of the sum of two complex numbers, $z_1 + z_2$ corresponds to the point $(x_1 + x_2, y_1 + y_2)$. It also corresponds to a vector with those coordinates as its components. Hence $z_1 + z_2$ is represented by the vector sum of the vectors z_1 and z_2, as shown in Fig. 2.

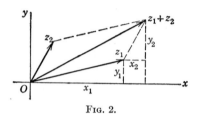
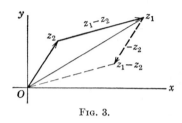

FIG. 2.   FIG. 3.

The difference $z_1 - z_2$ is represented by a vector from the point z_2 to the point z_1 (Fig. 3).

EXERCISES

In Exercises 1–4 find $z_1 + z_2$ and $z_1 - z_2$, and also exhibit them graphically.

1. $z_1 = -3 + i,$ $z_2 = 1 + 4i.$

2. $z_1 = -2i,$ $z_2 = 2 - 4i.$

3. $z_1 = 3,$ $z_2 = -3 + 5i.$

4. $z_1 = 4,$ $z_2 = -3i.$

5. Show that the vector representing the sum $z_1 + z_2 + z_3$ forms the closing side of the quadrilateral having the vectors z_1, z_2, z_3 as three of its sides. What is its direction?

6. Generalize Exercise 5 to the sum of four or more complex numbers.

7. In terms of the two points representing z_1 and z_2, what point represents $\frac{1}{2}(z_1 + z_2)$?

8. In terms of the two points representing z_1 and z_2, what point represents $z_1 + k(z_2 - z_1)$, where k is a real number?

5. Complex Conjugates. The complex conjugate, or simply the conjugate, of the complex number $z = x + iy$ is the number

$$\bar{z} = x - iy.$$

Geometrically the conjugate of z is the reflection of z in the axis of reals (Fig. 4).

If $z_1 = x_1 + iy_1$, $z_2 = x_2 + iy_2$, with the x's and y's real, then

$$\overline{z_1 + z_2} = (x_1 + x_2) - i(y_1 + y_2) = x_1 - iy_1 + x_2 - iy_2 = \bar{z}_1 + \bar{z}_2.$$

That is,

(1) $\overline{z_1 + z_2} = \bar{z}_1 + \bar{z}_2.$

Thus, the conjugate of the sum is the sum of the conjugates.

The reader can prove in like manner that

(2) $$\overline{z_1 - z_2} = \bar{z}_1 - \bar{z}_2,$$

(3) $$\overline{z_1 z_2} = \bar{z}_1 \bar{z}_2,$$

(4) $$\overline{\left(\frac{z_1}{z_2}\right)} = \frac{\bar{z}_1}{\bar{z}_2}.$$

The conjugate of $z_1 - z_2$ is exhibited as a vector in Fig. 4.

Note that the conjugate of $\bar{z}$ is z.

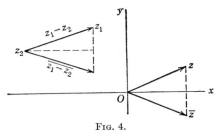

The conjugate of a real number is the number itself. Also it should be noted that the sum of a complex number and its conjugate is a real number; in fact

(5) $$z + \bar{z} = 2x = 2\Re(z).$$

FIG. 4.

Also, the difference of a complex number and its conjugate is a pure imaginary number, namely,

(6) $$z - \bar{z} = 2iy = 2i\Im(z).$$

6. Absolute Values. If x and y are real, the nonnegative real number $\sqrt{x^2 + y^2}$ is called the *absolute value* or *modulus* of the complex number $z = x + iy$. That is, by definition,

(1) $$|z| = |x + iy| = \sqrt{x^2 + y^2}.$$

Geometrically the absolute value of z is the length of the vector z; it is the distance of the point z from the origin. Consequently, $|z_1 - z_2|$ is the distance between the points z_1 and z_2. This is also evident from the definition (1), since

(2) $$|z_1 - z_2| = |(x_1 - x_2) + i(y_1 - y_2)| = \sqrt{(x_1 - x_2)^2 + (y_1 - y_2)^2}.$$

The statement $|z_1| > |z_2|$ means that the point z_1 is farther from the origin than is the point z_2. The elementary notion of order, greater than or less than, applies to absolute values because they are real numbers. We shall attach no meaning to the statement $z_1 > z_2$, unless z_1 and z_2 are both real. The complex numbers may be ordered in a variety of ways, but no ordering of them is needed for our purposes.

Associated with each complex number z are three real numbers already defined, the absolute value $|z|$, the real part $\Re(z)$, and the coefficient of the imaginary part $\Im(z)$. They are related by the equation

$$|z|^2 = [\Re(z)]^2 + [\Im(z)]^2,$$

and the resulting inequalities,

(3) $$|z| \geq |\Re(z)|, \qquad |z| \geq |\Im(z)|.$$

Since $z = x + iy$ and $\bar{z} = x - iy$ it is clear that

(4) $$z\bar{z} = x^2 + y^2 = |z|^2,$$

and that

(5) $$|\bar{z}| = |z|.$$

The absolute value of a product is the product of the absolute value of the factors; that is

(6) $$|z_1 z_2| = |z_1| \cdot |z_2|.$$

This follows from the definition of the product and of the absolute value but it can be shown simply with the aid of formula (4) above and the properties of conjugates. Thus,

$$|z_1 z_2|^2 = (z_1 z_2)(\overline{z_1 z_2}) = (z_1 z_2)(\bar{z}_1 \bar{z}_2)$$
$$= (z_1 \bar{z}_1)(z_2 \bar{z}_2) = |z_1|^2 \cdot |z_2|^2,$$

from which equation (6) follows, since the absolute value is nonnegative.

In the same way it can be shown that

(7) $$\left| \frac{z_1}{z_2} \right| = \frac{|z_1|}{|z_2|} \qquad\qquad (z_2 \neq 0).$$

Since no side of a triangle is greater than the sum of the other two sides in length, it follows (see Fig. 2) that

(8) $$|z_1 + z_2| \leq |z_1| + |z_2|.$$

Figure 3 shows a triangle with sides of length $|z_1|$, $|z_2|$, and $|z_1 - z_2|$. Since no side of a triangle is less than the difference of the other two sides in length, it follows that

(9) $$|z_1 - z_2| \geq \big||z_1| - |z_2|\big|.$$

In any specific case the notation can be chosen so that $|z_1| \geq |z_2|$, and then the outer absolute value signs on the right are not needed.

The properties (8) and (9) can of course be proved by purely algebraic means. There are some advantages in using conjugates in the proofs. Thus property (8) can be proved as follows:

$$|z_1 + z_2|^2 = (z_1 + z_2)(\bar{z}_1 + \bar{z}_2) = z_1 \bar{z}_1 + z_2 \bar{z}_2 + (z_1 \bar{z}_2 + \bar{z}_1 z_2).$$

Now $\bar{z}_1 z_2$ is the conjugate of $z_1 \bar{z}_2$. Therefore

$$z_1 \bar{z}_2 + \bar{z}_1 z_2 = 2\Re(z_1 \bar{z}_2).$$

But, according to equations (3) and (5) above, $\Re(z_1 \bar{z}_2) \leqq |z_1 \bar{z}_2| = |z_1 z_2|$. Hence

$$|z_1 + z_2|^2 \leqq |z_1|^2 + |z_2|^2 + 2|z_1 z_2| = (|z_1| + |z_2|)^2,$$

and by extracting the positive square root of each member we see that property (8) is true.

It follows from (8) that

$$|z_1 + z_2 + z_3| \leqq |z_1 + z_2| + |z_3| \leqq |z_1| + |z_2| + |z_3|.$$

The property is easily extended, by induction, to the form

$$(10) \qquad \left| \sum_{k=1}^{n} z_k \right| \leqq \sum_{k=1}^{n} |z_k| \qquad (n = 1, 2, \cdots).$$

EXERCISES

In Exercises 1–4 find $\bar{z}$, $\Re(z)$, $\mathcal{I}(z)$, and $|z|$.

1. $z = 3 - 4i$.

2. $z = -2i$.

3. $z = 4$.

4. $z = 2 - 2i$.

In Exercises 5–13 prove the formula stated.

5. $\overline{z_1 - z_2} = \bar{z}_1 - \bar{z}_2$.

6. $\overline{z_1 z_2} = \bar{z}_1 \bar{z}_2$.

7. $\overline{\left(\dfrac{z_1}{z_2}\right)} = \dfrac{\bar{z}_1}{\bar{z}_2}$ $(z_2 \neq 0)$.

8. $|z_1 z_2| = |z_1| \cdot |z_2|$, by writing the absolute values in the form $\sqrt{x^2 + y^2}$.

9. $\left|\dfrac{z_1}{z_2}\right| = \dfrac{|z_1|}{|z_2|}$ $(z_2 \neq 0)$.

10. $\overline{iz} = -i\bar{z}$.

11. $\overline{(z^4)} = (\bar{z})^4$.

12. $\overline{z_1 z_2 z_3} = \bar{z}_1 \bar{z}_2 \bar{z}_3$.

13. $\overline{\left(\dfrac{z_1}{z_2 z_3}\right)} = \dfrac{\bar{z}_1}{\bar{z}_2 \bar{z}_3}$ $(z_2 z_3 \neq 0)$.

14. If $z^2 = (\bar{z})^2$, show that z is either real or pure imaginary.

15. Give an algebraic proof of the property $|z_1 - z_2| \geqq ||z_1| - |z_2||$.

16. Show that $|z_1 + z_2| \geqq ||z_1| - |z_2||$.

17. If $|z_2| \neq |z_3|$, show that

$$\left| \frac{z_1}{z_2 + z_3} \right| \leqq \frac{|z_1|}{||z_2| - |z_3||}.$$

18. Prove that $|z| \geqq (|x| + |y|)/\sqrt{2}$.

19. Where does the point z lie if $|z| = 1$?

20. Where does the point z lie if $|z - 2| = 3$?

21. Where does the point z lie if $\Re(z) = \frac{1}{2}$?

22. Where does the point z lie if a and b are complex constants and z satisfies the equation

$$z\bar{z} - \bar{a}z - a\bar{z} + a\bar{a} = b\bar{b}?$$

23. Determine geometrically the conditions imposed upon z_1 and z_2 by the equation

$$|z_1 + z_2| = |z_1| + |z_2|.$$

24. Determine geometrically the conditions imposed upon z_1 and z_2 by the equation

$$|z_1 + z_2| = |z_1| - |z_2|.$$

7. The Polar Form. Let r and θ be the polar coordinates of the point representing z (Fig. 5). Then

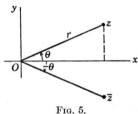

$$x = r\cos\theta, \qquad y = r\sin\theta,$$

and the complex number $z = x + iy$ can be written

$$(1) \qquad z = r(\cos\theta + i\sin\theta).$$

Fig. 5.

This is the *polar form* of z. The polar form of the conjugate of z is

$$\bar{z} = r[\cos(-\theta) + i\sin(-\theta)].$$

All points can be represented in polar coordinates without using negative values of r. We take $r \geq 0$. Since $r = \sqrt{x^2 + y^2}$, it is the absolute value of z,

$$(2) \qquad r = |z|.$$

The angle θ, also called the *argument* or amplitude of z, may be obtained from the formula

$$(3) \qquad \tan\theta = \frac{y}{x}$$

and the quadrant in which z lies. The argument, $\theta = \arg z$, is multiple-valued. For a given number z there is just one value of θ between zero and 2π; but there is also one between 2π and 4π, or one between $-\pi$ and π, etc. In fact for each number z there is one and only one value of θ in any given angular interval of range 2π,

$$\theta_0 \leq \theta < \theta_0 + 2\pi.$$

As an illustration, the number $2 + 2i$ has the absolute value $2\sqrt{2}$, and one value of its argument is $\theta = \pi/4$. Hence

$$2 + 2i = 2\sqrt{2}\left(\cos\frac{\pi}{4} + i\sin\frac{\pi}{4}\right).$$

Similarly,

$$-i = \cos\frac{3\pi}{2} + i\sin\frac{3\pi}{2},$$

and

$$-3 + 4i = 5(\cos\theta + i\sin\theta),$$

where $\tan\theta = -\frac{4}{3}$ and θ is in the second quadrant.

It is sometimes convenient to use the polar representation about some point other than the origin. The representation of $z - z_0$ in polar form,

(4) $$z - z_0 = \rho(\cos\phi + i\sin\phi),$$

can be interpreted graphically as shown in Fig. 6. That is, ρ is the distance between z and z_0, and ϕ is that angle between the real axis and the vector $z - z_0$ indicated in the figure.

As an illustration, the equation

$$z - i = 4(\cos\phi + i\sin\phi),$$

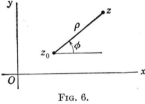

Fig. 6.

where ϕ can assume all values, represents a circle with center at $(0,1)$ and radius 4. Each point on that circle represents a number z that satisfies the above equation, and no other points represent solutions of the equation.

8. Products, Powers, and Quotients. The product of the two numbers

$$z_1 = r_1(\cos\theta_1 + i\sin\theta_1), \qquad z_2 = r_2(\cos\theta_2 + i\sin\theta_2)$$

is

$$z_1 z_2 = r_1 r_2[\cos\theta_1\cos\theta_2 - \sin\theta_1\sin\theta_2 + i(\sin\theta_1\cos\theta_2 + \cos\theta_1\sin\theta_2)],$$

and this formula reduces to the polar form of the product,

(1) $$z_1 z_2 = r_1 r_2[\cos(\theta_1 + \theta_2) + i\sin(\theta_1 + \theta_2)].$$

Thus the absolute value of the product of two complex numbers is the product of their absolute values, a property that was established earlier, and the argument of the product is the sum of the arguments of the factors,

$$\arg(z_1 z_2) = \arg z_1 + \arg z_2.$$

Fig. 7.

Geometrically, the length of the vector $z_1 z_2$ is equal to the product of the lengths of z_1 and z_2. The angle of inclination of the vector $z_1 z_2$ is the sum of the angles θ_1 and θ_2 (Fig. 7). In particular, when a complex number z is multiplied by i, the resulting vector iz is the one obtained by rotating the vector z through a right angle in the positive (counter-clockwise) direction, without changing the length of the vector, since

$$iz = \left(\cos\frac{\pi}{2} + i\sin\frac{\pi}{2}\right) r(\cos\theta + i\sin\theta)$$

$$= r\left[\cos\left(\theta + \frac{\pi}{2}\right) + i\sin\left(\theta + \frac{\pi}{2}\right)\right].$$

It follows from formula (1) that

$$z_1 z_2 \cdots z_n = r_1 r_2 \cdots r_n[\cos(\theta_1 + \theta_2 + \cdots + \theta_n) + i\sin(\theta_1 + \theta_2 + \cdots + \theta_n)].$$

Consequently if $z = r(\cos\theta + i\sin\theta)$ and if n is a positive integer,

$$(2) \qquad z^n = r^n(\cos n\theta + i\sin n\theta).$$

When $r = 1$, this formula reduces to *De Moivre's theorem* for positive integral exponents,

$$(3) \qquad (\cos\theta + i\sin\theta)^n = \cos n\theta + i\sin n\theta.$$

The quotient of two complex numbers is given in its polar form by the formula

$$(4) \qquad \frac{z_1}{z_2} = \frac{r_1}{r_2}[\cos(\theta_1 - \theta_2) + i\sin(\theta_1 - \theta_2)].$$

Since division is the inverse of multiplication this formula can be established easily from formula (1). As a special case it follows that

$$\frac{1}{z} = \frac{1}{r}[\cos(-\theta) + i\sin(-\theta)] = \frac{1}{r}(\cos\theta - i\sin\theta),$$

and, in view of equation (2),

$$(5) \qquad z^{-n} = \frac{1}{z^n} = \frac{1}{r^n}[\cos(-n\theta) + i\sin(-n\theta)].$$

Thus the formula (2) and De Moivre's theorem (3) are valid when the exponent is any negative integer.

EXERCISES

In Exercises 1–5 write z in the polar form and give several values of its argument.

1. $z = 1 + i\sqrt{3}$.   *Ans.* $\theta = \dfrac{\pi}{3}, \dfrac{\pi}{3} \pm 2n\pi$.

2. $z = i$.

3. $z = -2$.   *Ans.* $\theta = \pi, \ \pi \pm 2n\pi$.

4. $z = -2 - 2i$.

5. $z = 1 - 2i$.

Use the polar form to carry out the operations in Exercises 6–12.

6. $i(1 - i\sqrt{3})(\sqrt{3} + i)$.   *Ans.* $2 + 2i\sqrt{3}$.

7. $\dfrac{2 - 2i}{-1 - i}$

8. $\dfrac{3}{(\sqrt{3} - i)^2}$.

9. z^2, z^3, z^4 where $z = (1 + i\sqrt{3})/2$.

10. $(-2 - 2i)^7$.   *Ans.* $2^{10}(-1 + i)$.

11. $(1 - i)^4$.

12. $(\sqrt{3} + i)^{-3}$.   *Ans.* $-\tfrac{1}{8}i$.

13. Derive formula (4), Sec. 8.

14. Give a geometrical interpretation of the quotient z_1/z_2 as seen from formula (4), Sec. 8.

15. Prove that the triangle with vertices at the points z_1, z_2, and z_3 is similar to the triangle with vertices at z_1', z_2', and z_3' and that they are similarly placed, that is, that corresponding angles have the same sense, if and only if

$$\frac{z_3 - z_1}{z_2 - z_1} = \frac{z_3' - z_1'}{z_2' - z_1'}.$$

16. Establish the formula

$$1 + z + z^2 + \cdots + z^n = \frac{1 - z^{n+1}}{1 - z}$$

for the sum of a finite geometric series; then derive the formulas

$$(a)\ \ 1 + \cos\theta + \cos 2\theta + \cdots + \cos n\theta = \frac{1}{2} + \frac{\sin[(n + \tfrac{1}{2})\theta]}{2\sin(\theta/2)},$$

$$(b)\ \ \sin\theta + \sin 2\theta + \cdots + \sin n\theta = \frac{1}{2}\cot\frac{\theta}{2} - \frac{\cos[(n + \tfrac{1}{2})\theta]}{2\sin(\theta/2)}.$$

9. Extraction of Roots. The problem of extracting the nth roots of a complex number z is that of solving the equation

(1) $$z_0^n = z$$

for z_0, when z and the positive integer n are given.

Let the polar form of z be

$$z = r(\cos\theta + i\sin\theta),$$

and let

$$z_0 = r_0(\cos\theta_0 + i\sin\theta_0),$$

where r_0 and θ_0 are as yet unknown. Then equation (1) becomes

$$r_0^n(\cos n\theta_0 + i\sin n\theta_0) = r(\cos\theta + i\sin\theta).$$

Consequently

$$r_0^n = r, \qquad n\theta_0 = \theta \pm 2k\pi,$$

where k is either zero or any positive integer. Since we have taken r and r_0 as positive numbers, it follows that r_0 is the real positive nth root of r.

Now

$$\theta_0 = \frac{\theta}{n} \pm \frac{2k\pi}{n};$$

but these values of θ_0 yield the same value of z for any two integers k that differ by a multiple of n. Therefore there are just n distinct solutions of equation (1), namely,

(2) $$z_0 = \sqrt[n]{r}\left(\cos \frac{\theta + 2\pi k}{n} + i \sin \frac{\theta + 2\pi k}{n} \right)$$

where $k = 0, 1, 2, \cdots, n - 1$. These are the n values of $z^{1/n}$.

Geometrically the length of each of the n vectors $z^{1/n}$ is the positive number $\sqrt[n]{r}$. The amplitude of one of those vectors is the angle obtained by dividing θ by n, and the other amplitudes are obtained by adding multiples of $2\pi/n$ to θ/n.

It follows from formula (2) and the results of the preceding section that, if m and n are integers with no factor in common, then

(3) $$z^{m/n} = \sqrt[n]{r^m}\left\{ \cos\left[\frac{m}{n}(\theta + 2k\pi) \right] + i \sin\left[\frac{m}{n}(\theta + 2k\pi) \right] \right\},$$

where $k = 0, 1, 2, \cdots, n - 1$.

10. The nth Roots of Unity. Since

$$1 = \cos 0 + i \sin 0,$$

the nth roots of unity may be expressed as

(1) $$\cos \frac{2\pi k}{n} + i \sin \frac{2\pi k}{n} \quad (k = 0, 1, 2, \cdots, n - 1).$$

Let ω denote the particular root corresponding to $k = 1$,

(2) $$\omega = \cos \frac{2\pi}{n} + i \sin \frac{2\pi}{n};$$

then according to De Moivre's theorem (Sec. 8), the n roots (1) can be written as

(3) $$1, \quad \omega, \quad \omega^2, \quad \cdots, \quad \omega^{n-1}.$$

In the complex plane the nth roots of unity are the vertices of a regular polygon of n sides inscribed in the circle $|z| = 1$, with one vertex at the point $z = 1$. See Fig. 8 for $n = 3$ and Fig. 9 for $n = 6$.

If z_1 is any nth root of z, then

$$z_1, \qquad z_1\omega, \qquad z_1\omega^2, \qquad \cdots, \qquad z_1\omega^{n-1}$$

are the n nth roots of z.   This is easily seen geometrically, for the mul-

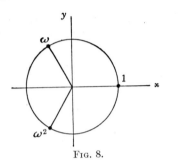

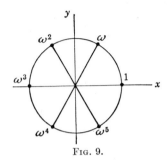

Fig. 8.   Fig. 9.

tiplication of a number z_1 by ω^k corresponds to increasing the argument of z_1 by the angle $2k\pi/n$.

EXERCISES

1. Show that the two square roots of i are

$$\frac{1}{\sqrt{2}}(1+i), \qquad -\frac{1}{\sqrt{2}}(1+i).$$

2. Show that the cube roots of 1 are

$$1, \qquad \tfrac{1}{2}(-1+i\sqrt{3}), \qquad \tfrac{1}{2}(-1-i\sqrt{3}),$$

and show all the numbers graphically.

3. Find the cube roots of -1 and check graphically.

4. Find the sixth roots of 64.

5. Find the sixth roots of $-i$.

6. Find the fourth roots of -9.

7. Find the cube roots of $(1+i)$ and check graphically.

8. Solve $x^4 + 4 = 0$, and factor $x^4 + 4$ into two quadratic factors with real coefficients.

9. Find the square roots of $x + iy$ in terms of x and y.

10. If ω is either imaginary cube root of unity, prove that

$$1 + \omega + \omega^2 = 0.$$

11. If ω is an imaginary nth root of unity, prove that

$$1 + \omega + \omega^2 + \cdots + \omega^{n-1} = 0.$$

12. If k is a real rational number, prove that

$$(a) \quad (z_1 z_2)^k = z_1^k z_2^k; \qquad (b) \quad \left(\frac{z_1}{z_2}\right)^k = \frac{z_1^k}{z_2^k}.$$

13. Prove that the usual quadratic formula applies to the quadratic equation $az^2 + bz + c = 0$, when the coefficients a, b, and c are complex numbers.

11. Regions in the Complex Plane.

Let us note first some particular regions in the z plane that will prove useful in the work that is to follow. A few definitions of technical terms will also be given at this time.

Let c denote a positive real number. Then according to the definition of the absolute value of a complex number, the points z that satisfy the inequality $|z| < c$ consist of all the points interior to the circle with center at the origin and radius c. Similarly, the inequality $|z - z_0| < c$, where z_0 is a fixed complex number, describes the interior of the circle with center at z_0 and radius c.

As another example, the points z for which

$$c_1 < |z| < c_2$$

are the points between the concentric circles $|z| = c_1$ and $|z| = c_2$; that is, the inequality describes an annular region. Again, the points for which

$$\Re(z) \geqq c$$

consist of all the points on and to the right of the vertical line $x = c$, where c is any real constant. Thus the inequality describes a half plane.

A *neighborhood* of a point z_0 is the circular region

$$|z - z_0| < \epsilon$$

where ϵ is a positive number. It therefore includes the point z_0 itself and excludes the points on the circle. The word *neighborhood* will be used consistently in this technical sense.

A point z_0 is called a *limit point* of a set of points in the plane if and only if every neighborhood of z_0 contains at least one point, other than z_0, of that set. The point z_0 may or may not be a point of the set.

As an illustration, each point on the circle $|z| = c$ is a limit point of the set $|z| < c$. These limit points do not belong to the set. But each point inside the circle is also a limit point that does belong to the set. As another illustration, every point z for which $c_1 \leqq |z| \leqq c_2$ is a limit point of the set $c_1 < |z| \leqq c_2$.

An *interior point* of a set of points is a point such that some neighborhood of it contains only points of the set.

An *open two-dimensional region* is a set such that every point of it is an interior point. As illustrations, the three sets of points $|z| < c$, $|z| > c$, and $\Re(z) > c$ are open two-dimensional regions. The word *region* will be used here to denote a *connected* region, one such that any two of its points can be joined by a continuous curve all of whose points belong to the region.   The set consisting of all the points interior to the two separated circles, $|z| < 1$ and $|z - 3| < 1$, for instance, makes up two regions rather than a single region.   A *two-dimensional region* is either such an open region or a set consisting of the region and some or all of its limit points that do not belong to the open region.   If the region includes all its limit points, such as the region $|z| \leq c$, it is called a *closed region.*

A region is *bounded* if all its points lie within some circle $|z| = c$ where c is a finite positive number.   Unless we make an explicit statement to the contrary, our points, and in particular all limit points, will represent finite complex numbers, and hence a closed region will signify a bounded closed region.

It will be noted that a region may be neither open nor closed.   This is illustrated by the region $2 \leq |z| < 3$, which includes the limit points z for which $|z| = 2$ but not those for which $|z| = 3$.

EXERCISES

Describe geometrically the regions in the z plane determined by the following inequalities:

1. $|x| < 3.$
3. $\mathcal{I}(z) > 1.$
5. $0 \leq \arg z \leq \dfrac{\pi}{4}.$

7. $-\pi < \arg z < \pi.$
9. $1 < |z - 2i| < 2.$

11. $\mathcal{I}(z^2) > 0.$

13. $|2z - 3| > 3.$
15. $|z - 1| + |z + 1| \leq 4.$

2. $|z - 4| \leq 1.$
4. $\mathcal{R}(z) \geq \frac{1}{2}.$
6. $0 \leq \arg z < \dfrac{\pi}{2}, \qquad |z| > 2.$

8. $|z + 3i| > 2.$
10. $\mathcal{R}(z^2) > 0.$

12. $\mathcal{R}\left(\dfrac{1}{z}\right) < \dfrac{1}{2}.$

14. $|3z + i| < 3.$
16. $|z| < |z - 4|.$

CHAPTER II

ANALYTIC FUNCTIONS

12. Functions of a Complex Variable. Let z denote the complex number represented by any point in some part R of the xy plane. We call z a *complex variable*. If a complex variable w is so related to z that to each value of z in R there corresponds a definite value or set of values of w, then w is a *function* of the complex variable z,

$$w = f(z).$$

If $w = z^3 - 1$, for instance, then w is a function of z. In this case there is just one value of w for each value of z. When there is a unique value of w for each value of z in some two-dimensional region, then w is called a *single-valued* function of z in that region. Other examples of single-valued functions are

$$w_1 = \frac{1}{z}, \qquad w_2 = \frac{z}{z^2 + 1}, \qquad w_3 = |z|.$$

The function w_1 is not defined at $z = 0$, and w_2 is not defined at $z = \pm i$. For the sake of brevity a function of a complex variable is sometimes called a *complex function*. However, w_3 is an example of a function of a complex variable that assumes only real values.

The functions $w = z^{\frac{1}{2}}$ and $w = \arg z$ are examples of multiple-valued functions. The first one assumes two values for each value of z other than $z = 0$. The function $\arg z$ assumes an infinite set of real values for each value of z other than $z = 0$; it is not defined when $z = 0$.

Functions obtained by applying the operations of addition, subtraction, multiplication, division, and extraction of roots to the variable z and to constants are called *algebraic functions*. For example,

$$2z^2 - 3 + z^{-1}$$

is a rational, fractional, algebraic function; *rational* because no fractional powers of z are involved, *fractional* because of the negative power of z. The algebraic function $(1 + z)^{\frac{1}{2}}$ is irrational. Every polynomial

$$a_0 + a_1 z + a_2 z^2 + \cdots + a_n z^n$$

is a rational, integral, algebraic function.

The functions described in the preceding paragraph include the most common algebraic functions, but not all algebraic functions. **Any variable** w that satisfies an equation of the type

$$P(z,w) = 0,$$

where P is a polynomial in z and w, is an *algebraic* function of z. A function that is not algebraic is called *transcendental*.

Let $z = x + iy$ and $w = u + iv$, where x, y, u, and v are real. Then, if w is a function of z,

$$u + iv = f(x + iy),$$

and each of the real variables u and v are determined by the pair of real variables x and y. That is,

$$u = u(x,y), \qquad v = v(x,y).$$

For example, if

$$w = z^2 + 2,$$

then

$$u + iv = x^2 - y^2 + 2 + 2xyi,$$

from which it follows that

$$u = x^2 - y^2 + 2, \qquad v = 2xy.$$

Since for each value of z, there is just one value of x and one of y, every function of x, y, and complex constants is a function of z. Thus

$$3x + 2yi = f(z);$$

when $z = 1 - i$, for instance, $x = 1$ and $y = -1$, so that

$$f(1 - i) = 3 - 2i.$$

Similarly, $f(0) = 0$ and $f(i) = 2i$. The function can be expressed in terms of z itself in many ways. For example,

$$f(z) = 3\Re(z) + 2i\Im(z) = 2z + \Re(z) = 2z + \tfrac{1}{2}(z + \bar{z}).$$

The two functions

$$x^2 + y^2 = |z|^2, \qquad x - iy = \bar{z},$$

are also functions of z. They are not algebraic.

We shall define other transcendental functions in the next chapter.

13. Limits. Let $f(z)$ be a single-valued function defined at all points in some neighborhood of a point z_0. The statement that the limit of the function $f(z)$ as z approaches z_0 is a number w_0,

$$\lim_{z \to z_0} f(z) = w_0,$$

means that the value of $f(z)$ can be made arbitrarily close to the value w_0 for all points z in a neighborhood of z_0, except possibly at the point z_0 itself, by taking the neighborhood sufficiently small. Let us express this definition in a more precise and useful form.

If for every positive number ϵ there exists a number δ such that

$$(1) \qquad |f(z) - w_0| < \epsilon \text{ when } |z - z_0| < \delta \ (z \neq z_0),$$

then

$$(2) \qquad \lim_{z \to z_0} f(z) = w_0,$$

and conversely.

The function need not be defined at z_0; but except for the point z_0 itself, the definition of the limit requires that the function be defined throughout some neighborhood of z_0 if the limit is to exist. For instance, the function

$$f(z) = \frac{z^2 - 1}{z - 1}$$

is not defined when $z = 1$, but for all other values of z it is equal to $z + 1$. Let us show by means of the definition of the limit that

$$\lim_{z \to 1} f(z) = 2.$$

In this case, when $z \neq 1$,

$$|f(z) - 2| = |z + 1 - 2| = |z - 1|,$$

and consequently

$$|f(z) - 2| < \epsilon \qquad\qquad \text{when } |z - 1| < \delta$$

provided we take $\delta = \epsilon$. Thus we have exhibited a value of δ corresponding to each number ϵ, and the limit is established.

As another example, let us show that

$$(3) \qquad \lim_{z \to 2i} (2x + iy^2) = 4i.$$

For each positive number ϵ we are to exhibit a number δ such that

$$(4) \qquad |2x + iy^2 - 4i| < \epsilon$$

when $|z - 2i| < \delta$. To simplify our problem, we write

$$|2x + iy^2 - 4i| \leq 2|x| + |y - 2||y + 2|,$$

and look for a value of δ such that

$$|2x| < \frac{\epsilon}{2}, \qquad |y - 2||y + 2| < \frac{\epsilon}{2}.$$

Now suppose $|y - 2| < \epsilon/10$, a number that appears to be sufficiently small, arrived at by a few rough trials. Then $-\epsilon/10 < y - 2 < \epsilon/10$, so that

$$4 - \frac{\epsilon}{10} < y + 2 < 4 + \frac{\epsilon}{10};$$

that is, $|y + 2| < 4 + \epsilon/10 < 5$, provided that $\epsilon < 10$, and therefore $|y - 2||y + 2| < \epsilon/2$. If $\epsilon \geq 10$, we can safely replace it by a number less than 10 in the inequality (4).

We have now shown that the inequality (4) is satisfied when the point z is inside the rectangular region

$$|x| < \frac{\epsilon}{4}, \qquad |y - 2| < \frac{\epsilon}{10},$$

when $\epsilon < 10$. When $\epsilon \geq 10$, we can replace the second inequality here by $|y - 2| < 1$. The neighborhood

$$|z - 2i| < \frac{\epsilon}{10}$$

lies inside the rectangular region. Therefore we can take

$$\delta = \frac{\epsilon}{10} \qquad\qquad \text{when } \epsilon < 10,$$

$$\delta < 1 \qquad\qquad \text{when } \epsilon \geq 10,$$

and the limit (3) is established.

When the limit of a single-valued function exists at z_0, that limit has a unique value. For suppose that it could have two distinct values w_0 and w_1. Then for every positive number ϵ, however small, a number δ would exist such that

$$|f(z) - w_0| < \epsilon, \qquad |f(z) - w_1| < \epsilon \qquad \text{when } |z - z_0| < \delta.$$

Then it would follow that

$$|[f(z) - w_0] - [f(z) - w_1]| \leq |f(z) - w_0| + |f(z) - w_1| < 2\epsilon;$$

that is, $|w_1 - w_0| < 2\epsilon$. But w_0 and w_1 are distinct constants, and hence $|w_1 - w_0|$ cannot be made arbitrarily small. The uniqueness of the limit is therefore proved.

We can expedite our treatment of limits here by establishing the connection between the limit of a function of a complex variable and limits of real functions of two real variables. The limits of the latter type are treated in advanced calculus. We shall be free to use their definitions and properties.

Suppose that according to the definition (1)

(5) $$\lim_{z \to z_0} f(z) = u_0 + iv_0,$$

where u_0 and v_0 are real constants. Let

$$f(z) = u + iv, \qquad z = x + iy, \qquad z_0 = x_0 + iy_0,$$

where u and v are real functions of x and y. Then the inequalities (1) become

(6) $$|u - u_0 + i(v - v_0)| < \epsilon \quad \text{when} \quad |x - x_0 + i(y - y_0)| < \delta.$$

Since the first absolute value here is not less than $|u - u_0|$, it follows that, given any positive number ϵ, a number δ exists such that

$$|u - u_0| < \epsilon \quad \text{when} \quad \sqrt{(x - x_0)^2 + (y - y_0)^2} < \delta.$$

Thus there is a neighborhood of the point (x_0, y_0) throughout which, except possibly at the point itself, $|u(x,y) - u_0| < \epsilon$. A square region inside the circular neighborhood will also answer the purpose, and according to the definition of a limit of a real function of two real variables, it follows that

(7) $$\lim_{\substack{x \to x_0 \\ y \to y_0}} u(x,y) = u_0.$$

Likewise, it follows from the condition (6) that

(8) $$\lim_{\substack{x \to x_0 \\ y \to y_0}} v(x,y) = v_0.$$

From our hypothesis (5) it therefore follows that

(9) $$\lim_{z \to z_0} f(z) = \lim_{\substack{x \to x_0 \\ y \to y_0}} u(x,y) + i \lim_{\substack{x \to x_0 \\ y \to y_0}} v(x,y).$$

Conversely, if the relations (7) and (8) are satisfied, then the relation (5) must be true. For, given any positive number ϵ, there exist numbers δ_1 and δ_2 such that the following two conditions are satisfied:

$$|u - u_0| < \frac{\epsilon}{2} \quad \text{when} \quad \sqrt{(x - x_0)^2 + (y - y_0)^2} < \delta_1,$$

$$|v - v_0| < \frac{\epsilon}{2} \quad \text{when} \quad \sqrt{(x - x_0)^2 + (y - y_0)^2} < \delta_2.$$

Let δ denote the smaller of the two numbers δ_1 and δ_2. Then since

$$|u - u_0 + i(v - v_0)| \leq |u - u_0| + |v - v_0|,$$

the condition (6) follows; that is,

$$\lim_{z \to z_0} f(z) = u_0 + iv_0.$$

14. Theorems on Limits. Let $f(z)$ and $F(z)$ be two functions whose limits exist as z approaches z_0:

(1) $$\lim_{z \to z_0} f(z) = w_0, \qquad \lim_{z \to z_0} F(z) = W_0.$$

Then

(2) $$\lim_{z \to z_0} [f(z) + F(z)] = w_0 + W_0,$$

(3) $$\lim_{z \to z_0} [f(z)F(z)] = w_0 W_0,$$

and, if $W_0 \neq 0$,

(4) $$\lim_{z \to z_0} \frac{f(z)}{F(z)} = \frac{w_0}{W_0}.$$

These three fundamental theorems on limits could be established directly from the definition of the limit of a function of a complex variable. But with the aid of the results of the last section they follow almost immediately from the corresponding theorems for real functions of two real variables.

Consider the proof of property (3), for example. Let

$$f(z) = u + iv, \qquad F(z) = U + iV,$$
$$w_0 = u_0 + iv_0, \qquad W_0 = U_0 + iV_0.$$

Then according to our hypothesis (1) the limits, as (x,y) approaches (x_0,y_0), of u, v, U, and V exist and have the values u_0, v_0, U_0, and V_0, respectively. The real and imaginary components of the function

$$f(z)F(z) = uU - vV + i(uV + vU)$$

therefore have the limits $(u_0U_0 - v_0V_0)$ and $(u_0V_0 + v_0U_0)$, according to the theorems on the limits of the sum and product of real functions. Therefore $f(z)F(z)$ has the limit

$$u_0U_0 - v_0V_0 + i(u_0V_0 + v_0U_0),$$

which is equal to w_0W_0, so that property (3) is established.

The proofs of properties (2) and (4) are similar. In proving (4) either a direct or an indirect use must be made of the property that, since $W_0 \neq 0$, there is a neighborhood of the point z_0 throughout which $F(z) \neq 0$. This property of a function whose limit exists and is different from zero follows from the fact that

$$|F(z) - W_0| < \epsilon \qquad \text{when } |z - z_0| < \delta:$$

thus if $F(z)$ vanishes at some point in every neighborhood of z_0, no value of δ would exist when ϵ is less than $|W_0|$, a conclusion that is contrary to the hypothesis that $F(z)$ has a limit W_0 where $W_0 \neq 0$.

For the function $f(z) = z$ we can take $\delta = \epsilon$ in the definition of the limit to see that

$$\lim_{z \to z_0} z = z_0.$$

It follows from property (3) on the limit of the product, and by induction that

$$\lim_{z \to z_0} z^n = z_0^n,$$

where n is a positive integer and z_0 is any complex number. Also, the limit of a constant is that constant. Then in view of property (2), the limit of a polynomial

$$P(z) = a_0 + a_1 z + a_2 z^2 + \cdots + a_n z^n$$

is equal to the value of the polynomial, for every number z_0; that is,

(5) $$\lim_{z \to z_0} P(z) = P(z_0).$$

15. Continuity. A single-valued function $f(z)$ is continuous at a point z_0 if and only if all three of the following conditions are satisfied:

(1) $$f(z_0) \quad \text{exists,}$$
(2) $$\lim_{z \to z_0} f(z) \quad \text{exists,}$$
(3) $$\lim_{z \to z_0} f(z) = f(z_0).$$

These three conditions imply that $f(z)$ is defined throughout some neighborhood of the point z_0. A natural modification of this definition is needed in order to define the continuity of a function at a point on the boundary of a region in which the function is defined. Suppose that $f(z)$ is defined throughout a region extending up to and including a curve C, but not extending across C. Then $f(z)$ is continuous at a point z_0 on C if and only if the conditions (2) and (3) are satisfied where, in this case, the limit is the limit from the interior of the region; that is, the neighborhood $|z - z_0| < \delta$ used in defining the limit is to be replaced by that part of the neighborhood which lies in the given region.

As a result of the theorems on limits, if any two functions are continuous, their sum and their product are also continuous, and their quotient is continuous except for those values of z for which the denominator vanishes.

Every polynomial in z is continuous at each point, according to formula (5), Sec. 14. The quotient of two polynomials is continuous for each value of z for which the denominator is different from zero.

The condition (3) can be written as follows, in view of the definition of the limit. For each positive number ϵ, there exists a number δ such that

(4) $$|f(z) - f(z_0)| < \epsilon \qquad \text{when } |z - z_0| < \delta.$$

The number δ corresponding to a given ϵ will in general depend upon z_0. However, if $f(z)$ is continuous at every point in a closed and bounded two-dimensional region R, then it is *uniformly continuous* there; that is, for each given ϵ, a number δ independent of z_0 exists such that the condition (4) is satisfied simultaneously for all z_0 in R.

If $f(z)$ is continuous in a bounded and closed two-dimensional region R, then there exists a constant M such that

$$|f(z)| < M$$

for all z in R; that is $f(z)$ is *bounded* in R.

Those properties of continuous functions may be obtained from the corresponding properties of real functions of two real variables, because a necessary and sufficient condition that the function

$$f(z) = u(x,y) + iv(x,y)$$

be continuous is that both u and v be continuous functions of the two variables x and y together. The function $f(z) = xy + ix^2$, for example, is continuous everywhere. The function $f(z) = e^x + i \sin (xy)$ is continuous everywhere as a result of the continuity of the real exponential and trigonometric functions and the continuity of xy.

A continuous function of a continuous function is continuous; that is, if $f(g)$ is continuous at $g = g_0$ and if $g(z)$ is continuous at $z = z_0$, where $g(z_0) = g_0$, then $f[g(z)]$ is a continuous function of z at $z = z_0$.

16. The Derivative. Let z_0 be a fixed complex number and let Δz be a complex variable. The derivative of a function $f(z)$ at $z = z_0$ is defined as follows:

(1) $$f'(z_0) = \lim_{\Delta z \to 0} \frac{f(z_0 + \Delta z) - f(z_0)}{\Delta z}.$$

The function $f(z)$ must be defined at all points in some neighborhood of the point z_0 if its derivative $f'(z_0)$ is to exist, for the above limit represents the limit of a function as defined in Sec. 13.

The derivative of the function $f(z) = z^2$, for example, is $2z$ at any point z, since

$$f'(z) = \lim_{\Delta z \to 0} \frac{(z + \Delta z)^2 - z^2}{\Delta z} = \lim_{\Delta z \to 0} (2z + \Delta z) = 2z.$$

It is important to remember that Δz is a complex variable, as indicated in Fig. 10. The argument ϕ of Δz may assume different values as Δz tends to zero. As a consequence, the derivative of a function of z may fail to exist because the expression

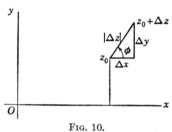

FIG. 10.

$$\frac{f(z_0 + \Delta z) - f(z_0)}{\Delta z}$$

depends in the limit upon ϕ.

Consider, for example, the function

$$f(z) = |z|^2.$$

In this case the limit (1) at any point z becomes

$$\lim_{\Delta z \to 0} \frac{|z + \Delta z|^2 - |z|^2}{\Delta z} = \lim_{\Delta z \to 0} \frac{(z + \Delta z)(\bar{z} + \overline{\Delta z}) - z\bar{z}}{\Delta z}$$

$$= \lim_{\Delta z \to 0} \left(\bar{z} + \overline{\Delta z} + z \frac{\overline{\Delta z}}{\Delta z} \right).$$

Now $\overline{\Delta z} \to 0$ when $\Delta z \to 0$. Therefore at the point $z = 0$ the limit is zero, and we have the result

$$f'(0) = 0.$$

But the derivative exists only at $z = 0$. When $z \neq 0$, let us write

$$\Delta z = |\Delta z|(\cos \phi + i \sin \phi).$$

Then

$$\frac{\overline{\Delta z}}{\Delta z} = \frac{|\Delta z|}{|\Delta z|} \frac{\cos (-\phi) + i \sin (-\phi)}{\cos \phi + i \sin \phi} = \cos 2\phi - i \sin 2\phi,$$

and the limit of this quotient does not exist as $\Delta z \to 0$, since the value of the expression depends upon the manner in which $\Delta z \to 0$.

If $f'(z_0)$ exists, then $f(z)$ is necessarily continuous at $z = z_0$, for $f(z_0 + \Delta z) - f(z_0)$ must approach zero as $\Delta z \to 0$ if the limit (1) is to exist. However, a function may be continuous and yet fail to have a derivative, as is illustrated above by the function $|z|^2$.

17. Differentiation Formulas. The definition of the derivative $f'(z)$ is identical in form to that of the derivative of a function of a real variable. We may therefore expect to establish the same fundamental formulas for differentiation as were previously obtained for functions of a real variable. These formulas do need to be proved, however. It is not safe to expect all results from real variables to carry over to complex variables. Note for instance, that the real function $f(x) = |x|^2$ of the real variable x has a derivative for every value of x, in contrast to the result obtained above relative to the function $f(z) = |z|^2$.

The results below can be obtained by the same steps as in the case of real variables. If c is a complex constant, then

$$(1) \qquad \frac{d}{dz}(c) = 0.$$

If the derivative of a function $w(z)$ exists, then

$$(2) \qquad \frac{d}{dz}(cw) = c\frac{dw}{dz}.$$

If n is a positive integer,

$$(3) \qquad \frac{d}{dz}(z^n) = nz^{n-1}.$$

If $w_1(z)$ and $w_2(z)$ are two functions whose derivatives exist, then

$$(4) \qquad \frac{d}{dz}(w_1 + w_2) = \frac{dw_1}{dz} + \frac{dw_2}{dz},$$

$$(5) \qquad \frac{d}{dz}(w_1 w_2) = w_1 \frac{dw_2}{dz} + w_2 \frac{dw_1}{dz},$$

$$(6) \qquad \frac{d}{dz}\left(\frac{w_1}{w_2}\right) = \frac{w_2(dw_1/dz) - w_1(dw_2/dz)}{w_2^2} \qquad (w_2 \neq 0);$$

and for a function of a function,

$$(7) \qquad \frac{d}{dz}\{w_1[w_2(z)]\} = \frac{dw_1}{dw_2}\frac{dw_2}{dz}.$$

As an example of the last formula, if $w_1 = z^5$ and $w_2 = 2z + 1$, then

$$\frac{d}{dz}(2z + 1)^5 = \frac{d}{dz}(w_2^5) = 5w_2^4 \frac{dw_2}{dz} = 5(2z + 1)^4 \cdot 2.$$

Formula (3) can be extended at once to the case in which n is a positive or negative integer or fraction.

Formula (5), for example, can be derived as follows:

$$\frac{d}{dz}(w_1 w_2) = \lim_{\Delta z \to 0} \frac{(w_1 + \Delta w_1)(w_2 + \Delta w_2) - w_1 w_2}{\Delta z}$$

where

$$\Delta w_1 = w_1(z + \Delta z) - w_1(z), \qquad \Delta w_2 = w_2(z + \Delta z) - w_2(z).$$

Since the derivatives of w_1 and w_2 are assumed to exist, Δw_2 tends to zero with Δz, and

$$\frac{d}{dz}(w_1 w_2) = \lim_{\Delta z \to 0}\left(w_1 \frac{\Delta w_2}{\Delta z} + w_2 \frac{\Delta w_1}{\Delta z} + \Delta w_2 \frac{\Delta w_1}{\Delta z}\right)$$

$$= w_1 \frac{dw_2}{dz} + w_2 \frac{dw_1}{dz}.$$

Formula (7) is obtained by writing

$$(8) \qquad \qquad \frac{\Delta w_1}{\Delta z} = \frac{\Delta w_1}{\Delta w_2}\frac{\Delta w_2}{\Delta z} \qquad \qquad (\Delta w_2 \neq 0),$$

and taking the limit as Δz tends to zero, noting that Δw_2 tends to zero with Δz. The identity (8) is valid only for those values of Δw_2 which are not zero, but since the derivatives of w_1 and w_2 exist, the limits here must be equal to those derivatives. For every positive ϵ, there are some values of Δz, where $|\Delta z| < \epsilon$, such that $\Delta w_2 \neq 0$, otherwise w_2 is a constant and formula (7) is of no interest.

EXERCISES

1. Derive formula (2) of this section.

2. Derive formula (3) of this section.

3. Derive formula (6) of this section.

In Exercises 4–7 use the formulas of this section to obtain dw/dz.

4. $w = 3z^2 - 4z + 7$.

5. $w = (1 - 4z^2)^3$.

6. $w = \dfrac{3z - 1}{2z + 1}$.

7. $w = (z^2 - 1)^3 (z^2 + 1)^4$.

8. Apply the definition of the derivative to show that, if $f(z) = \Re(z)$, then $f'(z)$ does not exist at any point.

9. Show that the function $f(z) = \bar{z}$ does not have a derivative anywhere.

10. Determine whether or not $f(z) = \mathcal{I}(z)$ has a derivative anywhere.

18. The Cauchy-Riemann Conditions. Suppose that a function $f(z)$ has a derivative at a point z, and let

$$f(z) = u(x,y) + iv(x,y).$$

Then the derivative is independent of the way in which Δz tends to zero, and Δz may be conveniently chosen as a real or as a pure imaginary variable. That is, if $\Delta w = \Delta x + i\,\Delta y$, we may choose to let Δy approach zero first, then let Δx approach zero, as in Fig. 11. With $\Delta z = \Delta x$ then,

$$f'(z) = \lim_{\Delta x \to 0} \frac{u(x + \Delta x, y) - u(x,y)}{\Delta x} + i \lim_{\Delta x \to 0} \frac{v(x + \Delta x, y) - v(x,y)}{\Delta x}.$$

The last two limits must exist because $f'(z)$ exists. They are the partial derivatives of u and v with respect to x. Hence whenever $f'(z)$ exists, it can be written

(1) $$f'(z) = \frac{\partial u}{\partial x} + i\frac{\partial v}{\partial x}.$$

Now let Δx approach zero first, then let Δy approach zero, as in Fig. 12. After Δx becomes zero, $\Delta z = i\,\Delta y$ and thus

$$f'(z) = \lim_{\Delta y \to 0} \frac{u(x, y + \Delta y) + iv(x, y + \Delta y) - u(x,y) - iv(x,y)}{i\,\Delta y}.$$

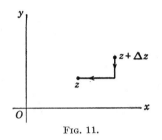

Fig. 11.

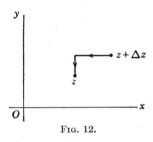

Fig. 12.

Therefore, if $f'(z)$ exists, it has the second representation

(2) $$f'(z) = -i\frac{\partial u}{\partial y} + \frac{\partial v}{\partial y}.$$

The right members of equations (1) and (2) are equal to the same complex number. Since u and v are real, their partial derivatives are real. Therefore it follows that

(3) $$\frac{\partial u}{\partial x} = \frac{\partial v}{\partial y} \quad \text{and} \quad \frac{\partial u}{\partial y} = -\frac{\partial v}{\partial x}.$$

These equations are the *Cauchy-Riemann* conditions, so named in honor of the French mathematician A. L. Cauchy (1789–1857), who discovered and used them, and in honor of the German mathematician G. F. B. Riemann (1826–1866), who made them fundamental in his development of the theory of analytic functions.

We have now shown that the Cauchy-Riemann conditions are *necessary* conditions for the existence of the derivative of the function

$$f(z) = u + iv.$$

As an illustration, we have seen earlier that the derivative of the function

$$f(z) = z^2 = x^2 - y^2 + 2xyi$$

exists at every point, in fact that $f'(z) = 2z$. Hence the Cauchy-Riemann conditions must be satisfied everywhere. In verification note that

$$u = x^2 - y^2, \quad v = 2xy,$$

and therefore

$$\frac{\partial u}{\partial x} = 2x = \frac{\partial v}{\partial y}, \qquad \frac{\partial u}{\partial y} = -2y = -\frac{\partial v}{\partial x}.$$

Also according to formula (1),

$$f'(z) = \frac{\partial u}{\partial x} + i\frac{\partial v}{\partial x} = 2x + 2yi = 2z.$$

19. Sufficient Conditions.   Conditions on u and v that are sufficient to ensure the existence of the derivative $f'(z)$ are included in the following theorem.

Theorem.   *Let the real single-valued functions $u(x,y)$ and $v(x,y)$, together with their partial derivatives of the first order with respect to x and y, be continuous in some neighborhood of a point (x_0,y_0). Then in order that the function $f(z) = u + iv$ have a derivative at a point $z = x + iy$ in the neighborhood, it is necessary and sufficient that u and v satisfy the Cauchy-Riemann conditions at that point.*

The necessity of the conditions was proved in the last section.

Since u and its partial derivatives of the first order are continuous in the neighborhood, then when the points (x,y) and $(x + \Delta x, y + \Delta y)$ are in the neighborhood, we can write

$$\Delta u = u(x + \Delta x, y + \Delta y) - u(x,y)$$
$$= \frac{\partial u}{\partial x}\Delta x + \frac{\partial u}{\partial y}\Delta y + \epsilon_1 \Delta x + \epsilon_2 \Delta y,$$

where $\partial u/\partial x$ and $\partial u/\partial y$ are the values of the partial derivatives at the point (x,y) and where ϵ_1 and ϵ_2 approach zero as both Δx and Δy approach zero.   The above formula for Δu is established in advanced calculus in connection with the definition of the differential of the function $u(x,y)$.

A similar formula may be written for Δv.   Therefore,

$$\Delta f = f(z + \Delta z) - f(z) = \Delta u + i\,\Delta v$$
$$= \frac{\partial u}{\partial x}\Delta x + \frac{\partial u}{\partial y}\Delta y + \epsilon_1 \Delta x + \epsilon_2 \Delta y$$
$$+ i\left(\frac{\partial v}{\partial x}\Delta x + \frac{\partial v}{\partial y}\Delta y + \epsilon_3 \Delta x + \epsilon_4 \Delta y\right).$$

Assuming now that the Cauchy-Riemann conditions are satisfied at the point (x,y), we can replace $\partial u/\partial y$ by $-\partial v/\partial x$ and $\partial v/\partial y$ by $\partial u/\partial x$ and write the last equation in the form

$$\Delta f = \frac{\partial u}{\partial x}(\Delta x + i\,\Delta y) + i\frac{\partial v}{\partial x}(\Delta x + i\,\Delta y) + \delta_1 \Delta x + \delta_2 \Delta y,$$

where δ_1 and δ_2 approach zero as Δz approaches zero ($\Delta z = \Delta x + i\,\Delta y$).

It follows that

(1)
$$\frac{\Delta f}{\Delta z} = \frac{\partial u}{\partial x} + i\,\frac{\partial v}{\partial x} + \delta_1 \frac{\Delta x}{\Delta z} + \delta_2 \frac{\Delta y}{\Delta z}.$$

Since $|\Delta x| \leq |\Delta z|$ and $|\Delta y| \leq |\Delta z|$, then

$$\left|\frac{\Delta x}{\Delta z}\right| \leq 1, \qquad \left|\frac{\Delta y}{\Delta z}\right| \leq 1,$$

so that the last two terms on the right of equation (1) tend to zero with Δz. Therefore

$$f'(z) = \lim_{\Delta z \to 0} \frac{\Delta f}{\Delta z} = \frac{\partial u}{\partial x} + i\,\frac{\partial v}{\partial x};$$

that is, the derivative of $f(z)$ exists, and the theorem is proved.

As an example of the use of our result, consider once more the function

$$f(z) = x^2 + y^2 = |z|^2.$$

Here $u = x^2 + y^2$ and $v = 0$; also

$$\frac{\partial u}{\partial x} = 2x, \qquad \frac{\partial v}{\partial y} = 0; \qquad \frac{\partial u}{\partial y} = 2y, \qquad \frac{\partial v}{\partial x} = 0.$$

All these functions are polynomials in x and y, and they are therefore continuous everywhere. The Cauchy-Riemann conditions are satisfied only at the origin. Consequently $f'(z)$ exists only at $z = 0$, as we found in Sec. 16.

EXERCISES

In Exercises 1–6 determine where the Cauchy-Riemann conditions are satisfied.

1. $w = 1 - z + 2z^2$.   *Ans.* Everywhere.

2. $w = \bar{z}$.

3. $w = z + \bar{z} = 2x$.

4. $w = az + b$, where a and b are complex constants.   *Ans.* Everywhere.

5. $w = \dfrac{1}{z}$.   *Ans.* $z \neq 0$.

6. $w = 2x + xy^2 i$.   *Ans.* Nowhere.

7. For the function $w = z^3 - 2z$, find dw/dz using the definition of the derivative. Also show that u and v satisfy the Cauchy-Riemann conditions, in order to establish in a second way that w has a derivative everywhere.

8. Consider the single-valued function $w = \sqrt{z}$ where $0 < \arg z < \pi$ and $|z| > 0$. Put $\sqrt{z} = \sqrt{r}\,[\cos (\theta/2) + i \sin (\theta/2)]$, and thus find u and v and show that they satisfy the Cauchy-Riemann conditions.

Ans. $u = \sqrt{(r + x)/2},\; v = \sqrt{(r - x)/2}$.

9. If $f(z) = u + iv$ and $z = r(\cos \theta + i \sin \theta)$, then u and v are functions of r and θ. Show that the Cauchy-Riemann conditions are satisfied if and only if u

and v satisfy both the conditions

$$\frac{\partial u}{\partial r} = \frac{1}{r}\frac{\partial v}{\partial \theta}, \qquad \frac{\partial v}{\partial r} = -\frac{1}{r}\frac{\partial u}{\partial \theta} \qquad\qquad (r \neq 0).$$

10. Use the polar form of the Cauchy-Riemann conditions established in Exercise 9 to show that those conditions are satisfied for the single-valued function

$$\sqrt{z} = \sqrt{r}\left(\cos\frac{\theta}{2} + i\sin\frac{\theta}{2}\right) \qquad (r > 0, 0 < \theta < 2\pi).$$

20. Analytic Functions. A single-valued function $f(z)$ is *analytic* at a point z_0 if and only if its derivative exists at every point in some neighborhood of z_0. When it exists, the derivative has, of course, a unique value. Note that the point z_0 is included in its neighborhood.

The function $|z|^2$, for example, is not analytic at any point, since its derivative exists only at $z = 0$, and therefore not throughout any neighborhood.

A function is analytic in a region of the z plane if it is analytic at every point in that region. The terms *holomorphic* and *regular* are often used in place of *analytic*.

If a function is analytic at some point in every neighborhood of z_0, but not analytic at z_0 itself, then the point z_0 is called a *singular point*, or a *singularity*, of the function. For instance, the function

$$f(z) = \frac{1}{z}$$

has for its derivative

$$f'(z) = -\frac{1}{z^2}$$

if $z \neq 0$. The function is analytic everywhere except at the point $z = 0$, which is a singular point of $f(z)$.

At present we have two methods of determining whether a function is analytic. First, if its derivative can be shown, directly from the definition or through the differentiation formulas, to exist throughout some open two-dimensional region, then the function is analytic at all points of the region.

Second, if $u(x,y)$ and $v(x,y)$, together with their partial derivatives of the first order, are continuous and single-valued and satisfy the Cauchy-Riemann conditions throughout some open two-dimensional region, then the function $f(z) = u + iv$ is analytic at all points of the region. If the Cauchy-Riemann conditions are satisfied in no such region, then $f(z)$ is nowhere analytic.

EXERCISES

In Exercises 1–4 determine where the given function is analytic and where it is continuous.

1. $f(z) = xy + iy$.   *Ans.* Nowhere; everywhere.

2. $f(z) = e^x \cos y + ie^x \sin y$.

3. $f(z) = \sin x \cosh y + i \cos x \sinh y$.   *Ans.* Everywhere; everywhere.

4. $f(z) = \dfrac{1}{z+1}$.

5. If in some region a function $f(z)$ and its conjugate $\overline{f(z)}$ are both analytic, prove that $f(z)$ is a constant.

21. Algebraic Functions. Every polynomial in z,

$$P(z) = a_0 + a_1 z + a_2 z^2 + \cdots + a_n z^n,$$

has a derivative at every point; in fact, according to the differentiation formulas,

$$P'(z) = a_1 + 2a_2 z + \cdots + na_n z^{n-1}.$$

Therefore $P(z)$ is analytic at every point in the complex plane.

Since the derivative of the product of two functions exists when the functions themselves have derivatives (Sec. 17), it follows that, if two functions are analytic in some region, their product is analytic there. Similarly for the sum and the quotient, provided that in the case of the quotient the region does not include any points where the denominator vanishes. Assuming that a polynomial is zero at only a finite number of points (Sec. 56), it follows that the quotient of two polynomials $P(z)/Q(z)$ is analytic everywhere except at the points for which $Q(z) = 0$.

Formula (7), Sec. 17, for the derivative of a function of a function shows *that an analytic function of an analytic function is analytic.*

For example, suppose that the function $\sqrt{z}$ is defined so as to be single-valued and continuous when $\Re(z) > 0$; then it is analytic there. The function $(2 - z^3)$ is everywhere analytic. Hence the function $\sqrt{2 - z^3}$ is analytic in any region where $\Re(2 - z^3) > 0$.

EXERCISES

Determine by inspection where each of the following functions fails to be analytic.

1. $\dfrac{z+2}{z(z^2+1)}$.   *Ans.* $z = 0, i, -i$.

2. $\dfrac{z}{z-1}$.

3. $\dfrac{z^2 - 2z + 4}{z^3(z^2 - 3z + 2)}$.

4. $z^3 - 2z + 1$.

5. $z^{-2}(z+2)^{-1}(z^2 + 2z + 2)^{-1}$.

22. Harmonic Functions.   Let the function $f(z) = u + iv$ be analytic in some region of the z plane.   Then

(1)
$$\frac{\partial u}{\partial x} = \frac{\partial v}{\partial y}, \qquad \frac{\partial u}{\partial y} = -\frac{\partial v}{\partial x},$$

and therefore

(2)
$$\frac{\partial^2 u}{\partial x^2} = \frac{\partial^2 v}{\partial x\,\partial y}, \qquad \frac{\partial^2 u}{\partial y^2} = -\frac{\partial^2 v}{\partial y\,\partial x},$$

provided these second derivatives exist.   We shall show in a later chapter (Sec. 53) that, when $f(z)$ is analytic, the partial derivatives of u and v of all orders exist and are continuous functions of x and y.   Granting this for the present, it follows that the two cross derivatives in equations (2) are equal, and therefore that

(3)
$$\frac{\partial^2 u}{\partial x^2} + \frac{\partial^2 u}{\partial y^2} = 0$$

throughout the region.

Equation (3) is *Laplace's* partial differential equation in two independent variables x and y.   Any function that has continuous partial derivatives of the second order and that satisfies Laplace's equation is called a *harmonic function*.

The function v, as well as u, is harmonic when the function

$$f(z) = u + iv$$

is an analytic function.   This can be shown by differentiating the first of equations (1) with respect to y, the second with respect to x, and subtracting to get the equation

(4)
$$\frac{\partial^2 v}{\partial x^2} + \frac{\partial^2 v}{\partial y^2} = 0.$$

If the function $f(z) = u + iv$ is analytic, then u and v are called *conjugate harmonic functions*.   This is a different use of the word *conjugate* from that employed in defining $\bar{z}$.

Given one of two conjugate harmonic functions, the Cauchy-Riemann equations (1) can be used to find the other.   We shall now illustrate one method of obtaining the conjugate harmonic of a given harmonic function.

The function

$$u = y^3 - 3x^2 y$$

is readily seen, by direct substitution into Laplace's equation, to be a harmonic function.   In order to find its harmonic conjugate v, we note that

$$\frac{\partial u}{\partial x} = -6xy,$$

from which, by using one of the Cauchy-Riemann equations, we may conclude that

$$\frac{\partial v}{\partial y} = -6xy.$$

Integrating this equation with respect to y with x held fixed, we find that

$$v = -3xy^2 + \phi(x),$$

where $\phi(x)$ is at present an arbitrary function of x. But since

$$\frac{\partial v}{\partial x} = -\frac{\partial u}{\partial y},$$

it follows that

$$-3y^2 + \phi'(x) = -3y^2 + 3x^2;$$

therefore $\phi'(x) = 3x^2$ and $\phi(x) = x^3 + c$, where c is an arbitrary constant. Hence the harmonic conjugate of the function $u = y^3 - 3x^2y$ is

$$v = -3xy^2 + x^3 + c.$$

The corresponding function $f(z) = u + iv$ is

(5) $$f(z) = y^3 - 3x^2y + i(x^3 - 3xy^2) + ic.$$

It is easily verified that

$$f(z) = i(z^3 + c).$$

This form is suggested by noting that when $y = 0$, equation (5) becomes

$$f(x) = i(x^3 + c).$$

Later on (Sec. 78) we shall show that, corresponding to each harmonic function u, a conjugate harmonic function v exists. We shall use a line integral to write an explicit formula for v in terms of u.

EXERCISES

In Exercises 1–4 show that the given function is harmonic, then determine its harmonic conjugate.

1. $u = \dfrac{1}{2}\log(x^2 + y^2)$.   *Ans.* $v = \arctan\dfrac{y}{x} + c.$

2. $u = 2x - x^3 + 3xy^2$
3. $u = \cos x \cosh y$.   *Ans.* $v = -\sin x \sinh y + c.$

4. $u = \dfrac{y}{x^2 + y^2}.$

5. Let $u(x,y)$ and $v(x,y)$ be conjugate harmonic functions. Their contour curves or level lines are the families of curves $u = c_1$ and $v = c_2$. Prove that these families of curves are orthogonal. More precisely, show that at any point (x_0, y_0) that is common to a curve $u = c_1$ and a curve $v = c_2$, the tangents to the two

curves are perpendicular, provided $\partial u/\partial x$ and $\partial u/\partial y$ do not both vanish at the point; that is, provided $f'(z_0) \neq 0$ where $f(z) = u + iv$.

6. Show that when

$$f(z) = u + iv = z^2,$$

the families of curves $u = c_1$ and $v = c_2$ are those shown in Fig. 13. Note the orthogonality of these curves as proved in Exercise 5. The curves $u = 0$ and

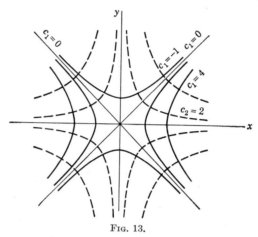

FIG. 13.

$v = 0$ intersect at the origin and are not orthogonal to each other. Why is this fact in agreement with the result of Exercise 5?

7. Sketch the families of curves $u = c_1$ and $v = c_2$ when

$$f(z) = \frac{1}{z},$$

and note the orthogonality proved in Exercise 5.

8. Sketch the families of curves $u = c_1$ and $v = c_2$ when

$$f(z) = \frac{z-1}{z+1},$$

and note how the results of Exercise 5 are illustrated here.

CHAPTER III

ELEMENTARY FUNCTIONS

23. The Exponential Function. We define the function e^z, where e is the base of the natural logarithm introduced in calculus, in terms of real functions by the formula

$$(1) \qquad e^z = e^x(\cos y + i \sin y),$$

when $z = x + iy$. The symbol exp z is also used to denote this same function.

As to the reasons for choosing this definition, we note first that when the argument is real, that is, when $z = x$, formula (1) reduces to e^x. Furthermore, in order that the exponential function of a complex variable may satisfy the basic laws of real exponential functions, we should like to be able to write the relation

$$e^{x+iy} = e^x e^{iy}.$$

We should also like to have the formal Maclaurin series expansion of e^{iy} apply, so that we could write for e^{iy} the series

$$(2) \qquad \sum_{n=0}^{\infty} \frac{(iy)^n}{n!} = \sum_{n=0}^{\infty} \frac{(iy)^{2n}}{(2n)!} + \sum_{n=0}^{\infty} \frac{(iy)^{2n+1}}{(2n+1)!},$$

where we have written $0! = 1$. Since $i^{2n} = (-1)^n$, the right-hand member becomes

$$\sum_{n=0}^{\infty} (-1)^n \frac{y^{2n}}{(2n)!} + i \sum_{n=0}^{\infty} (-1)^n \frac{y^{2n+1}}{(2n+1)!}.$$

Assuming that the Maclaurin series for the two functions $\cos y$ and $\sin y$ converge to these functions, and that the series (2) is to represent e^{iy}, we conclude that we should write

$$(3) \qquad e^{iy} = \cos y + i \sin y.$$

Formula (1) would then follow. That is, we expect to show later on that the manipulations carried out in the foregoing paragraph are all valid, and hence it seems that our definition (1) is a natural one.

The exponential function (1) is analytic for every value of z. This

37

follows from the Cauchy-Riemann conditions, for if we write

$$e^z = u + iv = e^x(\cos y + i \sin y),$$

then

$$u = e^x \cos y, \qquad v = e^x \sin y,$$

and therefore

$$\frac{\partial u}{\partial x} = e^x \cos y = \frac{\partial v}{\partial y}, \qquad \frac{\partial u}{\partial y} = -e^x \sin y = -\frac{\partial v}{\partial x}.$$

Since our function is analytic, its derivative is given by the formula

$$f'(z) = \frac{\partial u}{\partial x} + i\frac{\partial v}{\partial x} = e^x \cos y + ie^x \sin y;$$

that is,

(4) $$\frac{d}{dz}(e^z) = e^z.$$

If w is an analytic function of z, then exp w is an analytic function of z, since it is an analytic function of an analytic function. It follows from the formula for the derivative of a function of a function that

(5) $$\frac{d}{dz}(e^w) = e^w \frac{dw}{dz}.$$

24. Other Properties of the Exponential Function. Since

(1) $$e^z = e^{x+iy} = e^x(\cos y + i \sin y),$$

it follows, by setting $x = 0$, that

(2) $$e^{iy} = \cos y + i \sin y,$$

and that

(3) $$|e^z| = e^x.$$

Our definition (1) presents the complex number exp z in polar form, the absolute value of the number being given by formula (3) and the argument by the formula

$$\arg e^z = y.$$

The polar form of z, that is, $z = r(\cos \theta + i \sin \theta)$, can therefore be written in the more compact form

(4) $$z = re^{i\theta}.$$

The formula for the product of two complex numbers in polar form established in Sec. 8 can now be written

(5) $$z_1 z_2 = (r_1 e^{i\theta_1})(r_2 e^{i\theta_2}) = r_1 r_2 e^{i(\theta_1+\theta_2)}.$$

Similarly, we can now write

(6) $$\frac{z_1}{z_2} = \frac{r_1}{r_2} e^{i(\theta_1 - \theta_2)}, \qquad z^k = r^k (e^{ik\theta}),$$

where k is a real rational number.

The laws of exponents for the exponential functions follow immediately. In view of formula (5), for instance, we can write

$$e^{z_1} e^{z_2} = (e^{x_1} e^{iy_1})(e^{x_2} e^{iy_2}) = e^{(x_1 + x_2)} e^{i(y_1 + y_2)};$$

that is,

(7) $$e^{z_1} e^{z_2} = e^{(z_1 + z_2)}.$$

From formulas (6) we find that

(8) $$\frac{e^{z_1}}{e^{z_2}} = e^{(z_1 - z_2)},$$

(9) $$(e^z)^k = e^{k(z + 2n\pi i)},$$

where k is a real rational number. Here $n = 0, 1, 2, \cdots, m_2 - 1$, if $k = m_1/m_2$ where m_1 and m_2 are integers having no common factor.

From the definition it follows that the function exp z is periodic with period $2\pi i$; that is,

(10) $$e^{(z + 2\pi i)} = e^z.$$

It also follows that the number exp $\bar{z}$ is the complex conjugate of the number exp z.

EXERCISES

1. Show that $\exp \pi i = -1$; also that $\exp [(2n + 1)\pi i] = -1$, where n is any positive or negative integer.

2. Show that

$$\exp \frac{1 + \pi i}{4} = \frac{\sqrt[4]{e}}{\sqrt{2}} (1 + i).$$

3. Find the complex number $\exp (-2 + i\pi/2)$.

4. If $z = r \exp i\theta$, show that $\bar{z} = r \exp (-i\theta)$.

5. Prove that, for every finite value of z, $e^z \neq 0$.

6. By identifying the real and imaginary components, solve the equation $\exp z = -2$ for z.   *Ans.* $z = \log 2 \pm (2n + 1)\pi i$ $(n = 0, 1, 2, \cdots)$.

7. Solve the equation $\exp z = 1 + i \sqrt{3}$ for z.

8. Establish the properties (8), (9), and (10) of the last section.

9. Show that $\exp \bar{z} = \overline{\exp z}$.

10. Show that $\exp i\bar{z} \neq \overline{\exp iz}$ unless $z = \pm n\pi$, where $n = 0, 1, 2, \cdots$.

11. Find (a) $|\exp (i - 2z)|$; (b) $|\exp (z^2)|$.

12. Show that $|\exp (-2z)| < 1$ when z is any point in the half plane $x > 0$, and for no other points.

13. Show in two ways why the function $\exp(z^2)$ is everywhere analytic. What is its derivative?   *Ans.* $2z \exp(z^2)$.

14. Find $\Re[\exp(1/z)]$. Why is this a harmonic function of x and y in any region not including the origin?

15. Show in various ways that the function

$$w = e^z + e^{-z}$$

is analytic for all values of z.

16. Show that the function $\exp \bar{z}$ is not an analytic function of z.

25. The Trigonometric Functions. Since

$$e^{iy} = \cos y + i \sin y,$$

then

$$e^{-iy} = \cos y - i \sin y,$$

and the real trigonometric functions can be written

$$(1) \qquad \cos y = \frac{e^{iy} + e^{-iy}}{2}, \qquad \sin y = \frac{e^{iy} - e^{-iy}}{2i}.$$

It is therefore natural to define $\cos z$ and $\sin z$ for complex values of z by the equations

$$(2) \qquad \cos z = \frac{e^{iz} + e^{-iz}}{2}, \qquad \sin z = \frac{e^{iz} - e^{-iz}}{2i}.$$

Since $\exp z$, iz, and $-iz$ are analytic functions of z, both $\sin z$ and $\cos z$ as defined in equations (2) are analytic functions of z. It also follows that they have no singular points in the finite z plane. Knowing the derivative of the exponential function, we may obtain the formulas

$$(3) \qquad \frac{d}{dz} (\sin z) = \cos z, \qquad \frac{d}{dz} (\cos z) = - \sin z.$$

The remaining trigonometric functions are defined in terms of $\sin z$ and $\cos z$ by the usual relations,

$$(4) \qquad \begin{aligned} \tan z &= \frac{\sin z}{\cos z}, & \cot z &= \frac{1}{\tan z}, \\ \sec z &= \frac{1}{\cos z}, & \csc z &= \frac{1}{\sin z}. \end{aligned}$$

The function $\tan z$ is thus the quotient of two analytic functions; it is analytic except at the points for which $\cos z = 0$. The singular points of the remaining three functions are likewise evident. The derivatives of these four functions,

$$(5) \qquad \begin{aligned} \frac{d}{dz} (\tan z) &= \sec^2 z, & \frac{d}{dz} (\cot z) &= - \csc^2 z, \\ \frac{d}{dz} (\sec z) &= \sec z \tan z, & \frac{d}{dz} (\csc z) &= - \csc z \cot z, \end{aligned}$$

can be obtained by differentiating the right-hand members of equations (4).

From the definition of cos z it follows that

$$\begin{aligned}
\cos z = \cos (x + iy) &= \tfrac{1}{2}(e^{ix-y} + e^{-ix+y}) \\
&= \tfrac{1}{2}e^{-y}(\cos x + i \sin x) + \tfrac{1}{2}e^{y}(\cos x - i \sin x) \\
&= \frac{e^{y} + e^{-y}}{2} \cos x - i\,\frac{e^{y} - e^{-y}}{2} \sin x.
\end{aligned}$$

Thus the real and imaginary parts of cos z are displayed as follows:

(6) $\qquad \cos z = \cos (x + iy) = \cos x \cosh y - i \sin x \sinh y.$

In the same manner we find that

(7) $\qquad \sin z = \sin (x + iy) = \sin x \cosh y + i \cos x \sinh y.$

It is evident from these two formulas that

(8) $\qquad \sin (iy) = i \sinh y, \qquad \cos (iy) = \cosh y;$

also that sin $\bar{z}$ and cos $\bar{z}$ are the complex conjugates of sin z and cos z, respectively.

26. Further Properties of the Trigonometric Functions. By using either formulas (1) and (2) or formulas (7) and (6) of the last section the reader can show that

(1) $\qquad\qquad |\sin z|^2 = \sin^2 x + \sinh^2 y,$
(2) $\qquad\qquad |\cos z|^2 = \cos^2 x + \sinh^2 y.$

It is clear from these two formulas that the complex functions sin z and cos z are not bounded in absolute value, whereas in real variables the absolute values of the sine and cosine functions are never greater than unity.

The expected trigonometric identities are still valid in complex variables; thus

(3) $\qquad\qquad \sin^2 z + \cos^2 z = 1,$
(4) $\qquad\qquad \sin (z_1 + z_2) = \sin z_1 \cos z_2 + \cos z_1 \sin z_2,$
(5) $\qquad\qquad \cos (z_1 + z_2) = \cos z_1 \cos z_2 - \sin z_1 \sin z_2,$
(6) $\qquad\qquad \sin (-z) = - \sin z,$
(7) $\qquad\qquad \cos (-z) = \cos z,$
(8) $\qquad\qquad \sin \left(\frac{\pi}{2} - z \right) = \cos z,$
(9) $\qquad\qquad \sin 2z = 2 \sin z \cos z,$
(10) $\qquad\qquad \cos 2z = \cos^2 z - \sin^2 z,$

etc. Proofs may be based entirely upon the properties of the exponential function. They are left as exercises.

A value of z for which a function $f(z) = 0$ is called a *zero* of $f(z)$. The real zeros of the trigonometric functions are their only zeros. To establish this important property in the case of the sine function, we write

$$\sin z = 0;$$

then from equation (7) of Sec. 25 we conclude that both the equations

$$\sin x \cosh y = 0, \qquad \cos x \sinh y = 0,$$

must be satisfied. Since x and y are real, $\cosh y \geq 1$ and it does not vanish, while $\sin x$ vanishes only for $x = 0,\ \pm\pi,\ \pm2\pi,\ \pm3\pi$, etc. For these values of x, $\cos x$ does not vanish. Hence $\sinh y$ must be zero, and therefore $y = 0$. Thus the only values of z for which $\sin z$ is zero are the real values

$$z = 0,\ \pm n\pi \qquad\qquad (n = 1,2,\ \cdots).$$

EXERCISES

1. Establish the differentiation formulas (5), Sec. 25

2. Establish formulas (7) and (8), Sec. 25.

3. Establish formulas (1) and (2), Sec. 26.

4. Establish the identities (3), (4), and (5), Sec. 26.

5. Prove that $1 + \tan^2 z = \sec^2 z$.

6. Prove that $1 + \cot^2 z = \csc^2 z$.

7. Prove that

$$\tan 2z = \frac{2 \tan z}{1 - \tan^2 z}.$$

8. Prove that $\tan \bar{z} = \overline{\tan z}$.

9. Show that $\sin (i\bar{z}) \neq \overline{\sin (iz)}$ unless $z = \pm n\pi i$, where $n = 0, 1, 2, \cdots$.

10. Show that $\cos (i\bar{z}) = \overline{\cos (iz)}$.

11. Find $\Re (\tan z)$.

12. Show in two ways that each of the functions

$$(a)\ \sin x \sinh y, \qquad (b)\ \cos 2x \sinh 2y$$

is harmonic.

13. Prove that the only roots of the equation $\cos z = 0$ are the real roots $z = \pm(2n - 1)\pi/2 \quad (n = 1,2,\ \cdots)$.

14. Find all the roots of the equation $\sin z = \cosh 4$.

Ans. $z = (\pi/2) \pm 2n\pi \pm 4i$.

15. Find all the singular points of the function $\tan z$.

16. Show that the functions $(a)\ \sin \bar{z}$ and $(b)\ \cos \bar{z}$ are not analytic functions of z.

27. The Hyperbolic Functions. The hyperbolic sine and cosine of a complex argument are defined as they were with real arguments; that is,

$$(1) \qquad\qquad \sinh z = \frac{e^z - e^{-z}}{2}, \qquad \cosh z = \frac{e^z + e^{-z}}{2}.$$

The hyperbolic tangent of z is defined by the equation

$$\tanh z = \frac{\sinh z}{\cosh z},$$

and then coth z, sech z, and csch z are defined as the reciprocals of tanh z, cosh z, and sinh z, respectively.

Since e^z is analytic everywhere, it follows from formulas (1) that sinh z and cosh z are analytic everywhere. The function tanh z is analytic everywhere except at the zeros of cosh z. With the aid of the definition (1) the reader can show that cosh z vanishes at the points $z = \pm(n + \frac{1}{2})\pi i$, where $n = 0, 1, 2, \cdots$; these are the singular points of tanh z.

The calculus and algebra of the complex hyperbolic functions can be derived readily from the definitions above. The formulas are the same as those established for the corresponding functions of real variables; thus

$$(2) \qquad \frac{d}{dz}(\sinh z) = \cosh z, \qquad \frac{d}{dz}(\cosh z) = \sinh z,$$

$$(3) \qquad \frac{d}{dz}(\tanh z) = \operatorname{sech}^2 z, \qquad \frac{d}{dz}(\coth z) = -\operatorname{csch}^2 z,$$

$$(4) \quad \frac{d}{dz}(\operatorname{sech} z) = -\operatorname{sech} z \tanh z, \qquad \frac{d}{dz}(\operatorname{csch} z) = -\operatorname{csch} z \coth z.$$

Some of the most frequently used identities are

$$(5) \qquad \cosh^2 z - \sinh^2 z = 1,$$
$$(6) \qquad \sinh(z_1 + z_2) = \sinh z_1 \cosh z_2 + \cosh z_1 \sinh z_2,$$
$$(7) \qquad \cosh(z_1 + z_2) = \cosh z_1 \cosh z_2 + \sinh z_1 \sinh z_2,$$
$$(8) \qquad \sinh 2z = 2 \sinh z \cosh z,$$
$$(9) \qquad \sinh(-z) = -\sinh z, \qquad \cosh(-z) = \cosh z.$$

The relations between the hyperbolic and circular functions also follow from the definitions of those functions in terms of the exponential functions; thus

$$(10) \qquad \sinh(iz) = i \sin z, \qquad \cosh(iz) = \cos z,$$
$$(11) \qquad \sin(iz) = i \sinh z, \qquad \cos(iz) = \cosh z.$$

The real and imaginary components of the first two hyperbolic functions are shown in the formulas

$$(12) \qquad \sinh(x + iy) = \sinh x \cos y + i \cosh x \sin y,$$
$$(13) \qquad \cosh(x + iy) = \cosh x \cos y + i \sinh x \sin y.$$

The reader can show in various ways that

$$(14) \qquad |\sinh z|^2 = \sinh^2 x + \sin^2 y,$$
$$(15) \qquad |\cosh z|^2 = \sinh^2 x + \cos^2 y.$$

Since the function exp z has the period $2\pi i$, the function exp $(-z)$ also has that period. Consequently, the functions sinh z, cosh z, tanh z, etc., are periodic with the period $2\pi i$.

EXERCISES

1. Establish formulas (2) and (4) above.

2. Establish formula (5) above.

3. Establish formula (7) above.

4. Establish formula (13) above.

5. Establish formula (15) above.

6. Prove that tanh $(z + \pi i) = $ tanh z.

7. Prove that the only zeros of the function sinh z are $z = \pm n\pi i$, where $n = 0, 1, 2, \cdots$.

8. Find the zeros of the function cosh z.

9. Find all the roots of the equation cosh $z = \frac{1}{2}$.

Ans. $z = [(\pm\pi/3) \pm 2n\pi]i$.

10. Find all the roots of the equation sinh $z = i$.

Ans. $z = [(\pi/2) \pm 2n\pi]i$.

11. Find the singular points of the function tanh $(z + 1)$.

Ans. $z = -1 \pm (n - \frac{1}{2})\pi i$.

12. If w is an analytic function of z, write the formulas for the derivatives with respect to z of the hyperbolic functions of w: sinh w, cosh w, etc.

28. The Logarithmic Function. We define the function log z as follows:

(1) $$\log z = \log (re^{i\theta}) = \text{Log } r + i\theta,$$

when $z \neq 0$. We have written Log r here for the real natural logarithm of the positive number r. Our definition is a natural one in the sense that it is written by formally using the properties of real logarithms. Corresponding to the particular argument Θ of z such that

$$-\pi < \Theta \leq \pi,$$

we may write $z = r$ exp $[i(\Theta \pm 2n\pi)]$, where $n = 0, 1, 2, \cdots$. Thus formula (1) can be written

(2) $$\log z = \text{Log } r + i(\Theta \pm 2n\pi) \qquad (n = 0,1,2, \cdots);$$

that is, the function log z is multiple-valued with infinitely many values. We shall call the *principal value* of log z the number defined by formula (2) when $n = 0$, and write this as Log z; thus

(3) $$\text{Log } z = \text{Log } r + i\Theta \qquad (-\pi < \Theta \leq \pi).$$

Note that if z is real and positive, then $z = r$ so that the symbol Log r represents the principal value of log r.

The single-valued function (3) can be written

$$\text{Log } z = \frac{1}{2}\text{Log } (x^2 + y^2) + i \arctan \frac{y}{x},$$

where the inverse tangent here represents an angle between zero and π if $y > 0$, and between $-\pi$ and zero if $y < 0$. In either case, the usual formula for the derivative of the real function $\arctan t$ is valid. We can write, for instance,

$$\frac{\partial}{\partial x}\left(\arctan \frac{y}{x}\right) = \frac{-y/x^2}{1 + (y^2/x^2)} = -\frac{y}{x^2 + y^2},$$

and it is easy to show that the Cauchy-Riemann conditions are satisfied. The function $\text{Log } (x^2 + y^2)$ is continuous except at the origin. Our function $\arctan (y/x)$ is continuous at all points except the origin and the points on the negative half of the x axis, where its value is π while its limit from below the x axis is $-\pi$. The partial derivatives of the two functions are also continuous functions of (x,y) in the region of continuity of the functions. It follows that the single-valued function (3) is analytic in the region $-\pi < \Theta < \pi, r > 0$.

The function defined by formula (1) can be made single-valued by limiting θ so that

$$\theta_0 < \theta \leqq \theta_0 + 2\pi,$$

where θ_0 is any fixed angle. The function so defined differs from the principal value only by an imaginary constant, according to formula (3). Consequently, it too is analytic in the open region in which it is single-valued. Moreover, for every fixed θ_0,

$$\frac{d}{dz}(\log z) = \frac{1}{2}\frac{\partial}{\partial x}[\text{Log } (x^2 + y^2)] + i\frac{\partial}{\partial x}\left(\arctan \frac{y}{x}\right)$$

$$= \frac{x}{x^2 + y^2} - \frac{iy}{x^2 + y^2} = \frac{\bar{z}}{z\bar{z}}.$$

Therefore

(4) $$\frac{d}{dz}(\log z) = \frac{1}{z}.$$

The usual formulas for logarithms of products, quotients, and powers hold true for logarithms of complex numbers provided we use the appropriate one of the many values of the logarithm. Let

$$z_1 = r_1 e^{i\theta_1}, \qquad z_2 = r_2 e^{i\theta_2}.$$

Then, since $\text{Log } r_1 + \text{Log } r_2 = \text{Log } (r_1 r_2)$, we can write

$$\log z_1 + \log z_2 = \text{Log } (r_1 r_2) + i(\theta_1 + \theta_2).$$

But $z_1 z_2 = r_1 r_2 \exp [i(\theta_1 + \theta_2 + 2n\pi)]$; consequently

(5) $$\log z_1 + \log z_2 = \log (z_1 z_2),$$

provided that the value of the logarithm on the right is the one corresponding to $n = 0$.

Suppose, for example, that

$$z_1 = z_2 = e^{i\pi} = -1.$$

Taking $\log z_1 = \log z_2 = i\pi$, we see that formula (5) is true provided we write

$$\log (z_1 z_2) = 2\pi i;$$

it is not true when the principal value, Log $1 = 0$, is used for $\log (z_1 z_2)$.

Similarly, it can be shown that

(6) $$\log z_1 - \log z_2 = \log \frac{z_1}{z_2},$$

(7) $$k \log z = \log z^k,$$

where k is a real rational number, provided we use the appropriate values of the logarithms on the right.

The functions $\log z$ and $\exp z$ are inverses of each other; that is, if $w = \log z$, then $\exp w = z$, and conversely. For if $w = \log z$, then

$$e^w = \exp (\text{Log } r + i\theta) = \exp (\text{Log } r) \exp (i\theta) = re^{i\theta} = z.$$

Also, if $w = u + iv$ and $\exp w = z$, then, using the appropriate value of $\log z$, we have

$$\log z = \log (e^u e^{iv}) = u + iv = w.$$

Thus the two relations

(8) $$\exp (\log z) = z, \qquad \log (\exp w) = w,$$

are true provided that in the second one the value of the logarithm is properly chosen.

When k is a real rational number, the relation

(9) $$\exp (k \log z) = z^k$$

is a consequence of equations (7) and (8). If $\arg z$ is limited so that $\log z$ is single-valued and if $z \neq 0$, then equation (9) shows that the function z^k is analytic, since that equation presents z^k as an analytic function of an analytic function.

Equation (9) can be used to define z^c where c is any complex number:

(10) $$z^c = \exp (c \log z).$$

The function z^c is multiple-valued when c is not an integer. Its principal value is defined as the value corresponding to the principal value of $\log z$.

As an example of the definition (10), let us find the principal value of $(-i)^i$:

$$(-i)^i = \exp [i \operatorname{Log} (-i)] = \exp (i \operatorname{Log} e^{-i\pi/2}) = \exp \left[i \left(-\frac{i\pi}{2} \right) \right] = e^{\pi/2}.$$

With the aid of the formulas for the derivatives of the exponential and logarithmic functions it follows from equation (10) that

$$\frac{d}{dz} (z^c) = cz^{c-1},$$

(11)

where c is any complex constant. This is the general formula for the derivative of a power of z.

According to the definition (10), the general exponential function with a complex constant a as its base can be written $a^z = \exp (z \log a)$. For a specified value of $\log a$ this function is single-valued and analytic for all values of z.

EXERCISES

1. Show that $\log (-1) = \pm (2n + 1)\pi i$, where $n = 0, 1, 2, \cdots$.

2. Show that the principal value of $\log (1 - i)$ is $\frac{1}{2} \operatorname{Log} 2 - i\pi/4$.

3. Find $\log [(i)^{\frac{1}{3}}]$.   *Ans.* $(1 \pm 4n)\pi i/4$.

4. Solve the equation $e^z = -3$.   *Ans.* $z = \operatorname{Log} 3 \pm (2n + 1)\pi i$.

5. Solve the equation $\log z = i\pi/2$.   *Ans.* $z = i$.

6. Establish formulas (6) and (7) above.

7. Use the Cauchy-Riemann conditions in polar coordinates (Sec. 19, Exercise 9) to show that $\operatorname{Log} z$ is analytic.

8. Establish formula (11) above.

9. Show that the values of i^i are the real numbers $\exp [(-1 \pm 4n)\pi/2]$.

10. Find the values of $(1 + i)^i$.

11. Show in two ways that the function $\operatorname{Log} (x^2 + y^2)$ is harmonic. What is the conjugate harmonic function?

12. Let $z = r \exp i\theta$ and $z - 1 = \rho \exp i\phi$. Show that

$$\Re[\log (z - 1)] = \tfrac{1}{2} \operatorname{Log} (1 + r^2 - 2r \cos \theta).$$

13. Show that the derivative of the function a^z is $a^z \log a$.

29. The Inverse Trigonometric Functions.

The inverse trigonometric and hyperbolic functions may be expressed in terms of logarithms and algebraic functions.

Let us define the function

$$w = \sin^{-1} z$$

as the inverse of the function

$$z = \sin w = \frac{e^{iw} - e^{-iw}}{2i}.$$

Then we may obtain e^{iw} by solving the equation

$$e^{2iw} - 2ize^{iw} - 1 = 0,$$

which is a quadratic in e^{iw}. We find that

$$e^{iw} = iz + (1 - z^2)^{\frac{1}{2}},$$

where $(1 - z^2)^{\frac{1}{2}}$ is, as we know, a double-valued function of z. Finally we may write

(1) $$w = \sin^{-1} z = -i \log [iz + (1 - z^2)^{\frac{1}{2}}],$$

which is a multiple-valued function with infinitely many values. When the logarithm and the square root are made single-valued, the single-valued function (1) is analytic because it is a composite of analytic functions.

Similarly, the inverses of the functions $\cos w$ and $\tan w$ are found to be

(2) $$\cos^{-1} z = -i \log [z + (z^2 - 1)^{\frac{1}{2}}],$$

(3) $$\tan^{-1} z = \frac{i}{2} \log \frac{1 - iz}{1 + iz} = \frac{i}{2} \log \frac{i + z}{i - z}.$$

The derivatives of these three functions can be written by means of the above formulas. The derivative of the last one,

$$\frac{d}{dz} (\tan^{-1} z) = \frac{1}{1 + z^2},$$

does not depend on the manner in which the function is made single valued. The derivatives of the first two do depend on the values chosen for square roots; for instance,

$$\frac{d}{dz} (\sin^{-1} z) = (1 - z^2)^{-\frac{1}{2}},$$

and the last function here is double-valued.

The inverses of the hyperbolic functions can be written in the corresponding manner. It turns out that

(4) $$\sinh^{-1} z = \log [z + (z^2 + 1)^{\frac{1}{2}}],$$
(5) $$\cosh^{-1} z = \log [z + (z^2 - 1)^{\frac{1}{2}}],$$

(6) $$\tanh^{-1} z = \frac{1}{2} \log \frac{1 + z}{1 - z}.$$

The term *elementary function* signifies any function of z that can be expressed either in terms of the exponential and logarithmic functions, or by means of the operations of addition, subtraction, multiplication, and division, or both. These operations can involve constants as well as z. It is to be understood that only a finite number of operations need be involved to describe the function.

For example,

$$z^{\frac{1}{2}} = \exp\left(\tfrac{1}{2} \log z\right)$$

is an elementary function. Polynomials in z and quotients or roots of polynomials are elementary functions. We have seen above that the trigonometric, inverse trigonometric, hyperbolic, and inverse hyperbolic functions are elementary in the sense used here.

EXERCISES

1. Derive formula (2) above.

2. Derive formula (3) above.

3. Derive formula (6) above.

4. Solve the equation $\sin z = 2$ for z, (a) by identifying the real and imaginary components of $\sin z$ with those of 2; (b) by using formula (1) above.

Ans. $z = (1 \pm 4n)(\pi/2) \pm i \cosh^{-1} 2$.

5. Solve the equation $\cos z = 2$ for z.

6. Find (a) $\tan^{-1}(2i)$; (b) $\tan^{-1}(1 + i)$.

Ans. (a) $-(\pi/2) \pm n\pi + (i/2) \operatorname{Log} 3$.

7. Find (a) $\cosh^{-1} \tfrac{1}{2}$; (b) $\tanh^{-1} 0$. *Ans.* (b) $n\pi i$.

8. Show that the function 4^z is an elementary function, and find its derivative.

Ans. $4^z \log 4$.

CHAPTER IV

THE GEOMETRY OF ELEMENTARY FUNCTIONS

30. Mapping. Real functions of real variables, $y = f(x)$, can be exhibited graphically by plotting corresponding values of x and y as rectangular coordinates of points in the xy plane. The function $f(x)$ maps each point on the x axis into a point in the plane at a directed distance y above or below that point. The result of mapping all points of the x axis is a curve, the graph of the function.

When the variables are complex, the graphical representation of functions is more complicated, for if $w = f(z)$, each of the complex variables w and z are represented geometrically by points in the complex plane. It is generally simpler to use separate planes for the two variables. Then corresponding to each point (x,y) in the z plane for which $f(x + iy)$ is defined, there will be a point (u,v) in the w plane, where $w = u + iv$. That is, the function $f(z)$ maps points in the z plane upon the w plane.

The correspondence between points in the two planes is called a *mapping* or a *transformation* of points in the z plane into points in the w plane by function $f(z)$. Corresponding points are called *images* of each other. The word *image* is also applied to a curve or a region in one plane corresponding to a curve or region in the other.

The mapping of corresponding curves and regions in the two planes usually gives more information about the function than the mapping of individual points.

Even though two separate planes are used to represent w and z, it is often convenient to think of the mapping as effected in one plane, thus permitting the use of such graphic terms as *translation* and *rotation*. We may, for example, speak of the transformation $w = z + 2$ as moving each point and configuration in the z plane 2 units to the right. But the use of a separate w plane in the actual drawing of figures saves confusion.

We are particularly interested in the study of mapping by analytic functions because of its importance in certain physical applications. The problem of determining a function of two real variables that is harmonic in a given region and satisfies certain prescribed conditions on the boundary of the region can often be solved by means of mapping by analytic functions. For the purpose of solving such boundary value problems in Laplace's differential equation, it is desirable to see how various regions are transformed by the elementary analytic functions.

50

31. Linear Functions.   The mapping by means of the function

(1) $w = z + C,$

where C is a complex constant, is the translation of every point z through the vector representing C.   That is, if

$$z = x + iy, \qquad w = u + iv, \qquad C = C_1 + iC_2,$$

then the image of any point (x,y) in the z plane is the point

$$(x + C_1, y + C_2)$$

in the w plane.   Since every point in any region of the z plane is mapped upon the w plane in this same manner, the image of the region is simply a translation of the given region.   The two regions have the same shape, size, and orientation.

Let B be a complex constant whose polar form is $B = b \exp i\beta$.   Then if $z = r \exp i\theta$, the function

(2) $w = Bz = bre^{i(\theta+\beta)}$

maps the point (r,θ) in the z plane onto that point in the w plane whose polar coordinates are $br, \theta + \beta$.   That is, the mapping consists of a rotation of the radius vector of the point z about the origin through the angle $\beta = \arg B$ and an expansion or contraction of the radius vector by the factor $b = |B|$.   Every region in the z plane is transformed by this rotation and expansion into a geometrically similar region in the w plane.

By applying the transformation (1) to the variable w in equation (2), we see that the mapping by the general linear function

(3) $w = Bz + C$

consists of a rotation through the angle $\arg B$ and a magnification by the factor $|B|$, followed by a translation through the vector C.

As an illustration, the function

$$w = (1 + i)z + 2 - i$$

transforms the rectangular region shown in the z plane of Fig. 14 into

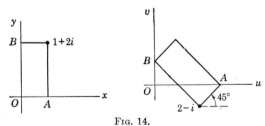

Fig. 14.

the rectangular region shown in the w plane. This is evident geometrically since $\arg (1 + i) = \pi/4$ and $|1 + i| = \sqrt{2}$.

As another illustration, let us note the image of the region $0 < x < 1$, the infinite strip between the lines $x = 0$ and $x = 1$, under the transformation

$$w = iz.$$

Since $i = \exp(i\pi/2)$, the transformation is a rotation through the angle $\pi/2$. Hence the image of the given strip is the strip $0 < v < 1$. This is also seen by noting that since $w = iz$, then $u = -y$ and $v = x$. When $0 < x < 1$ and y is unrestricted, it follows that $0 < v < 1$, and u is unrestricted.

32. Powers of z.   First let us consider the function

$$w = z^2.$$

This transformation can be described easily in terms of polar coordinates, for if $z = re^{i\theta}$ and $w = \rho e^{i\phi}$, then

$$\rho e^{i\phi} = r^2 e^{2i\theta}.$$

Thus the image of any point (r, θ) is that point in the w plane whose polar coordinates are $\rho = r^2$, $\phi = 2\theta$.

In particular, the function z^2 maps the entire first quadrant of the z plane, $0 \leqq \theta \leqq \pi/2$, $r \geqq 0$, upon the entire upper half of the w plane (Fig. 15).

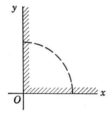

Fig. 15. $w = z^2$.

Circles about the origin, $r = r_0$, are transformed into circles $\rho = r_0^2$ in the w plane. The semicircular region $r \leqq r_0$, $0 \leqq \theta < \pi$ is mapped into the circular region $\rho \leqq r_0^2$, and the first quadrant of that semicircular region is mapped into the upper half of the circular region as indicated by the broken lines in Fig. 15.

In each of the above mappings of regions by the transformation $w = z^2$, there is just one point in the transformed region corresponding to a given point in the original region, and conversely; that is, there is a unique or one-to-one correspondence between points in the two regions. This uniqueness does not exist, however, for the circular region

$$r \leqq r_0, \qquad 0 \leqq \theta < 2\pi$$

and its image, since the image of that region covers the circular region $\rho \leqq r_0^2$ twice.

In rectangular coordinates the transformation $w = z^2$ becomes

$$u + iv = x^2 - y^2 + 2xyi.$$

Hence the hyperbolas $x^2 - y^2 = c_1$ and $2xy = c_2$, shown in Fig. 13, map into the vertical lines $u = c_1$ and the horizontal lines $v = c_2$, respectively. If $x > 0$, $y > 0$, and $xy < 1$, then $0 < v < 2$, and u can have any real value. Hence the region in the first quadrant of the z plane between the coordinate axes and the hyperbola $xy = 1$ maps into the horizontal strip between the lines $v = 0$ and $v = 2$ in the w plane.

The function

$$w = z^n$$

or

$$\rho e^{i\phi} = r^n e^{in\theta},$$

where n is a positive integer, transforms the angular region $0 \leqq \theta \leqq \pi/n$

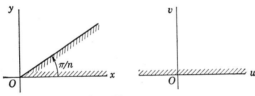

FIG. 16. $w = z^n$.

into the upper half of the w plane (Fig. 16), since $\phi = n\theta$. It transforms the circle $r = r_0$ into the circle $\rho = r_0^n$.

A discussion of cases in which n is not a positive integer will be given later.

EXERCISES

1. Under the transformation $w = iz + i$ show that the half plane $x > 0$ maps into the half plane $v > 1$.

2. Find the region into which the half plane $y > 0$ is mapped by the function $w = (1 + i)z$ (a) by using polar coordinates, (b) by using rectangular coordinates. Show the regions graphically.   *Ans.* The half plane $v > u$.

3. Find the image of the region $y > 1$ under the transformation $w = (1 - i)z$.

4. Find the image of the semiinfinite strip $x > 0$, $0 < y < 2$ under the transformation $w = iz + 1$. Show the regions graphically.

Ans. $-1 < u < 1$, $v > 0$.

5. If B and C are complex constants, give a geometrical description of the transformation $w = B(z + C)$.

6. If $w = Bz + C$, where $B = b \exp i\beta$ and $C = C_1 + iC_2$, find u and v in terms of x and y, and find x and y in terms of u and v.

Ans. $u = b(x \cos \beta - y \sin \beta) + C_1$, $v = b(x \sin \beta + y \cos \beta) + C_2$.

7. Describe the region into which the circular sector $0 < \theta < \pi/4$, $r < 1$ is mapped by the function (*a*) $w = z^2$; (*b*) $w = z^3$; (*c*) $w = z^4$.

8. What is the image in the z plane of the rectangular region bounded by the lines $u = 1$, $u = 2$, $v = 1$, $v = 2$, under the transformation $w = z^2$?

9. Show that the function $w = z^2$ maps the lines $y = c$ into parabolas with common foci at the point $w = 0$. What is the image of the line $y = 0$?

33. The Function $1/z$. In polar coordinates the transformation

$$w = \frac{1}{z}$$

becomes

$$\rho e^{i\phi} = \frac{1}{r} e^{-i\theta}.$$

FIG. 17. $w = \dfrac{1}{z}$.

This can be described by means of the consecutive transformations

$$w' = \frac{1}{r} e^{i\theta}, \qquad w = \overline{w'}.$$

The first is an *inversion* with respect to the unit circle; that is, the point w' lies on the radius drawn through the point z, and its distance from the center of the circle is such that $|w'||z| = 1$. This inversion is followed by a reflection $w = \overline{w'}$ in the real axis (Fig. 17). Thus points outside the unit circle are mapped into points inside the circle, and conversely.

When cartesian coordinates are used the equation

$$w = u + iv = \frac{1}{x + iy}$$

gives the relations

$$u = \frac{x}{x^2 + y^2}, \qquad v = -\frac{y}{x^2 + y^2},$$

and

$$x = \frac{u}{u^2 + v^2}, \qquad y = -\frac{v}{u^2 + v^2}.$$

If a, b, c, d represent real numbers, the equation

$$(1) \qquad\qquad a(x^2 + y^2) + bx + cy + d = 0$$

represents any circle or line, depending on whether $a \neq 0$ or $a = 0$. Under the transformation $w = 1/z$, equation (1) becomes

$$(2) \qquad\qquad d(u^2 + v^2) + bu - cv + a = 0.$$

Hence if a and d are different from zero, both the curve and its image are circles; that is, circles not passing through the point $z = 0$ transform into other circles not passing through the point $w = 0$.

Similarly, equations (1) and (2) show that every circle through the origin $z = 0$ transforms into a straight line in the w plane. Lines in the z plane transform into circles through the origin $w = 0$, unless the line passes through $z = 0$, in which case the image is a line through the origin $w = 0$.

If we consider lines as limiting cases of circles, we can say that the transformation always carries circles into circles. In particular, the lines $x = c_1$ transform into the circles

$$(3) \qquad u^2 + v^2 - \frac{u}{c_1} = 0$$

tangent to the v axis at the origin, and the lines $y = c_2$ into the circles

$$(4) \qquad u^2 + v^2 + \frac{v}{c_2} = 0,$$

as illustrated in Fig. 18.

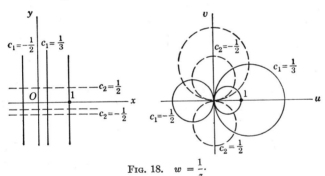

FIG. 18. $w = \dfrac{1}{z}.$

The half plane $x > c_1$ has for its image the region

$$(5) \qquad \frac{u}{u^2 + v^2} > c_1.$$

When $c_1 > 0$, it follows that

$$(6) \qquad \left(u - \frac{1}{2c_1}\right)^2 + v^2 < \left(\frac{1}{2c_1}\right)^2;$$

that is, the point w is inside a circle tangent to the v axis at the origin. Conversely, whenever u and v satisfy the inequality (6) and $c_1 > 0$, then the inequality (5) follows, and therefore $x > c_1$. Consequently, every point inside the circle is the image of some point in the half plane; thus the image of the half plane is the entire circular region (6).

34. The Point at Infinity.   Under the transformation $w = 1/z$, or

$$\rho e^{i\phi} = \frac{1}{r} e^{-i\theta},$$

the points z exterior to the circle $r = R$ map into points w interior to the circle $\rho = 1/R$ (Fig. 19).   The point $w = 0$ is not the image of any point in the finite z plane.   However, by making the radius R sufficiently large, the images of all points z outside the large circle $r = R$ are made to fall within an arbitrarily small neighborhood of the point $w = 0$.

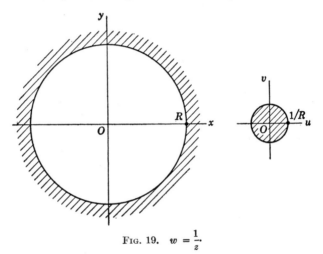

FIG. 19. $w = \dfrac{1}{z}$.

It is sometimes convenient to use the concept of the point at infinity or the infinite point, $z = \infty$.   Formally, this point is the image of the point $w = 0$ under the transformation $w = 1/z$.   That is, whenever a statement is made about the behavior of a function at $z = \infty$, we mean precisely the behavior of the function at $z' = 0$, where $z' = 1/z$.

We may say, for example, that the function

$$w = \frac{4z^2}{(1 - z)^2}$$

maps the point $z = \infty$ into the point $w = 4$.   This means that if we put $z = 1/z'$, so that

$$w = \frac{4/z'^2}{(1 - 1/z')^2} = \frac{4}{(z' - 1)^2},$$

then $w = 4$ when $z' = 0$.   Again, we may say that $w = \infty$ when $z = 1$;

for if we put $w = 1/w'$, then

$$w' = \frac{(1 - z)^2}{4z^2},$$

and $w' = 0$ when $z = 1$.

The notion of the infinite point is an abbreviation for a limiting process, and in case of doubt we should rely on the direct use of limits. Except when the contrary is stated, we shall continue to use the words *point* and *complex number* to signify points with finite coordinates and the complex numbers represented by such points.

EXERCISES

1. Find the image of the infinite strip $0 < y < 1/(2c)$ under the transformation $w = 1/z$. Show the regions graphically.   *Ans.* $u^2 + (v + c)^2 > c^2$, $v < 0$.

2. Show that the image of the half plane $y > c$, under the transformation $w = 1/z$, is the interior of a circle, provided $c > 0$. What is the image when $c = 0$; when $c < 0$?

3. Find the image of the quadrant $x > 1$, $y > 0$ under the transformation $w = 1/z$.   *Ans.* $\left|w - \frac{1}{2}\right| < \frac{1}{2}$, $v < 0$.

4. Find the image of the hyperbola $x^2 - y^2 = 1$ under the transformation $w = 1/z$.   *Ans.* $\rho^2 = \cos 2\phi$.

5. Describe geometrically the transformation of points z by the function

$$w = \frac{1}{z - 1}.$$

6. Describe geometrically the transformation of points z by the function $w = i/z$. Show that this function maps circles and lines into circles and lines.

7. Find the image of the semiinfinite strip $x > 0$, $0 < y < 1$ under the transformation $w = i/z$. Show the regions graphically.

35. The Linear Fractional Transformation.   The transformation

$$(1) \qquad\qquad w = \frac{\alpha z + \beta}{\gamma z + \delta} \qquad\qquad (\alpha\delta - \beta\gamma \neq 0),$$

where α, β, γ, and δ are complex constants, is called the *linear fractional transformation*.   It is also known as the *bilinear* or *Möbius transformation*. If $\alpha\delta - \beta\gamma = 0$, the right-hand member of equation (1) is either a constant or meaningless.

The inverse

$$(2) \qquad\qquad z = \frac{-\delta w + \beta}{\gamma w - \alpha}$$

of the transformation is also a linear fractional transformation.

We shall establish several properties of the transformation (1), most of which will be useful in connection with physical applications.   The linear fractional transformation plays a prominent role in some parts of geometry, however.   We shall not attempt to take up all the properties that are useful in that application.*

According to equation (1), each point in the z plane except the point $z = -\delta/\gamma$ maps into a unique point in the w plane.   According to equation (2), each point in the w plane except the point $w = \alpha/\gamma$ has a unique image in the z plane.   If the infinite point is included for each plane, then we can say that the transformation sets up a one-to-one correspondence between all points in the two planes.

We shall now show that the transformation (1) maps circles and lines into circles and lines.   We can show this by writing the transformation as a succession of transformations of the types studied above.

When $\gamma \neq 0$, equation (1) can be written

$$ w = \frac{\alpha}{\gamma} \left[\frac{z + (\beta/\alpha) + (\delta/\gamma) - (\delta/\gamma)}{z + (\delta/\gamma)} \right] = \frac{\alpha}{\gamma} \left[1 + \frac{(\beta/\alpha) - (\delta/\gamma)}{z + (\delta/\gamma)} \right] $$

$$ = \frac{\alpha}{\gamma} + \left(\frac{\beta\gamma - \alpha\delta}{\gamma} \right) \frac{1}{\gamma z + \delta}. $$

Now let us write

$$ (3) \qquad\qquad z' = \gamma z + \delta, \qquad z'' = \frac{1}{z'}, $$

and then if follows that

$$ (4) \qquad\qquad w = \frac{\alpha}{\gamma} + \frac{\beta\gamma - \alpha\delta}{\gamma} z''. $$

Equations (3) and (4) represent three successive transformations that map z into w.   The first and third are of the type

$$ (5) \qquad\qquad w = Bz + C $$

discussed in Sec. 31.   The second is the transformation $w = 1/z$ discussed in Sec. 33.   We found that the linear transformation (5) does not change the shape of a curve and that the transformation $w = 1/z$ always maps circles into circles, with lines as limiting cases.

When $\gamma = 0$, the transformation (1) is of the type (5).

Consequently, *the linear fractional transformation always transforms circles into circles, with lines as limiting cases.*

36. Further Properties of the Linear Fractional Transformation.   The equation

$$ (1) \qquad\qquad Azw + Bz + Cw + D = 0 $$

is linear in z and linear in w, but not linear in z and w together.   It

---

* For other properties of the transformation see, for instance, the books by Osgood or Burkhardt and Rasor listed in the Bibliography, Appendix I.

is called *bilinear* in z and w.   When it is solved for w, it has the form of the linear fractional transformation,

$$(2) \qquad\qquad w = \frac{\alpha z + \beta}{\gamma z + \delta};$$

hence the alternative name *bilinear transformation* applies to the form (2) as well as to (1).

The transformation (1) has three essential arbitrary constants, the ratios of some three of the constants A, B, C, and D to the fourth.   Therefore, it is to be expected that the transformation can be made to map any three distinct points z_1, z_2, and z_3 into any desired three points w_1, w_2, and w_3 that are distinct; for the substitution of corresponding values of z and w into equation (1) leads to three linear equations in the coefficients.   Now this mapping is made by the transformation

$$(3) \qquad \frac{(w - w_1)(w_2 - w_3)}{(w - w_3)(w_2 - w_1)} = \frac{(z - z_1)(z_2 - z_3)}{(z - z_3)(z_2 - z_1)},$$

which can be written in the bilinear form (1) by expanding the products in the equation

$$(4) \quad (z - z_3)(w - w_1)(z_2 - z_1)(w_2 - w_3)$$
$$= (z - z_1)(w - w_3)(z_2 - z_3)(w_2 - w_1).$$

For if $z = z_1$, the right-hand member of this last equation vanishes, and consequently $w = w_1$; similarly, if $z = z_3$, then $w = w_3$.   If $z = z_2$, two factors are common to both sides of equation (4), and the equation reduces to

$$(w - w_1)(w_2 - w_3) = (w - w_3)(w_2 - w_1);$$

the solution of this linear equation in w is clearly $w = w_2$.

Since the transformation (4) or (3) is bilinear in z and w, it is the linear fractional transformation that maps the three given points in the z plane into the three prescribed points in the w plane.   There cannot be more than one bilinear transformation that transforms those three points into the three prescribed points; for it can be shown that the three simultaneous linear equations in the ratios of the coefficients of equation (1) cannot have more than one solution.*

In geometry, the right-hand member of equation (3) is known as the *cross ratio* of the four points z, z_2, z_1, and z_3.   According to equation (3), the cross ratio of any four points is invariant under the linear fractional transformation.

In equation (3), the infinite point can be introduced as one of the

---

* Townsend, E. J., "Functions of a Complex Variable," p. 177.

prescribed points in the w plane or in the z plane. For example, let $z_1 = 1, z_2 = 0, z_3 = -1$, and $w_1 = i, w_2 = 1, w_3 = \infty$. Setting

$$w_3 = \frac{1}{w_3'},$$

we can write the transformation in the form

$$\frac{(w - w_1)(w_3'w_2 - 1)}{(w_3'w - 1)(w_2 - w_1)} = \frac{(z - z_1)(z_2 - z_3)}{(z - z_3)(z_2 - z_1)}.$$

When $w_3' = 0$ and the values of the remaining constants are inserted here the equation becomes

$$\frac{w - i}{1 - i} = \frac{z - 1}{(z + 1)(-1)},$$

or

$$w = \frac{(-1 + 2i)z + 1}{z + 1}.$$

Using either of these two forms, the reader can verify that the three given points map into the points specified, and in particular that w becomes infinite as z approaches -1.

Successive bilinear transformations are equivalent to a single bilinear transformation. That is, if

$$w = \frac{\alpha z + \beta}{\gamma z + \delta}$$

and

$$z = \frac{\alpha'z' + \beta'}{\gamma'z' + \delta'},$$

then it follows by direct substitution that

$$w = \frac{az' + b}{cz' + d},$$

where a, b, c, and d are complex constants.

The transformation (1) or (2) has at most two fixed, or invariant, points. They can be found by writing $w = z$ in equation (1) and solving the resulting quadratic equation for z.

Two points are *inverses* of each other with respect to a circle if they lie on the same radial line and if the product of their distances from the center of the circle is the square of the radius. Thus, if the points z' and z'' are inverses with respect to the circle $|z - z_0| = R$, we can write

$$z' = z_0 + \rho e^{i\phi}, \qquad z'' = z_0 + \frac{R^2}{\rho} e^{i\phi},$$

where ρ is the distance from the point z' to the center z_0, as indicated in Fig. 20.

Let w' and w'' be the images of the two inverse points z' and z'', under the transformation (2). Then w' and w'' are inverses with respect to the image of the circle $|z - z_0| = R$ under the transformation (2). The proof of this geometric property of the linear fractional transformation will be left for the exercises.

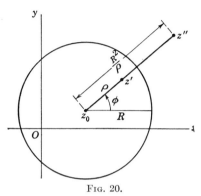

Fig. 20.

37. Special Linear Fractional Transformations. Let us determine all linear fractional transformations that map the upper half of the z plane $y \geqq 0$ into the unit circle $|w| \leqq 1$.

The boundary $y = 0$ of the half plane must have the boundary $|w| = 1$ of the unit circle as its image, for the transformation

$$(1) \qquad w = \frac{\alpha z + \beta}{\gamma z + \delta}$$

maps lines into circles or lines. In this case, the line $y = 0$ must map into a circle because the region in the w plane is of finite extent. Suppose that this circle is interior to the circle $|w| = 1$. Since w is a continuous single-valued function of z, points just below the x axis would map into points near that circle, interior to the circle $|w| = 1$, contrary to the required conditions.

If we make three specific points on the line $y = 0$ map into points on the circle $|w| = 1$, then the whole line will map into this circle, since the three image points determine the image circle. Conversely, every mapping of the line onto the circle must carry those three prescribed points into some three points on the circle.

According to equation (1), the requirement that $|w| = 1$ for each of the three points $z = 0$, $z = 1$, and $z = \infty$, leads to the equations

$$(2) \qquad |\beta| = |\delta|,$$
$$(3) \qquad |\alpha + \beta| = |\gamma + \delta|,$$
$$(4) \qquad |\alpha| = |\gamma|.$$

If either α or γ is zero, it follows from equation (4) that the other is also zero, and the transformation (1) maps the whole z plane onto a single point. Therefore $\alpha \neq 0$ and $\gamma \neq 0$, and we may write

$$w = \frac{\alpha\, z + (\beta/\alpha)}{\gamma\, z + (\delta/\gamma)},$$

or, since $|\alpha/\gamma| = 1$,

(5)
$$w = e^{i\theta_0} \frac{z - z_1}{z - z_2},$$

where θ_0 is any real number. According to equations (2) and (4), $|\beta/\alpha| = |\delta/\gamma|$; therefore $|z_1| = |z_2|$.

We have as yet made no use of condition (3). Let us now impose the corresponding condition, that $|w| = 1$ when $z = 1$, upon equation (5). Then

$$|1 - z_1| = |1 - z_2|,$$

or

$$(1 - z_1)(1 - \bar{z}_1) = (1 - z_2)(1 - \bar{z}_2).$$

But $z_1\bar{z}_1 = z_2\bar{z}_2$, since $|z_1| = |z_2|$, and the above relation reduces to

$$z_1 + \bar{z}_1 = z_2 + \bar{z}_2,$$

or $\mathfrak{R}(z_1) = \mathfrak{R}(z_2)$. Therefore either $z_2 = z_1$, or $z_2 = \bar{z}_1$. The condition $z_2 = z_1$ leads to the transformation $w = e^{i\theta_0}$ of the whole plane into a point.

The required transformation must therefore have the form

(6)
$$w = e^{i\theta_0} \frac{z - z_1}{z - \bar{z}_1},$$

where it is evident that the point $w = 0$ is the image of the point $z = z_1$, so that if the upper half plane is to map into the interior of the circle $|w| = 1$, it follows that z_1 must be in the upper half plane,

$$y_1 = \mathfrak{s}(z_1) > 0.$$

We can see that the transformation (6) does map the half plane into the unit circle by interpreting the equation

FIG. 21.

$$|w| = \frac{|z - z_1|}{|z - \bar{z}_1|}$$

geometrically. Keeping in mind that z and z_1 are in the upper half plane and $\bar{z}_1$ is in the lower half plane (Fig. 21), the distance $|z - z_1|$ from the point z to z_1 is not greater than the distance from z to $\bar{z}_1$. Thus $|w| \leq 1$. The transformation (6) is therefore the required transformation.

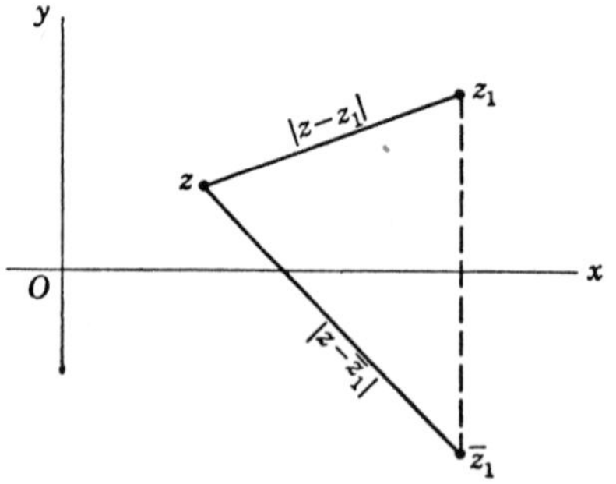

The identity transformation $w = z$ is not the only one that can map a region into itself.   In fact, all the transformations

$$(7) \qquad w = e^{i\theta_1} \frac{z - a}{\bar{a}z - 1},$$

where θ_1 is real and $|a| < 1$, map the unit circle $|z| \leq 1$ into the unit circle $|w| \leq 1$.   The proof is left for the exercises.

Two transformations each of which maps a region A onto a region B need not be identical.   This is illustrated by the transformation (6) with different sets of values of the constants θ_0 and z_1.

EXERCISES

1. Find the linear fractional transformation that maps the points $z_1 = 2$, $z_2 = i$, and $z_3 = -2$ into the points $w_1 = 1$, $w_2 = i$, and $w_3 = -1$.

Ans. $w = (3z + 2i)/(iz + 6)$.

2. Find the linear fractional transformation that maps the points $z_1 = -i$, $z_2 = 0$, and $z_3 = i$ into the points $w_1 = -1$, $w_2 = i$, and $w_3 = 1$.   Into what curve must this transformation map the y axis?

3. Find the linear fractional transformation that maps the points $z_1 = \infty$, $z_2 = i$, and $z_3 = 0$ into the points $w_1 = 0$, $w_2 = i$, and $w_3 = \infty$.

Ans. $w = -1/z$.

4. Find the linear fractional transformation that maps the points z_1, z_2, and z_3 into the points $w_1 = 0$, $w_2 = 1$, and $w_3 = \infty$.

Ans. $w = [(z - z_1)(z_2 - z_3)]/[(z - z_3)(z_2 - z_1)]$.

5. Find the fixed points of the transformation

$$w = \frac{z - 1 - i}{z + 2}.$$

Ans. $-1 + i, -i,$

6. Find the fixed points of the transformation

$$w = \frac{6z - 9}{z}.$$

Ans. 3, 3.

7. If the bilinear transformation maps all points on the real axis of the z plane upon the real axis of the w plane, prove that the coefficients in the transformation are all real, except possibly for a common complex factor.

8. If the linear fractional transformation is to map the half plane $y \geq 0$ into the circle $|w| \leq 1$, show that the coefficients must be such that the equation

$$|\alpha x + \beta| = |\gamma x + \delta|$$

is an identity in x.   Use this fact to give another derivation of the transformation (6) of the last section.

9. Derive formula (7) of the last section.   This may be done by successive linear fractional transformations, first mapping the circular region $|z| \leq 1$ into the upper half of a z' plane, and then mapping that half plane into the circle $|w| \leq 1$.

10. If the points z' and z'' are inverses with respect to a circle $|z - iR| = R$, and z' is kept fixed, prove that z'' approaches $\bar{z}'$ as R tends to infinity.

11. Under the transformation $w = 1/z$, show that the image of the center of a circle does not fall at the center of the image of the circle, except for point circles.

12. Let z' and z'' be inverse points with respect to a circle C, and let w' and w'' be their images under a linear fractional transformation. Then w' and w'' are inverses with respect to the image of C, provided that image is not a line. Prove this theorem in case C has its center at the origin for the particular transformation $w = 1/z$.

13. Prove the theorem in Exercise 12 for all circles C when the transformation is linear, $w = Az + B$.

14. Prove the theorem in Exercise 12 for the particular transformation $w = 1/z$ when C is any circle.

38. The Function $z^{\frac{1}{2}}$. Several of the functions we have considered take on more than one value for each value of z. One of the simplest of these is the function

$$(1) \qquad\qquad f(z) = z^{\frac{1}{2}} = \sqrt{r}\, e^{i\theta/2},$$

which takes on two values for each z, one the negative of the other depending on the choice of θ.

If $0 \leqq \theta_1 < 2\pi$, the function

$$(2) \qquad\qquad f_1(z) = \sqrt{r}\, e^{i\theta_1/2}$$

takes on just one value for each point z in the complex plane, and at each point its value is one of the two values of the function $z^{\frac{1}{2}}$.

A *branch* of the multiple-valued function $f(z)$ is any single-valued analytic function that for each z assumes one of the values of $f(z)$. The requirement of analyticity prevents a branch of a function from taking on a random selection of the values of the function.

As an example, the function $f_1(z)$ of equation (2), with $\theta_1 \neq 0$ and $r > 0$, is a branch of the function $z^{\frac{1}{2}}$. Corresponding to that branch, the second branch of the function $z^{\frac{1}{2}}$ is

$$f_2(z) = \sqrt{r}\, e^{i(\theta_1 + 2\pi)/2} = -\sqrt{r}\, e^{i\theta_1/2} = -f_1(z).$$

The branch $f_1(z)$ is not continuous at points on the positive real axis since

$$\lim_{\theta_1 \to 2\pi} (\sqrt{r}\, e^{i\theta_1/2}) = -\sqrt{r},$$

while

$$\lim_{\theta_1 \to 0} (\sqrt{r}\, e^{i\theta_1/2}) = \sqrt{r}.$$

Hence $f_1'(z)$ does not exist when z is real and positive.

The branch $f_1(z)$ is analytic in the region $0 < \theta_1 < 2\pi$, $r > 0$. That part of the real axis for which $x \geqq 0$ is called a *branch cut* for the branch

$f_1(z)$.   The branch is analytic except at points on this cut.   The cut is a boundary introduced so that the corresponding branch is single-valued and analytic throughout the open region bounded by the cut.

To define other branches of the function $z^{\frac{1}{2}}$ we need only limit θ to a range of 2π in formula (1).   If α is fixed and if $\alpha < \theta < \alpha + 2\pi$, then the equation

$$f_\alpha(z) = \sqrt{r}\, e^{i\theta/2} \qquad\qquad (r > 0) \qquad\qquad (1)$$

defines a branch of $z^{\frac{1}{2}}$.   The ray $\theta = \alpha$ is the branch cut.

Curves instead of lines running from the origin infinitely far out might be used as branch cuts.   But since the cut serves to make θ unique, it is clear that every branch cut for the function $z^{\frac{1}{2}}$ must begin at the point $z = 0$.   Such an origin of branch cuts for a multiple-valued function is called a *branch point* of the function.   For the function $z^{\frac{1}{2}}$, there is no neighborhood of the point $z = 0$ throughout which any branch of the function is analytic.   Hence no branch of that function is analytic at the branch point; but the derivative exists at some point in each neighborhood of the point.   Thus the branch point is a singular point of each branch.   For other functions a branch point may not be a singular point for every branch of the function, but it must be one for some of the branches.

Since $z = w^2$ when $w = z^{\frac{1}{2}}$, mapping by means of the latter function is the same as mapping with the inverse function $w = z^2$ and interchanging the w and z planes.   The function $f_1(z)$ described above maps the entire

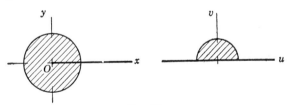

FIG. 22.

z plane upon the upper half of the w plane with the negative half of the u axis excluded, since $0 \leq \frac{1}{2}\theta_1 < \pi$.   If $0 < \theta_1 < 2\pi$, the branch $f_1(z)$ maps all points in the z plane except those on the branch cut $\theta_1 = 0$ in a one-to-one manner upon all points in the upper half of the w plane, excluding the points on the u axis (Fig. 22).   Circles about the origin map into semicircles.

39. Other Irrational Functions.   A branch cut for the function $w = z^{1/n}$, where n is an integer, can be selected as any ray from the origin.   Let us choose the negative real axis as a branch cut for the function $f(z) = z^{\frac{1}{2}}$, for example.   Then if $-\pi < \theta < \pi$ and $r > 0$, each of the three functions

$$f_1(z) = \sqrt[3]{r}\, e^{i\theta/3}, \qquad f_2(z) = \sqrt[3]{r}\, e^{i(\theta+2\pi)/3}, \qquad f_3(z) = \sqrt[3]{r}\, e^{i(\theta+4\pi)/3},$$

is a branch of $f(z)$. They are single-valued and analytic at all points in the finite z plane except for points on the cut $\theta = \pi$ and the branch point $z = 0$. The branch $f_1(z)$ maps the cut z plane into the angular region $-\pi/3 < \phi < \pi/3$ of the w plane.

A branch $f_1(z)$ of the function $f(z) = (z - z_0)^{\frac{1}{2}}$ is described by writing $z - z_0 = \rho e^{i\phi}$, where $0 < \phi < 2\pi$ and $\rho > 0$, so that

$$f_1(z) = \sqrt{\rho}\, e^{i\phi/2}.$$

This branch is defined everywhere in the z plane except on the branch cut $\phi = 0$ extending to the right of the branch point $z = z_0$.

As another example, the function

(1) $$f(z) = [(z - 1)(z - 3)]^{\frac{1}{2}}$$

can be written

(2) $$f(z) = \sqrt{\rho_1 \rho_2}\, e^{i(\phi_1+\phi_2)/2},$$

where

$$z - 1 = \rho_1 e^{i\phi_1}, \qquad z - 3 = \rho_2 e^{i\phi_2}.$$

If $0 \leq \phi_1 < 2\pi$ and $0 \leq \phi_2 < 2\pi$, then equation (2) defines a single-valued function. The limit of $\phi_1 + \phi_2$, as z approaches any point on the real axis to the right of the point $z = 3$, is zero if approached from above,

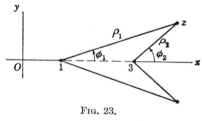

and 4π if approached from below (Fig. 23). Thus the two limiting values of $(\phi_1 + \phi_2)/2$ differ by 2π, and the function defined by equation (2) is continuous at such a point. At points on the line segment $1 < x < 3$, however, the limiting values of $\phi_1 + \phi_2$ from above and below are π and

FIG. 23.

3π, so that the function $\exp[i(\phi_1 + \phi_2)/2]$ is discontinuous there. At points to the left of the point $z = 1$, the angles ϕ_1 and ϕ_2 are continuous functions of z. Thus our single-valued function is continuous except at points on the segment $1 < x < 3$. It is a branch of the function (1) with branch points at $z = 1$ and $z = 3$, and with the line segment joining those points as a branch cut.

Branches of the function $[(z - z_1)(z - z_2)]^{\frac{1}{2}}$ can be described in a similar manner. The points $z = z_1$ and $z = z_2$ are branch points. The line segment joining them is a branch cut if we let the arguments of $(z - z_1)$ and $(z - z_2)$ range from α to $\alpha + 2\pi$, where

$$\alpha = \arg (z_2 - z_1).$$

40. The Transformation $w = \exp z$. If ρ and ϕ are the polar coordinates of the point w, the transformation

$$w = e^z$$

can be written

$$\rho e^{i\phi} = e^x e^{iy}.$$

Thus the coordinates of corresponding points in the two planes satisfy the relations

$$\rho = e^x, \qquad \phi = y.$$

The transformation therefore maps the lines $x = c$ into the circles $\rho = \exp c$, and the lines $y = c$ into the rays $\phi = c$.

The rectangular region $c_1 \leq x \leq c_2$, $c_3 \leq y \leq c_4$ maps into the region

$$e^{c_1} \leq \rho \leq e^{c_2}, \qquad c_3 \leq \phi \leq c_4$$

bounded by circles and rays. This mapping is one to one if $c_4 - c_3 < 2\pi$. The two regions and corresponding parts of their boundaries are shown in Fig. 24. In particular, if $c_3 = 0$ and $c_4 = \pi$ so that $0 \leq y \leq \pi$, the

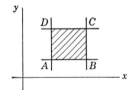 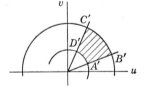

FIG. 24. $w = e^z$.

rectangle maps into half of a circular ring as shown in Fig. 8 of Appendix II.

When x ranges through all positive and negative values, the radius vector ρ ranges through all positive values; when $x \to -\infty$, $\rho \to 0$. When y varies from zero to π, ϕ varies from zero to π. Thus the infinite strip $0 \leq y \leq \pi$ maps into the upper half of the w plane, $0 \leq \phi \leq \pi$. The image of the point $z = 0$ is the point $w = 1$, and that of $z = \pi i$ is $w = -1$. Corresponding parts of the boundaries of the two regions are shown in Fig. 6 of Appendix II. This mapping of a strip upon a half plane is especially useful in the applications.

The semiinfinite strip $x \leq 0$, $0 \leq y \leq \pi$ maps into the semicircle $\rho \leq 1$, $0 \leq \phi \leq \pi$ (Fig. 7, Appendix II).

The infinite strip $-\pi \leq y \leq \pi$ maps into the entire w plane, but the mapping is not one to one on the ray $\phi = \pi$.

The transformation $w = \exp z$ can be written

$$z = \log w = \text{Log } \rho + i\phi.$$

A branch of this infinitely many valued function can be described by limiting ϕ to a range of 2π. If $-\pi < \phi < \pi$, the function is discontinuous at points on the branch cut $\phi = \pi$. This branch of log w is single-valued and analytic throughout the cut w plane, excluding the branch point $w = 0$.

EXERCISES

1. Show that a branch of the function $w = z^{\frac{1}{2}}$ maps the region between the two parabolas

$$r = \frac{2c_1^2}{1 - \cos\theta}, \qquad r = \frac{2c_2^2}{1 - \cos\theta}$$

in the z plane into the strip bounded by the lines $v = c_1$ and $v = c_2$ in the w plane, where c_1 and c_2 are positive constants.

2. If $w = (z^2 - 1)^{\frac{1}{2}}$, show that

$$\arg w = \frac{1}{2}\left(\arctan\frac{y}{x+1} + \arctan\frac{y}{x-1}\right),$$

and that

$$|w|^4 = (x^2 + y^2 + 1)^2 - 4x^2.$$

3. Write $z - 1 = \rho_1 \exp i\phi_1$, $z + 1 = \rho_2 \exp i\phi_2$, where $0 < \phi_1 < 2\pi$ and $-\pi < \phi_2 < \pi$. Give a formula for a branch of each of the functions

$$(a) \ w = (z^2 - 1)^{\frac{1}{2}}, \qquad (b) \ w = \left(\frac{z-1}{z+1}\right)^{\frac{1}{2}},$$

for which the branch cut consists of the two rays $\phi_1 = 0$ and $\phi_2 = \pi$.

Ans. (b) $w = \sqrt{\rho_1/\rho_2} \exp\left[i(\phi_1 - \phi_2)/2\right]$.

4. Describe a branch of the function $w = [z(z-1)(z-2)]^{\frac{1}{2}}$ having the positive half of the x axis, except for the segment between $z = 1$ and $z = 2$, as a branch cut.

5. Express the real and imaginary components of a branch of the function $w = (z^2 - 1)^{\frac{1}{2}}$ in terms of x and y.

6. Show that the transformation $w = z^2$ maps the triangle bounded by the lines $y = x$, $y = -x$, and $x = 1$ into the region bounded by the v axis and the parabola $\rho = 2/(1 + \cos\phi)$.

7. Under the transformation $w = \exp z$, show that the lines $ky = x$ map into the spirals $\rho = \exp k\phi$.

8. Verify the mapping indicated in Fig. 7 of Appendix II, under the transformation $w = \exp z$.

9. Find the image of the semiinfinite strip $x \geq 0$, $0 \leq y \leq \pi$ under the transformation $w = \exp z$.

10. Describe a branch of the function $w = \log(z - 1)$ that has as a branch cut the half of the real axis to the right of the point $z = 1$.

41. The Transformation $w = \sin z$. Since

$$\sin z = \sin x \cosh y + i \cos x \sinh y,$$

the transformation $w = \sin z$ can be written

$$u = \sin x \cosh y, \qquad v = \cos x \sinh y.$$

If $x = \pi/2$, then $u = \cosh y$ and $v = 0$. Thus the line $x = \pi/2$ maps into the part $u \geq 1$ of the real axis in the w plane. This mapping is one to one for either the upper or lower half of the line $x = \pi/2$; when y varies from zero to infinity through positive values, or through negative values, u varies from one to infinity.

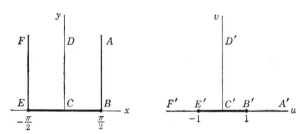

Fɪɢ. 25. $w = \sin z$.

If $y = 0$, then $u = \sin x$ and $v = 0$. Hence the entire x axis maps into the segment $-1 \leq u \leq 1$ of the u axis, but this mapping is not one to one. In fact, the segment $-\pi/2 \leq x \leq \pi/2$ of the x axis maps uniquely upon that segment. The upper half of the y axis maps into the upper half of the v axis, and the lower half into the lower half, since $u = 0$ and $v = \sinh y$ when $x = 0$. The mapping of those lines is shown in Fig. 25.

The line segment $y = c$, $-\pi/2 \leq x \leq \pi/2$ maps upon the semiellipse whose parametric equations are

$$u = \cosh c \sin x, \qquad v = \sinh c \cos x.$$

If $c > 0$, then $v \geq 0$, and these equations represent the upper half of the ellipse

$$\frac{u^2}{\cosh^2 c} + \frac{v^2}{\sinh^2 c} = 1;$$

if $c < 0$, they represent the lower half (Fig. 26). Each point of the line segment maps into one point of the semiellipse, and conversely, according to the above parametric equations. The foci of the ellipse are the points $w = +1$ independent of the value of c.

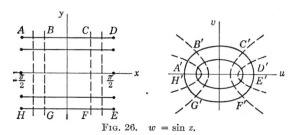

FIG. 26. $w = \sin z$.

The line $x = c$, where $-\pi/2 < c < \pi/2$, maps into the curve

$$u = \sin c \cosh y, \qquad v = \cos c \sinh y,$$

which is the right-hand half of the hyperbola

$$\frac{u^2}{\sin^2 c} - \frac{v^2}{\cos^2 c} = 1,$$

if $c > 0$, and the left-hand half if $c < 0$.   The mapping is one to one. The points $w = \pm 1$ are the foci of this hyperbola.

Each point in the upper half of the w plane is the intersection of just one pair of curves of this orthogonal system of ellipses and hyperbolas and corresponds to just one point in the semiinfinite strip

$$-\frac{\pi}{2} \leqq x \leqq \frac{\pi}{2}, \, y \geqq 0,$$

in the z plane.   Also, to each point of the strip there corresponds just one point w.   Hence the mapping of that strip upon the upper half of the w plane is one to one (Fig. 9, Appendix II).   The right-hand half of this strip maps into the first quadrant of the w plane (Fig. 10, Appendix II).

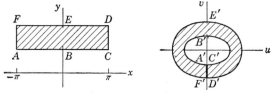

FIG. 27. $w = \sin z$.

The rectangle $-\pi \leqq x \leqq \pi$, $c_1 \leqq y \leqq c_2$ maps into the region bounded by two confocal ellipses as shown in Fig. 27.   But note that both the sides $x = \pm\pi$ map into the line segment $u = 0$, $v = -\sinh y$ $(c_1 \leqq y \leqq c_2)$; thus if $c_1 > 0$, the image of the rectangular region is the elliptic ring with a cut along the negative v axis.   As a point z describes the boundary of the rectangle, its image makes a circuit around one ellipse, then along the cut and around the other ellipse, and back again along the cut to the starting point, as shown in the figure.

The rectangular region $-\pi/2 \leq x \leq \pi/2$, $0 \leq y \leq c$ maps uniquely into a semielliptic region in the manner shown in Fig. 11 of Appendix II.

42. Successive Transformations. Since $\cos z = \sin (z + \pi/2)$, the transformation

$$w = \cos z$$

can be written successively as

$$w = \sin z', \qquad z' = z + \frac{\pi}{2}.$$

The last transformation is a translation of each point in the z plane to the right through the distance $\pi/2$. Therefore the transformation $w = \cos z$ is the same as the transformation $w = \sin z$ preceded by a translation to the right through $\pi/2$ units.

The transformation

$$w = \sinh z$$

can be written $iw = \sin(iz)$, or

$$w' = \sin z', \qquad z' = iz, \qquad w' = iw.$$

It is therefore the combination of the transformation $w = \sin z$ with a rotation of the axes in each plane through the angle $\pi/2$. Similarly, the transformation

$$w = \cosh z$$

is essentially the same as $w = \cos z$.

As another example of successive transformations, let

$$w = (\sin z)^{\frac{1}{2}},$$

which is the result of the two transformations

$$w' = \sin z, \qquad w = (w')^{\frac{1}{2}}.$$

We noted in the preceding section that the first maps the semiinfinite strip $0 \leq x \leq \pi/2$, $y \geq 0$ into the first quadrant. The second transforms the quadrant into an octant. The successive transformations of regions and boundaries that map the strip in the z plane into an octant of the w plane are shown in Fig. 28.

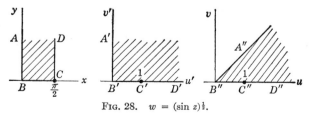

FIG. 28. $w = (\sin z)^{\frac{1}{2}}$.

The linear fractional transformation

$$w' = \frac{z - 1}{z + 1}$$

maps the half plane $x \geqq 0$ into the unit circle $|w| \leqq 1$ (Fig. 12, Appendix II). It is readily shown that this transformation also maps the half plane $y \geqq 0$ upon the half plane $v \geqq 0$. Since the transformation $w' = \text{Log } w$, or $w = \exp w'$, maps the half plane $v \geqq 0$ upon the strip $0 \leqq v' \leqq \pi$ (Fig. 6, Appendix II), it follows that the transformation

$$w' = \text{Log } \frac{z - 1}{z + 1}$$

maps the half plane into the strip. The order of corresponding points on the boundaries is shown in Fig. 19 of Appendix II.

43. Table of Transformations of Regions. Appendix II consists of a set of figures showing the transformation of a number of simple and useful regions by various elementary functions. In each case there is a one to one correspondence between points of the region and of its image. Corresponding parts of boundaries are indicated by the lettering. Some mappings that have not been discussed in the text are shown in that table. Their verification can be left as exercises for the student. Several of the transformations given in Appendix II can be derived by means of the Schwarz-Christoffel transformation (Chap. X).

EXERCISES

1. Determine the image of the rectangular region $0 \leqq y \leqq 1$, $-\pi \leqq x \leqq \pi$, and its boundary under the transformation $w = \sin z$.

2. Show that the transformation $w = \cosh z$ maps the points

$$z = iy, \ 0 \leqq y \leqq \frac{\pi}{2}$$

into the segment $0 \leqq u \leqq 1$ of the u axis. Show that it maps the strip $x \geqq 0$, $0 \leqq y \leqq \pi/2$ into the first quadrant of the w plane, and indicate corresponding parts of the boundaries of the regions.

3. Describe the transformation $w = \cosh z$ in terms of the transformation $w = \sin z$ and rotations and translations.

4. Show that the transformation $w = \sin^2 z$ maps the region $0 \leqq x \leqq \pi/2$, $y \geqq 0$ into the region $v \geqq 0$, and indicate corresponding parts of the boundaries.

5. Under the transformation $w = (\sin z)^{\frac{1}{2}}$, show that the strip

$$-\frac{\pi}{2} \leqq x \leqq \frac{\pi}{2}, \qquad y \geqq 0$$

maps into the part of the first quadrant lying below the line $v = u$, and determine the corresponding parts of the boundaries.

6. Verify the mapping, under the transformation $w = 1/z$, of the regions and parts of the boundaries indicated (*a*) in Fig. 4, Appendix II; (*b*) in Fig. 5, Appendix II.

7. Verify the mapping, under the transformation $w = (z - 1)/(z + 1)$, shown in Fig. 12, Appendix II.

8. Using the polar representation of z, show that the transformation

$$w = z + 1/z$$

maps both the upper and lower half of the circle $r = 1$ into the line segment $-2 \leq u \leq 2$, $v = 0$.

9. Show that the transformation $w = z + 1/z$ maps the circle $r = c$ into the ellipse

$$u = \left(c + \frac{1}{c} \right) \cos \theta, \qquad v = \left(c - \frac{1}{c} \right) \sin \theta.$$

10. Verify the mapping indicated in Fig. 16, Appendix II, under the transformation $w = z + 1/z$.

11. Describe the mapping by the function $w = \cosh z$ in terms of the transformations $w = e^z$ and $2w = z + 1/z$.

12. Verify the mapping indicated in Fig. 19, Appendix II, under the transformation

$$w = \operatorname{Log} \frac{z - 1}{z + 1}.$$

13. Describe geometrically, in terms of neighborhoods of the points z_0 and w_0, the definition of the limit of a function $f(z)$ as z approaches z_0 (Sec. 13).

CHAPTER V

INTEGRALS

The reader may pass directly to the chapters on conformal mapping and applications at this time if he wishes. It would seem natural to present that chapter next, since we have just completed a study of mapping by elementary functions. However, we have not yet established the continuity of the second-order partial derivatives of the real and imaginary components, $u(x,y)$ and $v(x,y)$, of an analytic function. If we take up the subject of conformal mapping at this time, we shall have to assume that continuity; to establish it we need to use some of the theory of integrals of analytic functions, which is presented below.

The theory of line integrals together with the theory of power series and residues constitutes a very important portion of the theory of functions of complex variables. The theory is noted for its mathematical elegance. The theorems are generally concise and powerful, and most of the proofs are quite simple. But the theory is also noted for its great utility in both pure and applied mathematics. We present a substantial introduction to that theory in this and succeeding chapters.

44. Line Integrals. The definite integral of a real function,

$$\int_a^b f(x) \, dx,$$

is a number that is determined by the values of the function $f(x)$ at the points along the segment of the x axis between the points $(a,0)$ and $(b,0)$. The definite integral of a complex function,

$$\int_\alpha^\beta f(z) \, dz,$$

between the points represented by the complex numbers α and β is defined in terms of the values of $f(z)$ at the points along some curve from α to β. The

Fig. 29.

integral is called a *line integral*, or a *curvilinear integral*, over the curve. Its value may depend upon the curve selected.

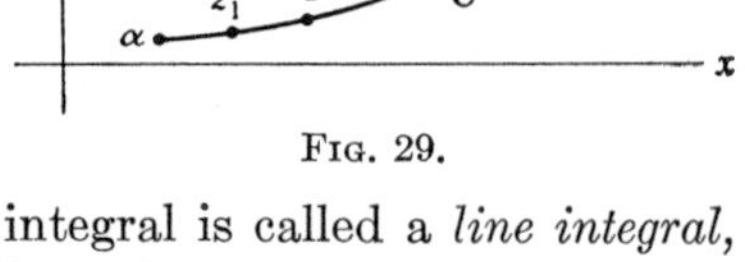

Let C be some curve of finite length joining the points α and β, and let the complex numbers z_0, z_1, $\cdots$, z_n represent a sequence of points cn C, where $z_0 = \alpha$ and $z_n = \beta$ (Fig. 29). We write

$$\Delta_j z = z_j - z_{j-1} \qquad (j = 1,2, \cdots ,n).$$

Also let z_j' denote any point on the arc from z_{j-1} to z_j. Then the limit of the sum

$$\sum_{j=1}^{n} f(z_j') \, \Delta_j z$$

as n tends to infinity, where the set of n points z_j on C is always so chosen that the maximum of the n chord lengths $|\Delta_j z|$ tends to zero as n increases, is called the *line integral* of $f(z)$ along C:

(1) $$\int_\alpha^\beta f(z) \, dz = \lim_{n \to \infty} \sum_{j=1}^{n} f(z_j') \, \Delta_j z \qquad (\text{max. } |\Delta_j z| \to 0).$$

The integral is also written

$$\int_C f(z) \, dz;$$

here the path C is directed from α to β.

We may describe this integral in terms of real line integrals or real definite integrals. Let

$$f(z) = u(x,y) + iv(x,y)$$

and write

$$\Delta_j z = z_j - z_{j-1} = x_j - x_{j-1} + i(y_j - y_{j-1}) = \Delta_j x + i \, \Delta_j y$$
$$(j = 1,2, \cdots ,n).$$

Then, the definition (1) can be written

$$\int_\alpha^\beta f(z) \, dz = \lim_{n \to \infty} \sum_{j=1}^{n} [u(x_j',y_j') + iv(x_j',y_j')](\Delta_j x + i \, \Delta_j y)$$

$$= \lim_{n \to \infty} \sum_{j=1}^{n} [u(x_j',y_j') \, \Delta_j x - v(x_j',y_j') \, \Delta_j y]$$

$$+ i \lim_{n \to \infty} \sum_{j=1}^{n} [v(x_j',y_j') \, \Delta_j x + u(x_j',y_j') \, \Delta_j y].$$

In breaking up the limit as n tends to infinity into two real limits here, we have used a modified form of our earlier theorem, equation (9), Sec. 13, on limits of complex functions. The modified form can be established in a manner similar to that used in Sec. 13.

The last two limits represent real line integrals, so that

(2) $$\int_\alpha^\beta f(z) \, dz$$

$$= \int_C [u(x,y) \, dx - v(x,y) \, dy] + i \int_C [v(x,y) \, dx + u(x,y) \, dy],$$

provided that the two real line integrals here exist. Their existence implies that the limits of the sums written above have values independent of the choice of the points (x_j, y_j) and (x'_j, y'_j).

Let C be a curve that can be represented by real parametric equations,

$$(3) \qquad\qquad x = \phi(t), \qquad y = \psi(t),$$

where the functions ϕ and ψ are single-valued and have continuous derivatives of the first order. If $f(z)$ is a single-valued continuous function of z, then u and v are single-valued continuous functions of x and y, and therefore of t, when the point z is on C. The first integral on the right of equation (2) is then the same as the real definite integral

$$(4) \qquad\qquad \int_{t_\alpha}^{t_\beta} [u\phi'(t) - v\psi'(t)]\, dt,$$

where t_α and t_β are the values of the parameter t corresponding to the end points α and β of C. We note that the integral (4) exists because its integrand is a continuous function of t.

Likewise, the last integral in equation (2) can be written as a definite integral of a continuous function of t. The line integral

$$\int_\alpha^\beta f(z)\, dz$$

therefore exists when the path C has the parametric representation (3) and when $f(z)$ is continuous at all points on C.

If C consists of a finite number of arcs $C_1, C_2, \cdots , C_m$, each of which has the parametric representation described above, the integral can be written as the sum of the integrals along those arcs:

$$(5) \qquad \int_C f(z)\, dz = \int_{C_1} f(z)\, dz + \int_{C_2} f(z)\, dz + \cdots + \int_{C_m} f(z)\, dz.$$

If the parameter t is the variable x itself, the equations (3) of the curve C reduce to the ordinary equation of the curve, $y = \psi(x)$. If $t = y$, the equations become $x = \phi(y)$. All straight lines, circles, and conics—in fact, nearly all the curves considered in analytic geometry—have parametric representations of the type described above.

The representation (2) of the complex integral in terms of real integrals shows that we can replace dz by $(dx + i\, dy)$ and expand the integrand; that is,

$$\int_C f(z)\, dz = \int_C (u + iv)(dx + i\, dy)$$
$$= \int_C (u\, dx - v\, dy) + i \int_C (v\, dx + u\, dy).$$

The real definite integral can be interpreted as an area. It has other interpretations. No corresponding useful interpretation, geometrical or physical, of the complex integral is available except in special cases. Nevertheless, as noted above the theory of integration in the complex plane is remarkably useful in physics, engineering, and mathematics.

45. Examples. First, let us find the value of the integral

$$I_1 = \int_0^{2+i} z^2 \, dz$$

along the straight-line path OA (Fig. 30) between the limits $\alpha = 0$ and $\beta = 2 + i$. Setting

$$z^2 = x^2 - y^2 + 2xyi, \qquad dz = dx + i \, dy,$$

we can write

$$I_1 = \int_{(0,0)}^{(2,1)} [(x^2 - y^2) \, dx - 2xy \, dy] + i \int_{(0,0)}^{(2,1)} [2xy \, dx + (x^2 - y^2) \, dy].$$

Since $x = 2y$ on OA, $dx = 2 \, dy$ and

$$I_1 = \int_0^1 (6y^2 - 4y^2) \, dy + i \int_0^1 (8y^2 + 3y^2) \, dy = \tfrac{2}{3} + \tfrac{11}{3}i.$$

If the curve C is the path OBA shown in the figure, let us evaluate the integral

$$I_2 = \int_0^{2+i} z^2 \, dz = \int_{OB} z^2 \, dz + \int_{BA} z^2 \, dz.$$

Along OB, $z = x$ and $dz = dx$. Along BA, $z = 2 + iy$ and $dz = i \, dy$. Hence

$$I_2 = \int_0^2 x^2 \, dx + \int_0^1 [i(4 - y^2) - 4y] \, dy = \tfrac{8}{3} + \tfrac{11}{3}i - 2 = \tfrac{2}{3} + \tfrac{11}{3}i.$$

Thus $I_2 = I_1$; in fact

$$I_1 = I_2 = \tfrac{1}{3}z^3 \Big]_0^{2+i} = \tfrac{1}{3}(2 + i)^3 = \tfrac{2}{3} + \tfrac{11}{3}i.$$

Also, the integral of z^2 around the closed curve $OBAO$ is zero. We shall soon see that these properties of the integrals here are a consequence of the fact that the integrand z^2 is analytic throughout a region including the triangle OAB.

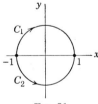

As another example, let $f(z) = \bar{z}$. The integral

$$I_3 = \int_{-1}^1 \bar{z} \, dz = \int_{-1}^1 (x - iy)(dx + i \, dy)$$

over the path C_1 of Fig. 31, consisting of the upper half of the circle $r = 1$, can be evaluated by using the angle θ as the parameter t. Then $x = \cos \theta$ and $y = \sin \theta$ along C_1; that is, $z = e^{i\theta}$ and $dz = ie^{i\theta} \, d\theta$ and

$$I_3 = \int_\pi^0 e^{-i\theta} ie^{i\theta} \, d\theta = i \int_\pi^0 d\theta = -\pi i.$$

Fig. 31.

The line integral between the same limits along the lower semicircle C_2 is

$$I_4 = \int_{-1}^{1} \bar{z}\, dz = i \int_{\pi}^{2\pi} d\theta = \pi i.$$

Hence $I_4 \neq I_3$. The integral around the entire circle C in a counterclockwise direction does not vanish;

$$I_C = I_4 - I_3 = 2\pi i.$$

Since $1/z = \bar{z}/|z|^2 = \bar{z}$ on the unit circle, the integrand of the integrals I_3, I_4, and I_C can be replaced by $1/z$. Thus

$$I_C = \int_C \frac{dz}{z} = 2\pi i.$$

46. Properties of Integrals. If the limits of a line integral are interchanged without changing the curve C, the same sets of points z_j and z_j' may be used in the definition of both integrals. Thus, if z_j and z_j' are the points used in defining the integral from α to β and $\Delta_j z$ are the differences used there (Sec. 44), we can write

$$\int_\beta^\alpha f(z)\, dz = \lim_{n \to \infty} \sum_{j=n}^{j=1} f(z_j')(z_{j-1} - z_j)$$

$$= \lim_{n \to \infty} \sum_{j=1}^{n} f(z_j')(-\Delta_j z).$$

Consequently, when the same curve is used in both integrals,

(1) $$\int_\beta^\alpha f(z)\, dz = - \int_\alpha^\beta f(z)\, dz.$$

The properties

(2) $$\int_\alpha^\beta k f(z)\, dz = k \int_\alpha^\beta f(z)\, dz,$$

where k is any complex constant, and

(3) $$\int_\alpha^\beta [f(z) + g(z)]\, dz = \int_\alpha^\beta f(z)\, dz + \int_\alpha^\beta g(z)\, dz$$

follow directly from the definition of the line integral given in Sec. 44, provided it is understood that the same curve C is used as the path of integration for all the integrals appearing in either equation. If α, β, and γ are three points on the path C, it also follows that

(4) $$\int_\alpha^\gamma f(z)\, dz = \int_\alpha^\beta f(z)\, dz + \int_\beta^\gamma f(z)\, dz.$$

Properties (1) to (4) are also consequences of the corresponding properties of real line integrals, in view of the representation (2), Sec. 44.

The integral

(5) $$\int_C |f(z)||dz| = \lim_{n\to\infty} \sum_{j=1}^{n} |f(z_j')| \sqrt{(\Delta_j x)^2 + (\Delta_j y)^2}$$

is the real line integral

$$\int_C \sqrt{u^2 + v^2}\, ds,$$

where s is arc length along the curve C. In particular, when $f(z) = 1$ for all z, the integral (5) represents the length L of C:

(6) $$\int_C |dz| = L.$$

Since the absolute value of the sum of n complex numbers is not greater than the sum of their absolute values, it is true that

$$\left| \sum_{j=1}^{n} f(z_j')\, \Delta_j z \right| \leq \sum_{j=1}^{n} |f(z_j')||\Delta_j z|$$

for every integer n. As n increases, the value of the left-hand member approaches

$$\left| \int_C f(z)\, dz \right|,$$

and the right-hand member approaches the integral (5). Therefore

(7) $$\left| \int_C f(z)\, dz \right| \leq \int_C |f(z)||dz|.$$

According to equation (5), when $|f(z)| \leq M$ for every point z on C, where M is a real positive constant, then

$$\int_C |f(z)||dz| \leq M \int_C |dz|.$$

In view of formulas (6) and (7), this important property of integrals follows:

(8) $$\left| \int_C f(z)\, dz \right| \leq ML,$$

where M is the maximum value of $|f(z)|$ on C and L is the length of C.

EXERCISES

1. (*a*) Calculate the value of the integral

$$\int_{-2}^{2} \frac{2z - 3}{z}\, dz$$

when the path C is the upper half of the circle $|z| = 2$. (*b*) Calculate the value when C is the lower half of that circle.   (c) Find the value of the integral around the entire circle in the counterclockwise sense.

$$Ans. \ (a) \ 8 + 3\pi i; \ (b) \ 8 - 3\pi i; \ (c) \ -6\pi i.$$

2. Find the value of the integral

$$\int_0^{1+i} (x - y + ix^2) \, dz$$

(a) along the straight line between the limits; (b) over the path along the lines $y = 0$ and $x = 1$; (c) over the path along the lines $x = 0$ and $y = 1$.

$$Ans. \ (a) \ (-1 + i)/3; \ (b) \ (-3 + 5i)/6; \ (c) \ -(3 + i)/6.$$

3. Show that

$$\int_C (z + 1) \, dz = 0$$

when C is the boundary of the square with vertices at the points $z = 0$, $z = 1$, $z = 1 + i$, and $z = i$.

4. Find the value of the integral

$$\int_C e^{iz} \, dz$$

where C is the boundary of the square in Exercise 3.

5. Find the value of the integral

$$\int_{\pi i}^1 e^z \, dz$$

(a) along the straight line between the limits; (b) over the path along the coordinate axes joining the limits.   *Ans.* $1 + e$.

6. Show that, for every path joining the points α and β,

$$\int_\alpha^\beta dz = \beta - \alpha.$$

Note that the definition (1), Sec. 44, may be used here.

7. Without evaluating the integral show that

$$\left| \int_i^{2+i} \frac{dz}{z^2} \right| \leq 2,$$

where the path is the straight line between the limits.

8. (a) Without calculating the integral, show that

$$\left| \int_{-i}^i (x^2 + iy^2) \, dz \right| \leq 2$$

when the path is along the y axis.   (b) When the path is a semicircle with the points $z = \pm i$ as ends of a diameter, show that the absolute value of the integral does not exceed π.

9. Compute the value of the integral

$$\int_{-i}^i (x^2 + iy^2) \, dz$$

(a) along the path $x = 0$; (b) along the right-hand half of the circle $|z| = 1$. Compare the results with those given in Exercise 8.

10. Show that

$$\int_C \frac{dz}{z - 2} = 2\pi i$$

where C is the circle $z - 2 = r_0 e^{i\theta}$ described in the counterclockwise sense.

47. The Cauchy-Goursat Theorem. According to Green's theorem on real line integrals, if two functions $P(x,y)$ and $Q(x,y)$, together with their partial derivatives of the first order, are continuous in a region R bounded by a closed curve C, where R includes its boundary C, then

$$\int_C (P\, dx + Q\, dy) = \int\int_R \left(\frac{\partial Q}{\partial x} - \frac{\partial P}{\partial y}\right) dx\, dy.$$

Now consider a function

$$f(z) = u(x,y) + iv(x,y)$$

which is analytic at all points within and on a closed curve C, *and such that $f'(z)$ is continuous there.* Then u and v and their partial derivatives of the first order are continuous there, and consequently

$$\int_C (u\, dx - v\, dy) = -\int\int_R \left(\frac{\partial v}{\partial x} + \frac{\partial u}{\partial y}\right) dx\, dy,$$

$$\int_C (v\, dx + u\, dy) = \int\int_R \left(\frac{\partial u}{\partial x} - \frac{\partial v}{\partial y}\right) dx\, dy.$$

In view of the Cauchy-Riemann conditions, the integrands of the two double integrals vanish throughout the region R. Since the line integrals on the left are the real and imaginary coefficients of the complex number representing the line integral of $f(z)$, it follows that

$$\int_C f(z)\, dz = 0.$$

This result was originated by Cauchy in the early part of the last century.

As elementary examples of it, we note that when C denotes a closed curve,

$$\int_C dz = 0, \qquad \int_C z\, dz = 0, \qquad \int_C z^2\, dz = 0,$$

etc.; for the functions $f(z) = 1$, $f(z) = z$, $f(z) = z^2$, etc., are analytic and have continuous derivatives.

Goursat was the first to prove that the condition that $f'(z)$ be continuous can be omitted from the hypotheses in the theorem. The removal of that condition is of prime importance to the theory of analytic functions. As one of the consequences, for example, we shall show that the derivatives of analytic functions are also analytic. The revised form of the theorem, the *Cauchy-Goursat* theorem, can be stated as follows:

Theorem. *If a function $f(z)$ is single-valued and analytic within and on a closed curve C, then*

(1)
$$\int_C f(z) \, dz = 0.$$

In order to ensure the existence of the integral, it is to be understood that C consists of a finite number of arcs each of which has a parametric representation of the type described under equations (3), Sec. 44. The curve is closed in the sense that it forms a single unbroken loop in the finite plane. It will be a simple matter to extend the result to curves that are more general including, for example, the entire boundary of the region between two polygons, one inside the other.

The proof of the theorem is presented in the following sections.

48. A Preliminary Theorem. The derivative $f'(z_0)$ exists when $f(z)$ is analytic at the point z_0; that is, given any positive number ϵ, a positive number δ_0, depending upon z_0 and ϵ, exists such that

(1)
$$\left| \frac{f(z) - f(z_0)}{z - z_0} - f'(z_0) \right| < \epsilon \qquad \text{when } |z - z_0| < \delta_0.$$

In order to prove the Cauchy-Goursat theorem, we first show that a sufficiently fine subdivision of the region bounded by the closed curve C can be made so that the first inequality here is true for every point z in each subdivision when z_0 is properly chosen in that subdivision. Thus there is some degree of uniformity in the approach of $\Delta f / \Delta z$ to $f'(z)$.

Lemma. *Let $f(z)$ be analytic at all points of a region R bounded by a closed curve C, where our region R includes the points on C itself. Given any positive number ϵ, it is always possible to divide R into a finite number of squares and partial squares, whose boundaries will be denoted by C_j, such that a point z_j exists within or on each C_j for which the inequality*

(2)
$$\left| \frac{f(z) - f(z_j)}{z - z_j} - f'(z_j) \right| < \epsilon$$
$$(j = 1,2, \cdots ,n)$$

is satisfied by every point z within or on C_j.

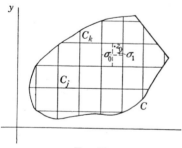

FIG. 32.

Let the region R be covered with a set of equal squares formed by drawing lines parallel to the coordinate axes. Those portions of any square which lie outside of R are to be removed, leaving R subdivided into squares and partial squares (Fig. 32).

Now suppose that for a given positive number ϵ, there is at least one of these subregions in which no point z_j exists such that the inequality (2) is true at every point z in that subregion. If it is a square, let it be divided into four equal squares. If it is a partial square, let the whole square be so divided, and let the portions that lie outside of R be discarded. If in any one of those smaller regions no point z_j exists such that (2) is satisfied there, let that region be subdivided in the same manner, etc.

After a finite number of such steps of subdividing every subregion that requires it, we may arrive at a subdivision such that the inequality (2) is true for every subregion present. In that case the lemma is true.

But suppose that points z_j do not exist such that (2) is satisfied after subdividing one of the original subregions, denoted by σ_0, a finite number of times. Then after σ_0 is subdivided once, there is at least one of the smaller regions σ_1 in which no appropriate z_j's exist when σ_1 is subdivided any finite number of times. After σ_1 is subdivided once, there is at least one of its subregions σ_2 that fails to qualify after any finite number of subdivisions, etc.

Each region of this sequence of regions

$$\sigma_0, \qquad \sigma_1, \qquad \sigma_2, \qquad \cdots, \qquad \sigma_k, \qquad \cdots$$

is contained in the preceding one. There is a point z_0 common to all the regions $\sigma_0, \sigma_1, \cdots, \sigma_k$ for every integer k. But the dimensions of σ_k approach zero as k increases. Hence for each positive number δ_0, there is an integer k_0 such that all points of σ_k are interior to the circle

$$|z - z_0| = \delta_0$$

when $k \geqq k_0$. Since there are no points z_k for which the inequality (2) is satisfied in any of the regions σ_k, it follows that the inequality (1) is not satisfied at z_0 for the given ϵ. But z_0 is a point in the region R, and hence $f'(z_0)$ exists. Thus we have arrived at a contradiction, and the proof of the lemma is complete.

49. Proof of the Cauchy-Goursat Theorem. We shall show that the inequality

(1)
$$\left| \int_C f(z)\, dz \right| < \epsilon'$$

is true for every positive number ϵ'. For the given closed curve C and the given function $f(z)$, the integral here has a definite constant value. The integral must therefore have the value zero.

For a given positive number ϵ, let C_j $(j = 1, 2, \cdots, n)$ be the boundaries of a set of squares and partial squares into which the region R can be subdivided, according to the above lemma, so that points z_j

exist for which the inequality (2) of the preceding section is true. We can state that inequality in the following form. Each of the functions

$$(2) \qquad \delta_j(z) = \frac{f(z) - f(z_j)}{z - z_j} - f'(z_j) \qquad (j = 1, 2, \cdots, n)$$

satisfies the inequality

$$(3) \qquad |\delta_j(z)| < \epsilon.$$

Note that each function $\delta_j(z)$ is continuous; in particular, its limit as z approaches z_j is zero, and we shall define $\delta_j(z_j)$ to be zero.

We now let z represent any point on the boundary C_j. The value of $f(z)$ at any point on C_j can be written, according to equation (2),

$$(4) \qquad f(z) = f(z_j) - z_j f'(z_j) + f'(z_j)z + (z - z_j)\delta_j(z).$$

Integrating around C_j and recalling that (Sec. 47)

$$\int_{C_j} dz = 0, \qquad \int_{C_j} z \, dz = 0,$$

we see that

$$(5) \qquad \int_{C_j} f(z) \, dz = \int_{C_j} (z - z_j)\delta_j(z) \, dz.$$

Let the integral around each C_j be taken in the counterclockwise sense. The sum of all those integrals is the integral around the closed curve C in the counterclockwise sense; that is,

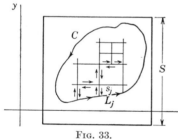

FIG. 33.

$$\sum_{j=1}^{n} \int_{C_j} f(z) \, dz = \int_{C} f(z) \, dz,$$

because the line integrals along the common boundary line of every pair of adjacent subregions cancel each other; the integral is taken in one sense along that line in one region and in the opposite sense in the other (Fig. 33). Only the integrals along the arcs that are parts of C remain. Therefore, in view of equation (5),

$$\int_{C} f(z) \, dz = \sum_{j=1}^{n} \int_{C_j} (z - z_j)\delta_j(z) \, dz,$$

and hence

$$\left| \int_{C} f(z) \, dz \right| \leqq \sum_{j=1}^{n} \left| \int_{C_j} (z - z_j)\delta_j(z) \, dz \right|$$

$$\leqq \sum_{j=1}^{n} \int_{C_j} |z - z_j| |\delta_j(z)| |dz|.$$

It follows from the inequality (3) that

(6) $$\left| \int_C f(z) \, dz \right| < \epsilon \sum_{j=1}^{n} \int_{C_j} |z - z_j| |dz|.$$

Each boundary C_j coincides either entirely or partially with the boundary of a square. In either case let s_j denote the length of a side of that square. Now z is on C_j, and z_j is either interior to or on C_j, so that

$$|z - z_j| \leq s_j \sqrt{2},$$

and

(7) $$\int_{C_j} |z - z_j| |dz| \leq s_j \sqrt{2} \int_{C_j} |dz|.$$

The last integral represents the length of C_j. It is $4s_j$ if C_j is a square, and it does not exceed $(4s_j + L_j)$ if C_j is a partial square, where L_j is the arc of C that forms a part of C_j. When C_j is a square and A_j denotes the area of that square, then according to the inequality (7),

(8) $$\int_{C_j} |z - z_j| |dz| \leq 4 \sqrt{2} \, s_j^2 = 4 \sqrt{2} \, A_j.$$

When C_j is a partial square,

(9) $$\int_{C_j} |z - z_j| |dz| < s_j \sqrt{2} \, (4s_j + L_j) < 4 \sqrt{2} \, A_j + \sqrt{2} \, SL_j,$$

where S is the length of a side of some square that encloses the entire curve C as well as all squares used originally in covering C (Fig. 33). Thus the sum of all A_j's does not exceed S^2.

If L denotes the length of C, it now follows from the inequalities (6), (8), and (9) that

$$\left| \int_C f(z) \, dz \right| < \epsilon(4 \sqrt{2} \, S^2 + \sqrt{2} \, SL).$$

For each positive number ϵ', the right-hand member here can be made equal to ϵ' by assigning the proper value to the positive number ϵ. Hence the inequality (1) is established, and the Cauchy-Goursat theorem is proved.

50. Multiply Connected Regions. A region R is *simply connected* if every closed curve within it encloses only points of R. The region bounded by each closed curve C of the types considered above is simply connected. But the annular region between two concentric circles, for example, is not simply connected; its boundary consists of two closed curves. A region that is not simply connected is called *multiply connected*.

By introducing as additional boundary lines certain lines joining the inner curves to the outer curve, the region can be made simply con-

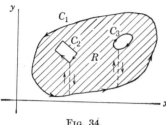

FIG. 34.

nected. This is illustrated in Fig. 34, where the broken lines are the additional boundary lines. The boundary consisting of the curves C_1, C_2, C_3, and the broken lines forms a closed curve that can be used in the Cauchy-Goursat theorem. The broken lines are traversed twice in describing that closed curve, and the integrals along each of them in the two

directions cancel each other. Thus the statement of the Cauchy-Goursat theorem can be extended as follows:

Theorem. *Let $f(z)$ be single-valued and analytic in a multiply connected region R and on the boundary of R. If B denotes the boundary of R, where B consists of a finite number of disconnected closed curves each of which is described in such a sense that the points of R are on the left, then*

$$\int_B f(z)\, dz = 0.$$

As an example, we note that

$$\int_C \frac{dz}{z^2(z^2 + 9)} = 0,$$

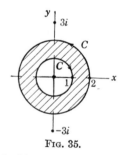

FIG. 35.

if the path C consists of the circle $|z| = 2$ described in the counterclockwise sense and the circle $|z| = 1$ described in the clockwise sense (Fig. 35); for the integrand here is a single-valued function that is analytic except at the points $z = 0$ and $z = \pm 3i$, and these three points lie outside the annular region bounded by the path C.

An integral over the entire boundary of a region is often called a *contour integral*.

The curves and regions that arise in the mathematical and physical applications can generally be limited to quite simple ones. For this reason, and in order to keep our treatment of integration reasonably brief, we have relied on intuitive notions of certain geometric concepts such as *closed curves* and *inside* or *outside* a closed curve, concepts that are treated with care in the subject of topology. In order to define the inside of a closed curve, it is convenient to restrict further the closed curves we have considered to simple closed contours, closed curves that are cut by parallels to the coordinate axes in not more than two points. The restriction can be removed easily after first establishing the Cauchy-

Goursat theorem for simple closed curves. This procedure is followed, for example, on page 74 of the book by Titchmarsh listed in Appendix I.

51. Indefinite Integrals. Let z_0 and z represent two points in a simply connected region R throughout which $f(z)$ is single-valued and analytic. If C_1 and C_2 are two curves drawn from z_0 to z and lying entirely within R, then C_1 and C_2 together form a closed curve in R (Fig. 36). If points on the curves are denoted by z', the Cauchy-Goursat theorem states that

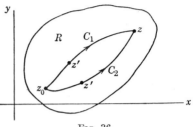

FIG. 36.

$$\int_{C_2} f(z') \, dz' - \int_{C_1} f(z') \, dz' = 0;$$

that is, the integral from z_0 to z has the same value along all paths. When z_0 is fixed, the integral is therefore a single-valued function $F(z)$ for all paths in the simply connected region R:

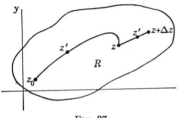

FIG. 37.

$$(1) \qquad F(z) = \int_{z_0}^{z} f(z') \, dz'.$$

We shall now show that the derivative of $F(z)$ is $f(z)$. Let $z + \Delta z$ be a point in R (Fig. 37). Then

$$F(z + \Delta z) - F(z) = \int_{z_0}^{z+\Delta z} f(z') \, dz' - \int_{z_0}^{z} f(z') \, dz' = \int_{z}^{z+\Delta z} f(z') \, dz',$$

where the path of integration from z to $z + \Delta z$ may be selected as a straight line. Since we can write

$$f(z) = \frac{f(z)}{\Delta z} \int_{z}^{z+\Delta z} dz' = \frac{1}{\Delta z} \int_{z}^{z+\Delta z} f(z) \, dz',$$

then

$$\frac{F(z + \Delta z) - F(z)}{\Delta z} - f(z) = \frac{1}{\Delta z} \int_{z}^{z+\Delta z} [f(z') - f(z)] \, dz'.$$

But $f(z)$ is continuous at the point z. Hence for each positive number ϵ, a positive number δ exists for which

$$|f(z') - f(z)| < \epsilon$$

when $|z' - z| < \delta$, or in particular, when $|\Delta z| < \delta$. Therefore, when $|\Delta z| < \delta$,

$$\left|\frac{F(z + \Delta z) - F(z)}{\Delta z} - f(z)\right| < \frac{\epsilon}{|\Delta z|} \int_{z}^{z+\Delta z} |dz'| = \epsilon;$$

that is,

$$\lim_{\Delta z \to 0} \frac{F(z + \Delta z) - F(z)}{\Delta z} = f(z).$$

Thus the derivative of the integral (1) exists at each point z in R, and

(2) $$F'(z) = f(z).$$

The integral of an analytic function is therefore an analytic function of its upper limit, provided the path of integration is confined to a simply connected region throughout which the integrand is analytic.

We can see from its definition (1) that $F(z)$ is changed by an additive constant when the lower limit z_0 is replaced by a new constant. The function $F(z)$ is an *indefinite integral* or antiderivative of $f(z)$, written

$$F(z) = \int f(z)\, dz;$$

that is, it is an analytic function whose derivative is $f(z)$. In view of formula (1), the definite integral can be evaluated as the *change in the value of the indefinite integral*, as in the case of real integrals; for

(3) $$\int_{\alpha}^{\beta} f(z)\, dz = \int_{z_0}^{\beta} f(z)\, dz - \int_{z_0}^{\alpha} f(z)\, dz = F(\beta) - F(\alpha).$$

It is assumed that the paths of integration are confined to a simply connected region in which $f(z)$ is analytic.

It should be noted that if $G(z)$ is any single-valued analytic function other than $F(z)$ such that $G'(z) = f(z)$, then the derivative of the function

$$w = G(z) - F(z)$$

is zero. Thus if $w = u + iv$, then

$$\frac{\partial u}{\partial x} + i\frac{\partial v}{\partial x} = 0,$$

and therefore $\partial u/\partial x$ and $\partial v/\partial x$ both vanish throughout the region in which the functions $F(z)$ and $G(z)$ are analytic. In view of the Cauchy-Riemann conditions, $\partial u/\partial y$ and $\partial v/\partial y$ also vanish, and therefore u and v are constant. Thus w is a constant, and it follows that the two indefinite integrals $F(z)$ and $G(z)$ differ by a constant. As a consequence, any indefinite integral of $f(z)$ can be used in place of $F(z)$ in formula (3).

An indefinite integral of the function $f(z) = z^2$, for example, is the single-valued analytic function $F(z) = z^3/3$. Since the function z^2 is analytic everywhere, we can write

$$\int_0^{1+i} z^2 \, dz = \tfrac{1}{3}z^3 \Big]_0^{1+i} = \tfrac{1}{3}(1 + i)^3$$

for every path between the points $z = 0$ and $z = 1 + i$.

As another example, let us evaluate

(4) $$\int_{-1}^1 z^{\frac{1}{2}} \, dz$$

along any path lying in the upper half of the z plane and joining the two limits, where $z^{\frac{1}{2}} = \sqrt{r} \exp{(i\theta/2)}$ and $0 \le \theta < 2\pi$. The function $z^{\frac{1}{2}}$ and its indefinite integral

(5) $$\tfrac{2}{3}z^{\frac{3}{2}} = \tfrac{2}{3}r^{\frac{3}{2}}e^{3i\theta/2}$$

are single-valued and analytic when $r > 0$ and $-\pi/2 < \theta < 3\pi/2$, a region that includes every path under consideration, and such that the integrand $z^{\frac{1}{2}}$ has the values prescribed above in the upper half plane. Hence

$$\int_{-1}^1 z^{\frac{1}{2}} \, dz = \tfrac{2}{3}r^{\frac{3}{2}}e^{3i\theta/2}\Big]_{z=-1}^{z=1} = \tfrac{2}{3}(1 - e^{3i\pi/2}) = \tfrac{2}{3}(1 + i).$$

The integral (4) over every path below the x axis has another value. The integrand and its indefinite integral (5) are single-valued and analytic when $r > 0$ and $\pi/2 < \theta < 5\pi/2$, a region that includes the paths now under consideration and such that $z^{\frac{1}{2}}$ has the values prescribed in the lower half plane. Thus

$$\int_{-1}^1 z^{\frac{1}{2}} \, dz = \tfrac{2}{3}r_{\frac{3}{2}}e^{3i\theta/2}\Big]_{z=-1}^{z=1} = \tfrac{2}{3}(e^{3\pi i} - e^{3\pi i/2}) = \tfrac{2}{3}(-1 + i).$$

The integral in the positive sense around the closed curve consisting of a path of the second group combined with one of the first group therefore has the value

$$\tfrac{2}{3}(-1 + i) - \tfrac{2}{3}(1 + i) = -\tfrac{4}{3}.$$

EXERCISES

1. If the closed curve C is the circle $|z| = 1$ described in either the counter-clockwise or clockwise sense, prove that the value of each of the following integrals is zero:

(a) $\displaystyle\int_C \frac{z \, dz}{z - 2}$;   (b) $\displaystyle\int_C \frac{dz}{z^2 + 2z + 2}$;   (c) $\displaystyle\int_C ze^{2z} \, dz$;

(d) $\displaystyle\int_C \frac{dz}{\cos z}$;   (e) $\displaystyle\int_C \tanh z \, dz$.

2. What is the value of the contour integral

$$\int_C \frac{dz}{z - 2 - i}$$

when the closed curve C is the boundary of (a) the square bounded by the real and imaginary axes and the lines $x = 1$ and $y = 1$; (b) the rectangle bounded by the real and imaginary axes and the lines $x = 3$ and $y = 2$, described in the counterclockwise sense?   *Ans.* (a) 0; (b) $2\pi i$.

3. Show that for every path between the limits

$$\int_{-2}^{-2+i} (z+2)^2 \, dz = -\tfrac{1}{3} i.$$

4. Evaluate each of the following integrals where the path is any curve from the point representing the lower limit to the point representing the upper limit:

(a) $\displaystyle\int_0^{\pi+2i} \cos \frac{z}{2} \, dz;$ (b) $\displaystyle\int_{-\pi i}^{0} e^{-z} \, dz;$

(c) $\displaystyle\int_{-1}^{i} (1 + 4iz^3) \, dz;$ (d) $\displaystyle\int_{1-\pi i}^{1+\pi i} \sinh 2z \, dz.$

Ans. (a) $e + 1/e$; (c) $1 + i$.

5. Use the indefinite integral to find the value of

$$\int_{-2i}^{2i} \frac{dz}{z}$$

over every path from $z = -2i$ to $z = 2i$ lying to the right of the imaginary axis. Note that Log z, the principal value of log z, is a single-valued analytic indefinite integral of $1/z$ in the half plane $x > 0$.   *Ans.* πi.

6. Solve Exercise 5 for every path lying to the left of the imaginary axis.

Ans. $-\pi i$.

52. The Cauchy Integral Formula.   Another fundamental result will now be established.

   Theorem.   *Let $f(z)$ be single-valued and analytic within and on a closed curve C.   If z_0 is any point interior to C, then*

(1) $$f(z_0) = \frac{1}{2\pi i} \int_C \frac{f(z)}{z - z_0} \, dz,$$

where the integral is taken in the positive sense around C.

   Formula (1) is *Cauchy's integral formula*.   It shows that the value of a function that is analytic in a region is determined throughout the region by its values on the boundary.   Thus there is no choice of ways in which the function can be defined at points away from the boundary once the function is defined on the boundary.   Every alteration of values of the function at interior points must be accompanied by a change of its values on the boundary, if the function is to remain analytic.   We shall see further evidence of this *organic* character of analytic functions as we proceed.

According to the Cauchy integral formula, for example, if C is the circle $|z| = 2$ described in the positive sense, then, taking $z_0 = -i$,

$$\int_C \frac{z\,dz}{(9 - z^2)(z + i)} = 2\pi i \left(\frac{-i}{9 - i^2}\right) = \frac{\pi}{5},$$

since the function $f(z) = z/(9 - z^2)$ is analytic within and on C.

To prove the theorem, let C_0 be a circle about z_0,

$$|z - z_0| = r_0,$$

whose radius r_0 is small enough that C_0 is interior to C (Fig. 38). The function $f(z)/(z - z_0)$ is analytic at

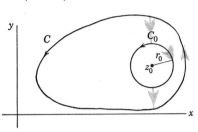

FIG. 38.

all points within and on C except the point z_0. Hence its integral around the boundary of the ring-shaped region between C and C_0 is zero, according to the Cauchy-Goursat theorem; that is,

$$\int_C \frac{f(z)\,dz}{z - z_0} - \int_{C_0} \frac{f(z)\,dz}{z - z_0} = 0,$$

where both integrals are taken counterclockwise.

Since the integrals around C and C_0 are equal, we can write

(2) $$\int_C \frac{f(z)\,dz}{z - z_0} = f(z_0) \int_{C_0} \frac{dz}{z - z_0} + \int_{C_0} \frac{f(z) - f(z_0)}{z - z_0}\,dz.$$

But $z - z_0 = r_0 e^{i\theta}$ on C_0 and $dz = i r_0 e^{i\theta}\,d\theta$, so that

(3) $$\int_{C_0} \frac{dz}{z - z_0} = i \int_0^{2\pi} d\theta = 2\pi i,$$

for every positive r_0. Also, $f(z)$ is continuous at $z = z_0$. Hence if we select any positive number ϵ, then a positive number δ exists such that

$$|f(z) - f(z_0)| < \epsilon \qquad\qquad \text{when } |z - z_0| \leqq \delta.$$

We take r_0 equal to that number δ. Then $|z - z_0| = \delta$, and

$$\left|\int_{C_0} \frac{f(z) - f(z_0)}{z - z_0}\,dz\right| \leqq \int_{C_0} \frac{|f(z) - f(z_0)|}{|z - z_0|}\,|dz| < \frac{\epsilon}{\delta}\,(2\pi\delta) = 2\pi\epsilon.$$

The absolute value of the last integral in equation (2) can therefore be made arbitrarily small by taking r_0 sufficiently small. But since the other two integrals in that equation are independent of r_0, in view of equation (3), this one must be independent of r_0 also. Its value must therefore be zero.   Equation (2) then reduces to the formula

$$\int_C \frac{f(z)\,dz}{z - z_0} = 2\pi i f(z_0),$$

and the theorem is proved.

53. Derivatives of Analytic Functions.   A formula for the derivative $f'(z_0)$ can be written formally by differentiating the integral in Cauchy's integral formula

(1) $$f(z_0) = \frac{1}{2\pi i} \int_C \frac{f(z)}{z - z_0}\,dz$$

with respect to z_0, inside the integral sign.   Thus,

(2) $$f'(z_0) = \frac{1}{2\pi i} \int_C \frac{f(z)}{(z - z_0)^2}\,dz.$$

As before we assume that $f(z)$ is single-valued and analytic within and on the closed curve C and that z_0 is within C.   To establish formula (2), we first note that, according to (1),

$$\frac{f(z_0 + \Delta z_0) - f(z_0)}{\Delta z_0} = \frac{1}{2\pi i\,\Delta z_0} \int_C \left(\frac{1}{z - z_0 - \Delta z_0} - \frac{1}{z - z_0} \right) f(z)\,dz$$

$$= \frac{1}{2\pi i} \int_C \frac{f(z)\,dz}{(z - z_0 - \Delta z_0)(z - z_0)}.$$

The last integral approaches the integral

$$\int_C \frac{f(z)\,dz}{(z - z_0)^2}$$

as Δz_0 approaches zero; for the difference between that integral and this one reduces to

$$\Delta z_0 \int_C \frac{f(z)\,dz}{(z - z_0)^2(z - z_0 - \Delta z_0)}.$$

Let M be the maximum value of $|f(z)|$ on C and let L be the length of C. Then if d_0 is the shortest distance from z_0 to C and if $|\Delta z_0| < d_0$, we can write

$$\left| \Delta z_0 \int_C \frac{f(z)\,dz}{(z - z_0)^2(z - z_0 - \Delta z_0)} \right| < \frac{ML|\Delta z_0|}{d_0^2(d_0 - |\Delta z_0|)},$$

and the last fraction approaches zero when Δz_0 approaches zero.   Consequently,

$$\lim_{\Delta z_0 \to 0} \frac{f(z_0 + \Delta z_0) - f(z_0)}{\Delta z_0} = \frac{1}{2\pi i} \int_C \frac{f(z)\,dz}{(z - z_0)^2},$$

and formula (2) is established.

If we differentiate both members of equation (2) and assume that the order of differentiation with respect to z_0 and integration with respect to z can be interchanged, we find that

(3)
$$f''(z_0) = \frac{2!}{2\pi i} \int_C \frac{f(z)\, dz}{(z - z_0)^3}.$$

This formula can be established by the same method that was used to establish formula (2). For it follows from formula (2) that

$$2\pi i \frac{f'(z_0 + \Delta z_0) - f'(z_0)}{\Delta z_0} = \int_C \left[\frac{1}{(z - z_0 - \Delta z_0)^2} - \frac{1}{(z - z_0)^2} \right] \frac{f(z)\, dz}{\Delta z_0}$$

$$= \int_C \frac{2(z - z_0) - \Delta z_0}{(z - z_0 - \Delta z_0)^2 (z - z_0)^2} f(z)\, dz.$$

Following the same procedure that was used before, we can show that the limit of the last integral, as Δz_0 approaches zero, is

$$2 \int_C \frac{f(z)\, dz}{(z - z_0)^3},$$

and formula (3) follows at once.

We have now established the existence of the derivative of the function $f'(z_0)$ at each point interior to the region bounded by the curve C.

We recall our definition that a function $f(z)$ is analytic at a point z_1 if and only if there is a neighborhood about z_1 at each point of which $f'(z)$ exists. Hence $f(z)$ is analytic in some neighborhood of the point. If the curve C used above is a circle $|z - z_1| = r_1$ in that neighborhood, then $f''(z)$ exists at each point inside the circle, and therefore $f'(z)$ is analytic at $z = z_1$. We can apply the same argument to the function $f'(z)$ to conclude that its derivative $f''(z)$ is analytic at $z = z_1$, etc. Thus the following fundamental result is a consequence of formula (3).

Theorem. *If a single-valued function $f(z)$ is analytic at a point, then its derivatives of all orders, $f'(z), f''(z), \cdots$, are also analytic functions at that point.*

Since $f'(z)$ is analytic and therefore continuous, and since

$$f'(z) = \frac{\partial u}{\partial x} + i \frac{\partial v}{\partial x} = \frac{\partial v}{\partial y} - i \frac{\partial u}{\partial y},$$

it follows that the partial derivatives of $u(x,y)$ and $v(x,y)$ of the first order are continuous. Since $f''(z)$ is analytic and

$$f''(z) = \frac{\partial^2 u}{\partial x^2} + i \frac{\partial^2 v}{\partial x^2} = \frac{\partial^2 v}{\partial x\, \partial y} - i \frac{\partial^2 u}{\partial x\, \partial y},$$

etc., it follows that the partial derivatives of u and v of all orders are continuous functions of x and y at each point where $f(z)$ is analytic. This result was anticipated in Sec. 22, for the partial derivatives of the second order, in the discussion of harmonic functions.

The argument used in establishing formulas (2) and (3) can be applied successively to obtain a formula for the derivative of any given order. But mathematical induction can now be applied to establish the general formula

(4) $$f^{(n)}(z_0) = \frac{n!}{2\pi i} \int_C \frac{f(z)\, dz}{(z - z_0)^{n+1}} \qquad (n = 1,2, \cdots).$$

That is, if we assume that this formula is true for any particular integer $n = k$, we can show by proceeding as before that it is true if $n = k + 1$. The details of the proof can be left to the reader, with the suggestion that in the algebraic simplifications he retain the difference $(z - z_0)$ throughout as a single term.

The curve C here, as well as in Cauchy's integral formula, can be replaced by the boundary of a multiply connected region containing the point z_0 in its interior. This can be shown by the same argument that was used to generalize the curve in the Cauchy-Goursat theorem; that is, we can introduce lines that connect the inner boundaries to the outer one so as to make the region bounded by these lines and the original curves a simply connected region. The new boundary is a closed curve to which the above results apply; but the integrals in opposite directions along each line that was introduced cancel each other.

54. Morera's Theorem. In Sec. 51 we proved that the derivative of the function

$$F(z) = \int_{z_0}^{z} f(z')\, dz'$$

exists at each point of a simply connected region R, in fact, that

$$F'(z) = f(z).$$

We assumed there that $f(z)$ is analytic in R. But in our proof we used only two properties of the analytic function $f(z)$, namely, that it is continuous in R and that its integral around every closed curve in R vanishes. Thus when $f(z)$ satisfies those two conditions, the function $F(z)$ is analytic in the region R.

We proved in Sec. 53 that the derivative of every analytic function is analytic. Since $F'(z) = f(z)$, it follows that $f(z)$ is analytic. The following theorem, due to E. Morera (1856–1909), is therefore established when R is simply connected.

Theorem. *If the function $f(z)$ is continuous in a region R, and if*

$$\int_C f(z)\, dz = 0,$$

*for every path C that is the entire boundary of some subregion of R, then f(z)
is analytic in R.*

The theorem is true when R is a multiply connected region; for additional boundaries can be introduced, as illustrated in Fig. 34, so as to make the region simply connected, and the hypotheses of the theorem are satisfied in this simply connected region when they are satisfied in the multiply connected region.

The theorem serves as a converse of the Cauchy-Goursat theorem. In view of the latter theorem we can now state that *a necessary and sufficient condition for a continuous function to be analytic in a region is that every integral of the function, taken around the entire boundary of each part of the region, should vanish.*

55. Integral Functions. Let $f(z)$ be analytic at $z = z_0$. If C_0 denotes any one of the circles $|z - z_0| = r_0$ within and on which $f(z)$ is analytic, then according to Cauchy's integral formula

$$f(z_0) = \frac{1}{2\pi i} \int_{C_0} \frac{f(z)\, dz}{z - z_0}.$$

If M is the maximum value of $|f(z)|$ on C_0, it follows that

(1) $$|f(z_0)| \leq \frac{1}{2\pi}\left(\frac{M}{r_0}\right)(2\pi r_0) = M.$$

Therefore the real variable $|f(z)|$ *cannot have a maximum value at any point where f(z) is analytic;* for the value of $|f(z)|$ at the point is not greater than its maximum value on each circle about the point. Thus in every neighborhood of z_0 there are values of $|f(z)|$, where $z \neq z_0$, that are at least as great as $|f(z_0)|$.

A somewhat more general form of this *maximum modulus theorem* states that if $f(z)$ is analytic within and on a closed curve C, and if M is the maximum value of $|f(z)|$ on C, then $|f(z)| < M$ at each point inside C unless $|f(z)|$ is a constant, in which case $|f(z)| = M$. Proofs will be found in books listed in Appendix I, for example, in Titchmarsh, Chap. V.

Let $f(z) = u + iv$. Then as a consequence of the maximum modulus theorem, *the harmonic function u(x,y) assumes its maximum value on the boundary C.* For the function $\exp f(z)$ is analytic within and on C and therefore its modulus e^u assumes its maximum value on C; hence u itself has its maximum value on C.

The integral formula for the derivatives, in case C is the circle C_0, becomes

$$f^{(n)}(z_0) = \frac{n!}{2\pi i} \int_{C_0} \frac{f(z)\, dz}{(z - z_0)^{n+1}} \qquad (n = 1, 2, \cdots).$$

It follows as before that

(2)
$$|f^{(n)}(z_0)| \leqq \frac{n!M}{r_0^n}.$$

This is called *Cauchy's inequality*. If $n = 1$ and M' is such that $|f(z)| < M'$ within and on the circle C_0, then

(3)
$$|f'(z_0)| < \frac{M'}{r_0},$$

from which we can establish *Liouville's theorem:*

Theorem. *If $f(z)$ is analytic and $|f(z)|$ is bounded for all values of z in the complex plane, then $f(z)$ must be a constant.*

Under the hypothesis a constant M' exists such that $|f(z)| < M'$ for all z. Therefore at each point z_0 the inequality (3) is true for every positive number r_0. Since we can take r_0 as large as we please, it follows that $f'(z_0) = 0$ at every point, and hence $f(z)$ is a constant.

A function that is analytic for all finite values of z is called an *integral function*. Every polynomial in z is an integral function. Other examples are the functions e^z, sin z, cos z, sinh z, and cosh z. Liouville's theorem states that no integral function except a constant is bounded for all values of z.

56. The Fundamental Theorem of Algebra. This theorem states that if $P(z)$ is a polynomial in z of degree one or greater,

$$P(z) = a_0 + a_1 z + a_2 z^2 + \cdots + a_m z^m \quad (m = 1,2, \cdots ; a_m \neq 0),$$

then the equation $P(z) = 0$ has at least one root.

The proof of this theorem by purely algebraic methods is difficult, but it follows easily from Liouville's theorem. For let us suppose that $P(z)$ is not zero for any value of z. Then the function

$$f(z) = \frac{1}{P(z)}$$

is everywhere analytic. Also $|f(z)|$ approaches zero as $|z|$ tends to infinity, so that $|f(z)|$ is bounded for all z. Consequently $f(z)$ is a constant. We have therefore arrived at a contradiction, for $P(z)$ is not a constant when $m = 1, 2, \cdots$, and $a_m \neq 0$. Hence $P(z)$ is zero for at least one value of z.

In elementary algebra courses the fundamental theorem is usually stated without proof; then as a consequence it is shown that an algebraic equation of degree m has not more than m roots.

EXERCISES

1. Show that for every closed curve C inclosing the point z_0 and described in the positive sense,

$$\int_C \frac{dz}{z - z_0} = 2\pi i.$$

2. When the curve C is described in the positive sense, show that

$$\int_C \frac{dz}{(z - z_0)^n} = 0 \qquad\qquad (n = 2,3, \cdots),$$

(a) when C is the circle $|z - z_0| = r_0$; (b) when C is any closed curve enclosing the point z_0; (c) when C is any closed curve with the point z_0 outside C.

3. If C is the circle $|z| = 2$ described in the positive sense, and if

$$g(z_0) = \int_C \frac{2z^2 - z + 1}{z - z_0} \, dz,$$

show in two ways that $g(1) = 4\pi i$. What is the value of $g(z_0)$ when $|z_0| > 2$?

4. Evaluate each of the following integrals, where C is the boundary of the square whose sides lie along the lines $x = \pm 2$ and $y = \pm 2$, described in the positive sense:

(a) $\displaystyle\int_C \frac{e^z \, dz}{z + \pi i/2}$;

(b) $\displaystyle\int_C \frac{\cos z}{z} \, dz$;

(c) $\displaystyle\int_C \frac{\tan (z/2)}{(z - x_0)^2} \, dz \quad (-2 < x_0 < 2)$;

(d) $\displaystyle\int_C \frac{\sinh 2z}{z^4} \, dz$.

Ans. (a) 2π; (b) $2\pi i$; (c) $\pi i \sec^2 (x_0/2)$; (d) $8\pi i/3$.

5. If C is a closed curve described in the positive sense and

$$g(z_0) = \int_C \frac{z^3 - z}{(z - z_0)^3} \, dz,$$

show that $g(z_0) = 6\pi z_0 i$ when z_0 is inside C, and $g(z_0) = 0$ when z_0 is outside C.

6. Give an example to show that $|f(z)|$ may assume a minimum value at a point where $f(z)$ is analytic.

7. Complete the derivation of formula (3) of Sec. 53.

8. Carry out the mathematical induction to establish formula (4), Sec. 53, for every positive integer n.

CHAPTER VI

POWER SERIES

57. Taylor's Series.   We begin with one of the most important results of this chapter.

Theorem.   *Let $f(z)$ be analytic at all points within a circle C_0 with center at z_0 and radius r_0.   Then at each point z inside C_0*

$$(1) \quad f(z) = f(z_0) + f'(z_0)(z - z_0) + \frac{f''(z_0)}{2!} (z - z_0)^2 + \cdots$$

$$+ \frac{f^{(n)}(z_0)}{n!} (z - z_0)^n + \cdots ;$$

that is, the infinite series here converges to $f(z)$.

This is the expansion of the function $f(z)$ by Taylor's series about the point z_0.   As a special case, when z, z_0, and $f(z)$ are real, it includes the expansions of real functions by Taylor's series that were treated in a formal manner in elementary calculus.

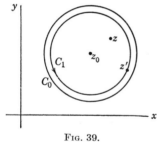

FIG. 39.

To prove the theorem, let z be any fixed point inside the circle C_0 and put $|z - z_0| = r$; thus $r < r_0$. Let z' denote any point on a circle $|z' - z_0| = r_1$, denoted by C_1, where $r < r_1 < r_0$.   As illustrated in Fig. 39 then, z is inside C_1, and $f(z)$ is analytic within and on C_1.   According to the Cauchy integral formula, it follows that

$$(2) \qquad\qquad f(z) = \frac{1}{2\pi i} \int_{C_1} \frac{f(z') \, dz'}{z' - z}.$$

Now

$$\frac{1}{z' - z} = \frac{1}{(z' - z_0) - (z - z_0)} = \frac{1}{z' - z_0} \frac{1}{1 - \dfrac{z - z_0}{z' - z_0}}.$$

But when α is any complex number other than unity, we note that

$$\frac{1}{1 - \alpha} = 1 + \alpha + \alpha^2 + \cdots + \alpha^{n-1} + \frac{\alpha^n}{1 - \alpha},$$

an identity that becomes evident when both its members are multiplied

98

by $(1 - \alpha)$.   Hence the equation above can be written

$$\frac{1}{z' - z} = \frac{1}{z' - z_0}\left[1 + \frac{z - z_0}{z' - z_0} + \cdots + \left(\frac{z - z_0}{z' - z_0}\right)^{n-1} \right.$$
$$\left. + \frac{1}{1 - \dfrac{z - z_0}{z' - z_0}}\left(\frac{z - z_0}{z' - z_0}\right)^n\right],$$

and therefore

$$\frac{f(z')}{z' - z} = \frac{f(z')}{z' - z_0} + (z - z_0)\frac{f(z')}{(z' - z_0)^2} + \cdots$$
$$+ (z - z_0)^{n-1}\frac{f(z')}{(z' - z_0)^n} + (z - z_0)^n\frac{f(z')}{(z' - z)(z' - z_0)^n}.$$

We now divide through by $2\pi i$ and integrate each term counterclockwise around C_1.   In view of formula (2) and the integral formulas (Sec. 53)

$$\frac{1}{2\pi i}\int_{C_1}\frac{f(z')\,dz'}{(z' - z_0)^{j+1}} = \frac{1}{j!}f^{(j)}(z_0) \qquad (j = 1, 2, \cdots),$$

we can write the result as follows:

$$(3)\quad f(z) = f(z_0) + f'(z_0)(z - z_0) + \cdots + \frac{f^{(n-1)}(z_0)}{(n - 1)!}(z - z_0)^{n-1} + R_n,$$

where

$$(4)\qquad\qquad R_n = \frac{(z - z_0)^n}{2\pi i}\int_{C_1}\frac{f(z')\,dz'}{(z' - z)(z' - z_0)^n}.$$

Let M be the maximum value of $|f(z')|$ on C_1.   Since $|z - z_0| = r$ and $|z' - z_0| = r_1$ and $|z' - z| \geqq (r_1 - r)$, it follows from equation (4) that

$$|R_n| \leqq \frac{r^n}{2\pi}\frac{2\pi r_1 M}{(r_1 - r)r_1^n} = \frac{r_1 M}{r_1 - r}\left(\frac{r}{r_1}\right)^n.$$

But $r/r_1 < 1$, and therefore

$$\lim_{n \to \infty} R_n = 0.$$

Thus as n tends to infinity, the limit of the sum of the first n terms in the right-hand member of equation (3) is $f(z)$.   That is, $f(z)$ is represented by Taylor's series,

$$(5)\qquad\qquad f(z) = f(z_0) + \sum_{n=1}^{\infty}\frac{f^{(n)}(z_0)}{n!}(z - z_0)^n.$$

When $z_0 = 0$, this reduces to *Maclaurin's series*,

$$(6)\qquad\qquad f(z) = f(0) + \sum_{n=1}^{\infty}\frac{f^{(n)}(0)}{n!}z^n.$$

58. Observations and Examples. When it is known that $f(z)$ is analytic at all points within the circle C_0, the convergence of Taylor's series to $f(z)$ is assured; no test for the convergence of the series is required. The maximum radius of C_0 is the distance from the point z_0 to the singular point of $f(z)$ that is nearest to z_0, since the function is to be analytic at all points inside C_0. We shall see (Sec. 62) that the series generally diverges at all points outside that circle of maximum radius. That circle is then called the *circle of convergence* of the series.

As our first example of a Maclaurin series expansion, let $f(z) = e^z$. Then $f^{(n)}(z) = e^z$ and $f^{(n)}(0) = 1$. Since e^z is analytic for every value of z, then

$$(1) \qquad e^z = 1 + \sum_{n=1}^{\infty} \frac{z^n}{n!} \qquad \text{when } |z| < \infty.$$

Similarly, we find that

$$(2) \qquad \sin z = \sum_{n=1}^{\infty} (-1)^{n+1} \frac{z^{2n-1}}{(2n-1)!} \qquad \text{when } |z| < \infty,$$

$$(3) \qquad \cos z = 1 + \sum_{n=1}^{\infty} (-1)^n \frac{z^{2n}}{(2n)!} \qquad \text{when } |z| < \infty,$$

$$(4) \qquad \sinh z = \sum_{n=1}^{\infty} \frac{z^{2n-1}}{(2n-1)!} \qquad \text{when } |z| < \infty,$$

$$(5) \qquad \cosh z = 1 + \sum_{n=1}^{\infty} \frac{z^{2n}}{(2n)!} \qquad \text{when } |z| < \infty,$$

and

$$(6) \qquad \frac{1}{1+z} = \sum_{n=0}^{\infty} (-1)^n z^n \qquad \text{when } |z| < 1.$$

As a special case of the expansion (1), for example, when z is real, the representation

$$e^x = 1 + \sum_{n=1}^{\infty} \frac{x^n}{n!}$$

is valid for every real x.

By substituting Z^2 for z in the expansion (6), we note that

$$\frac{1}{1+Z^2} = \sum_{n=0}^{\infty} (-1)^n Z^{2n} \qquad \text{when } |Z| < 1.$$

Such substitutions in the expansions of the elementary functions are often useful.

The derivatives of the function $f(z) = z^{-1}$ are

$$f^{(n)}(z) = (-1)^n n! \; z^{-n-1} \qquad (n = 1, 2, \cdots),$$

and therefore $f^{(n)}(1) = (-1)^n n!$. Hence the expansion of this function by Taylor's series about the point $z = 1$ is

(7)
$$\frac{1}{z} = \sum_{n=0}^{\infty} (-1)^n (z-1)^n.$$

This expansion is valid when $|z - 1| < 1$, since the function is analytic at all points except $z = 0$.

As another example, let us expand the function

$$f(z) = \frac{1 + 2z}{z^2 + z^3} = \frac{1}{z^2}\left(2 - \frac{1}{1+z}\right)$$

in a series of positive and negative powers of z. We cannot apply Maclaurin's series to $f(z)$ itself, since this function is not analytic at $z = 0$; but we can apply it to the function $1/(1 + z)$. Thus, when $0 < |z| < 1$, it is true that

$$\frac{1 + 2z}{z^2 + z^3} = \frac{1}{z^2}\left(2 - 1 + z - z^2 + z^3 - \cdots\right)$$

$$= \frac{1}{z^2} + \frac{1}{z} - 1 + z - z^2 + z^3 - \cdots;$$

EXERCISES

1. Show that, for every finite value of z,

$$e^z = e + e \sum_{n=1}^{\infty} \frac{(z-1)^n}{n!}.$$

2. Show that

(a) $\dfrac{1}{z^2} = 1 + \displaystyle\sum_{n=1}^{\infty} (n+1)(z+1)^n$ when $|z + 1| < 1$;

(b) $\dfrac{1}{z^2} = \dfrac{1}{4} + \dfrac{1}{4}\displaystyle\sum_{n=1}^{\infty} (-1)^n(n+1)\left(\dfrac{z-2}{2}\right)^n$ when $|z - 2| < 2$.

3. Expand $\cos z$ by Taylor's series about the point $z = \pi/2$.

4. Expand $\sinh z$ by Taylor's series about the point $z = \pi i$.

5. Within what circle does the Maclaurin series for the function $\tanh z$ converge to the function? Write the first few terms of that series.

6. Prove that, when $0 < |z| < 4$,

$$\frac{1}{4z - z^2} = \sum_{n=0}^{\infty} \frac{z^{n-1}}{4^{n+1}}.$$

7. Prove that when $x \neq 0$,

$$\frac{\sin (x^2)}{x^4} = \frac{1}{x^2} - \frac{x^2}{3!} + \frac{x^6}{5!} - \frac{x^{10}}{7!} + \cdots .$$

8. Represent the function

$$f(z) = \frac{z}{(z-1)(z-3)}$$

by a series of positive and negative powers of $(z-1)$, which converges to $f(z)$ when $0 < |z - 1| < 2$.

$$Ans.\ f(z) = \frac{-1}{2(z-1)} - 3 \sum_{n=1}^{\infty} \frac{(z-1)^{n-1}}{2^{n+1}}.$$

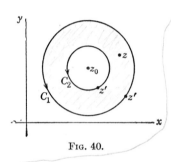

FIG. 40.

59. Laurent's Series. Let z' denote a point on either of two concentric circles C_1 and C_2,

$$|z' - z_0| = r_1, \qquad |z' - z_0| = r_2,$$

about a point z_0, where $r_2 < r_1$ (Fig. 40). We shall prove the following theorem.

Theorem. *If $f(z)$ is analytic on C_1 and C_2 and throughout the region between those two circles, then at each point z between them $f(z)$ is represented by a convergent series of positive and negative powers of $(z - z_0)$,* $f(z)$ is not analy. at z_0

(1) $$f(z) = \sum_{n=0}^{\infty} a_n(z - z_0)^n + \sum_{n=1}^{\infty} \frac{b_n}{(z - z_0)^n},$$

where

(2) $$a_n = \frac{1}{2\pi i} \int_{C_1} \frac{f(z')\ dz'}{(z' - z_0)^{n+1}} \qquad (n = 0,1,2, \cdots),$$

(3) $$b_n = \frac{1}{2\pi i} \int_{C_2} \frac{f(z')\ dz'}{(z' - z_0)^{-n+1}} \qquad (n = 1,2, \cdots),$$

each integral being taken counterclockwise.

The series here is called *Laurent's series.*

In case $f(z)$ is analytic at every point on and inside C_1 except the point z_0 itself, the radius r_2 may be taken arbitrarily small. The expansion (1) is then valid when $0 < |z - z_0| < r_1$. If $f(z)$ is analytic at all points on and inside C_1, the integrand of the integral (3) is an analytic function of z' inside and on C_2, because $-n + 1 \leq 0$; it therefore has the value zero and the series becomes Taylor's series.

Since the integrands of the integrals in formulas (2) and (3) are analytic functions of z' throughout the annular region, any closed curve C around the annulus can be used as the path of integration in place of the circular paths C_1 and C_2. Thus Laurent's series can be written

$$(4) \qquad\qquad f(z) = \sum_{n=-\infty}^{\infty} A_n(z - z_0)^n \qquad (r_2 < |z - z_0| < r_1),$$

where

$$(5) \qquad\qquad A_n = \frac{1}{2\pi i} \int_C \frac{f(z')\, dz'}{(z' - z_0)^{n+1}} \qquad (n = 0, \pm 1, \pm 2, \cdots).$$

In particular cases, of course, some of the coefficients may be zero. In fact, the function

$$f(z) = \frac{1}{(z - 1)^2},$$

for example, already has the form (4) with $z_0 = 1$. Here $A_{-2} = 1$ while all other A_n's are zero, which is·in agreement with formula (5). Since this function is analytic everywhere except at the point $z = 1$, the curve C can be any closed curve enclosing that point.

The coefficients are usually found by other means than the use of the above formulas. For example, when $|z| > 0$ the expansions

$$\frac{e^z}{z^2} = \frac{1}{z^2} + \frac{1}{z} + \frac{1}{2!} + \frac{z}{3!} + \frac{z^2}{4!} + \cdots$$

and

$$e^{1/z} = 1 + \sum_{n=1}^{\infty} \frac{1}{n!\, z^n}$$

follow from Maclaurin's series. We shall see that such representations are unique, so that these must be the Laurent series with $z_0 = 0$.

To prove the theorem we first note that, according to Cauchy's integral formula,

$$(6) \qquad\qquad f(z) = \frac{1}{2\pi i} \int_{C_1} \frac{f(z')\, dz'}{z' - z} - \frac{1}{2\pi i} \int_{C_2} \frac{f(z')\, dz'}{z' - z},$$

since C_1 and C_2 form the boundary of a region throughout which $f(z)$ is analytic. In the first integral, as in the above proof of Taylor's theorem, we put

$$\frac{1}{z' - z} = \frac{1}{(z' - z_0) - (z - z_0)} = \frac{1}{z' - z_0} + \frac{z - z_0}{(z' - z_0)^2} + \cdots$$
$$+ \frac{(z - z_0)^{n-1}}{(z' - z_0)^n} + \frac{(z - z_0)^n}{(z' - z_0)^n(z' - z)}.$$

In the second integral we put

$$-\frac{1}{z' - z} = \frac{1}{(z - z_0) - (z' - z_0)}$$

and factor $(z - z_0)$ from the demoninator to write

$$-\frac{1}{z' - z} = \frac{1}{z - z_0} + \frac{z' - z_0}{(z - z_0)^2} + \cdots$$
$$+ \frac{(z' - z_0)^{n-1}}{(z - z_0)^n} + \frac{(z' - z_0)^n}{(z - z_0)^n(z - z')}.$$

Then it follows from equation (6) that

$$f(z) = a_0 + a_1(z - z_0) + a_2(z - z_0)^2 + \cdots + a_{n-1}(z - z_0)^{n-1} + R_n$$
$$+ \frac{b_1}{z - z_0} + \frac{b_2}{(z - z_0)^2} + \cdots + \frac{b_n}{(z - z_0)^n} + S_n,$$

where a_n and b_n are the numbers represented by formulas (2) and (3) and

$$R_n = \frac{(z - z_0)^n}{2\pi i} \int_{C_1} \frac{f(z') \, dz'}{(z' - z_0)^n(z' - z)},$$
$$S_n = \frac{1}{2\pi i (z - z_0)^n} \int_{C_2} \frac{(z' - z_0)^n f(z')}{z - z'} \, dz'.$$

Let $r = |z - z_0|$; then $r_2 < r < r_1$. The proof that R_n approaches zero as n tends to infinity is the same as that used in establishing Taylor's series. If M is the maximum value of $|f(z')|$ on C_2, then

$$|S_n| \leqq \left(\frac{r_2}{r}\right)^n \frac{Mr_2}{r - r_2},$$

and therefore S_n approaches zero as n tends to infinity. This completes the proof of the theorem.

60. Properties of Power Series. Let S_N represent the sum of the first N terms of any infinite series of complex numbers,

$$(1) \qquad \sum_{n=1}^{\infty} z_n.$$

Then if $z_n = x_n + iy_n$, we can write

$$(2) \qquad S_N = \sum_{n=1}^{N} z_n = \sum_{n=1}^{N} x_n + i \sum_{n=1}^{N} y_n,$$

and in order that the limit of S_N may exist as N tends to infinity, it is necessary and sufficient that the limits of each of the above sums of the real numbers x_n and y_n exist. For if those limits exist and are denoted by X and Y, that is, if

$$(3) \qquad X = \sum_{n=1}^{\infty} x_n, \qquad Y = \sum_{n=1}^{\infty} y_n,$$

then

$$\lim_{N \to \infty} S_N = X + iY = \sum_{n=1}^{\infty} z_n.$$

On the other hand if $X + iY$ represents the limit of S_N, it follows that $X + iY - S_N$ approaches zero; that is, if X_N and Y_N represent the two sums on the right of equation (2), then

$$\lim_{N \to \infty} |X - X_N + i(Y - Y_N)| = 0.$$

This makes it necessary that X_N approach X and Y_N approach Y, so that both the series (3) must converge.

A necessary condition for the convergence of a series of real numbers is that the nth term approach zero as n tends to infinity. If the series (1) is to converge, then the series (3) must both converge, and so x_n and y_n must approach zero as n tends to infinity. Therefore z_n must approach zero; that is, a *necessary condition for the convergence of the series* (1) *is that*

(4) $$\lim_{n \to \infty} |z_n| = 0.$$

In particular, the terms of a convergent series are bounded: $|z_n| < M$ for every positive integer n, where M is some positive constant.

If the series (1) is *absolutely convergent*, that is, if the series

$$\sum_{n=1}^{\infty} |z_n| = \sum_{n=1}^{\infty} \sqrt{x_n^2 + y_n^2}$$

converges, then it follows from the comparison test for series of positive real numbers that the two series

$$\sum_{n=1}^{\infty} |x_n|, \qquad \sum_{n=1}^{\infty} |y_n|,$$

both converge. The series (3) are thus absolutely convergent, and they are therefore convergent, because the absolute convergence of a series of real numbers implies the convergence of the series itself. Since the series (3) converge, the series (1) converges; that is, *absolute convergence of a series of complex numbers implies the convergence of the series itself.*

Theorem. *If a power series*

(5) $$\sum_{n=0}^{\infty} a_n z^n$$

converges when $z = z_1$, *it is absolutely convergent for every value of* z *such that* $|z| < |z_1|$.

Since the series whose terms are $a_n z_1^n$ converges, those terms are all bounded,

$$|a_n z_1^n| < M \qquad\qquad (n = 0,1,2, \cdots),$$

for some positive constant M. Let $|z|/|z_1| = k$, where $|z| < |z_1|$; then

$$|a_n z^n| = |a_n z_1^n| \left|\frac{z}{z_1}\right|^n < M k^n.$$

The series whose terms are the positive real numbers $M k^n$ is a geometric series; it is convergent, since $k < 1$. We conclude from the comparison test that the series

$$\sum_{n=0}^{\infty} |a_n z^n|$$

converges, so the theorem is proved.

The region of convergence of the power series (5) is therefore a circle about the origin. The greatest circle about the origin such that the series converges at each point inside is called the *circle of convergence* of the power series. The series cannot converge at any point z_1 outside that circle, according to the above theorem, for in that case it must converge everywhere inside the circle about the origin passing through z_1. Thus the first circle could not be the circle of convergence.

If z is replaced by $(z - z_0)$, it follows that the region of convergence of the series

$$(6) \qquad\qquad \sum_{n=0}^{\infty} a_n (z - z_0)^n$$

is a circle about the point z_0. Similarly, we can see at once that if the series

$$(7) \qquad\qquad \sum_{n=1}^{\infty} \frac{b_n}{(z - z_0)^n}$$

converges when $z = z_1$, then it is absolutely convergent for every value of z such that

$$|z - z_0| > |z_1 - z_0|.$$

The region of convergence of the series (7) is therefore the exterior of some circle about the point z_0.

61. Uniform Convergence. Let C_0 denote a circle $|z| = r_0$ interior to which a power series converges, and let the function $S(z)$ represent the sum of that series,

$$(I) \qquad\qquad S(z) = \lim_{N \to \infty} \sum_{n=0}^{N} a_n z^n = \sum_{n=0}^{\infty} a_n z^n.$$

The remainder after N terms can be written

(2) $$R_N(z) = S(z) - \sum_{n=0}^{N-1} a_n z^n = \lim_{m \to \infty} \sum_{n=N}^{m} a_n z^n.$$

When $|z| \leqq |z_1|$, where $|z_1| < r_0$, we can write

(3) $$\left| \sum_{n=N}^{m} a_n z^n \right| \leqq \sum_{n=N}^{m} |a_n z^n| \leqq \sum_{n=N}^{m} |a_n||z_1|^n.$$

The limit of this last sum, as m tends to infinity, is the remainder in the series of the absolute values of the terms of the series (1). But according to the theorem in the preceding section, the series (1) is absolutely convergent when $z = z_1$, and hence the remainder

$$\rho_N = \lim_{m \to \infty} \sum_{n=N}^{m} |a_n||z_1|^n$$

approaches zero as N tends to infinity; that is, given any positive number ϵ, an integer N_ϵ exists such that $\rho_N < \epsilon$ whenever $N \geqq N_\epsilon$. Since the terms of the last series are all nonnegative real numbers, it follows that, for every integer m greater than N,

$$\sum_{n=N}^{m} |a_n||z_1|^n \leqq \rho_N.$$

In view of the relation (3) then,

$$\left| \sum_{n=N}^{m} a_n z^n \right| \leqq \rho_N$$

for every integer m greater than N, and hence the remainder (2) satisfies the relation

$$|R_N(z)| \leqq \rho_N < \epsilon \qquad \text{when } N \geqq N_\epsilon.$$

Now N_ϵ is independent of z when $|z| \leqq |z_1|$, so that the following theorem is established.

Theorem. *The power series (1) is uniformly convergent for all points z within and on any circle $|z| = |z_1|$ that is interior to the circle of convergence.*

The partial sum

$$S_N(z) = \sum_{n=0}^{N-1} a_n z^n$$

of the series (1) is a polynomial, and hence it is a continuous function of z. To show that its limit $S(z)$ is continuous when $|z| \leqq |z_1|$, we first note that since

$$S(z) = S_N(z) + R_N(z),$$

then

(4) $\quad |S(z + \Delta z) - S(z)| = |S_N(z + \Delta z) - S_N(z) + R_N(z + \Delta z) - R_N(z)|$
$$\leqq |\Delta S_N| + |R_N(z + \Delta z)| + |R_N(z)|,$$

where $\Delta S_N = S_N(z + \Delta z) - S_N(z)$. We want to show that, given any positive number ϵ, a positive number δ exists such that

(5) $\qquad\qquad\qquad |S(z + \Delta z) - S(z)| < \epsilon \qquad$ when $|\Delta z| < \delta$.

In view of the uniform convergence established above, an integer N_ϵ exists such that $|R_N| < \epsilon/3$ for every point in the region $|z| \leqq |z_1|$, when $N \geqq N_\epsilon$. When $N = N_\epsilon$, a number δ exists such that $|\Delta S_N| < \epsilon/3$ when $|\Delta z| < \delta$, because $S_N(z)$ is continuous. The value of the right-hand member of the inequality (4) is therefore less than ϵ, and the inequality (5) is established.

We have now shown that a power series represents a continuous function of z at each point interior to its circle of convergence.

By substituting $(z - z_0)$ or its reciprocal for z, the above results can be extended at once to series of the types

$$\sum_{n=0}^{\infty} a_n (z - z_0)^n, \qquad \sum_{n=0}^{\infty} \frac{b_n}{(z - z_0)^n},$$

with obvious modifications. Thus if the second series here is convergent in the annulus $r_1 \leqq |z - z_0| \leqq r_2$, it is uniformly convergent for all values of z in that annulus and its sum represents a continuous function of z there.

62. Integration and Differentiation of Power Series. It was shown above that a power series represents a continuous function $S(z)$ interior to the circle of convergence. We shall prove in this section that $S(z)$ is analytic within that circle.

Theorem 1. *Let C denote any curve interior to the circle of convergence of a power series, and let $g(z)$ be any function that is continuous on C. The series formed by multiplying each term of the power series by $g(z)$ can be integrated term by term over C; that is,*

(1) $\qquad\qquad \sum_{n=0}^{\infty} a_n \int_C z^n g(z) \, dz = \int_C S(z) g(z) \, dz.$

We assume as before that the curve C consists of a finite number of arcs having the parametric representation described in Sec. 44. Since the sum $S(z)$ of the power series is a continuous function, the integral of the product

$$S(z)g(z) = \sum_{n=0}^{N-1} a_n z^n g(z) + R_N(z)g(z)$$

exists. The terms of the finite sum here are also continuous on the curve C, so their integrals over C exist, and consequently the integral of the remainder $R_N(z)g(z)$ must exist. Thus

$$(2) \qquad \int_C S(z)g(z)\,dz = \sum_{n=0}^{N-1} a_n \int_C z^n g(z)\,dz + \int_C R_N(z)g(z)\,dz.$$

Let M represent the maximum value of $|g(z)|$ at all points z on C, and let L denote the length of C. In view of the uniform convergence of the power series established in Sec. 61, for every positive number ϵ, an integer N_ϵ exists such that for all points z on C,

$$|R_N(z)| < \epsilon \qquad\qquad \text{when } N \geqq N_\epsilon.$$

Since ϵ and N_ϵ are independent of z, we can write

$$\left| \int_C R_N(z)g(z)\,dz \right| < \epsilon ML \qquad\qquad \text{when } N \geqq N_\epsilon.$$

It follows, therefore, from equation (2) that

$$\int_C S(z)g(z)\,dz = \lim_{N\to\infty} \sum_{n=0}^{N-1} a_n \int_C z^n g(z)\,dz,$$

which is the same as equation (1), so Theorem 1 is proved.

When $g(z) = 1$ for all values of z and C is any closed curve interior to the circle of convergence of the power series, then, for every integer n,

$$\int_C z^n g(z)\,dz = \int_C z^n\,dz = 0.$$

It follows from equation (1) that

$$\int_C S(z)\,dz = 0$$

for every closed curve interior to the circle of convergence, and according to Morera's theorem, the function $S(z)$ is analytic. The result can be stated as follows:

Theorem 2. *A power series represents an analytic function at every point interior to its circle of convergence.*

If a function $f(z)$ is analytic inside a circle C about the origin and has a singular point z_0 on C such that either $f(z)$ or its derivative of some order has no limit as z tends to z_0 within C then the Maclaurin series for $f(z)$ must diverge outside C. If it converged it would represent an analytic function $F(z)$ in a circle enclosing C. Since $F(z) = f(z)$ in C then $f(z)$ and its derivatives would have limits at z_0.

Theorem 3. *A power series can be differentiated term by term at every point z interior to the circle of convergence; that is,*

$$(3) \qquad\qquad S'(z) = \sum_{n=1}^{\infty} n a_n z^{n-1} \qquad\qquad (|z| < r_0).$$

To establish this theorem, let z_1 denote any point interior to the circle and let C be some closed curve about z_1 and interior to the circle.   Then since $S(z)$ is analytic,

$$S'(z_1) = \frac{1}{2\pi i} \int_C \frac{S(z)\ dz}{(z - z_1)^2}.$$

In equation (1) we take

$$g(z) = \frac{1}{2\pi i(z - z_1)^2};$$

then

$$\int_C z^n g(z)\ dz = \frac{1}{2\pi i} \int_C \frac{z^n\ dz}{(z - z_1)^2} = \frac{d}{dz_1}(z_1^n),$$

and

$$\int_C S(z)g(z)\ dz = S'(z_1).$$

Therefore

$$S'(z_1) = \sum_{n=0}^{\infty} a_n \frac{d}{dz_1}(z_1^n),$$

and the theorem is proved.

The results here can be extended at once to series of positive or negative power of $(z - z_0)$.

63. Uniqueness of Representations by Power Series. The series in equation (3) of the preceding section is a power series that converges to $S'(z)$ within the circle of convergence C_0 of the series

(1)
$$\sum_{n=0}^{\infty} a_n z^n = S(z).$$

Consequently, that series can be differentiated term by term; that is,

$$S''(z) = \sum_{n=2}^{\infty} n(n - 1)a_n z^{n-2} \qquad\qquad (|z| < r_0).$$

Similarly, the derivative of $S(z)$ of any order can be found by successively differentiating the series term by term.   Moreover,

$$S(0) = a_0, \qquad S'(0) = a_1, \qquad S''(0) = 2!a_2, \qquad \cdots ,$$

so that the coefficients are those of the Maclaurin series expansion of $S(z)$,

$$a_n = \frac{S^{(n)}(0)}{n!}.$$

The generalization to series of positive powers of $(z - z_0)$ is immediate. Thus we have the following theorem on the uniqueness of the representation of functions in power series.

Theorem 1. *If the series*

(2)
$$\sum_{n=0}^{\infty} a_n(z - z_0)^n$$

converges to a function $f(z)$ at all points interior to some circle $|z - z_0| = r_0$, that series is the Taylor series expansion of $f(z)$ in powers of $(z - z_0)$.

As an example, we find by substituting z^2 for z in the Maclaurin series for $\sin z$ that

$$\sin (z^2) = \sum_{n=1}^{\infty} (-1)^{n-1} \frac{z^{4n-2}}{(2n - 1)!} \qquad (|z| < \infty).$$

This series must be identical to the series that would be found by expanding the function $\sin (z^2)$ directly in Maclaurin's series.

It follows from Theorem 1 that if the series (2) converges to zero at every point in some neighborhood of z_0, then each of the coefficients a_n must vanish.

Theorem 2. *If the series*

(3)
$$\sum_{n=-\infty}^{\infty} A_n(z - z_0)^n = \sum_{n=0}^{\infty} a_n(z - z_0)^n + \sum_{n=1}^{\infty} \frac{b_n}{(z - z_0)^n}$$

converges to a function $f(z)$ at all points in some annular region about z_0, then it is the Laurent series expansion of $f(z)$ in powers of $(z - z_0)$ for that region.

The proof of this theorem follows from Theorem 1 of the preceding section, extended to series of positive and negative powers of $(z - z_0)$. If we take the curve C as a closed curve around the annulus and interior to it and take

$$g(z) = \frac{1}{2\pi i (z - z_0)^{m+1}},$$

the term by term integration shows that

$$A_m = \frac{1}{2\pi i} \int_C \frac{f(z)\, dz}{(z - z_0)^{m+1}}.$$

These are the coefficients in the Laurent series.

64. Multiplication and Division. Suppose that the two power series

(1)
$$\sum_{n=0}^{\infty} a_n z^n = f(z), \qquad \sum_{n=0}^{\infty} b_n z^n = g(z)$$

both converge in the interior of some circle $|z| = r_0$. The sums $f(z)$ and $g(z)$ are then analytic functions in that region, and hence their product has a Maclaurin series expansion in the region,

$$(2) \qquad f(z)g(z) = \sum_{n=0}^{\infty} c_n z^n \qquad (|z| < r_0).$$

The coefficients c_n are given by the formulas

$$c_0 = f(0)g(0) = a_0 b_0,$$
$$c_1 = f(0)g'(0) + f'(0)g(0) = a_0 b_1 + a_1 b_0,$$
$$c_2 = \frac{1}{2!} [f(0)g''(0) + 2f'(0)g'(0) + f''(0)g(0)]$$
$$= a_0 b_2 + a_1 b_1 + a_2 b_0,$$

etc., where we have made use of the fact that the two series (1) are the same as the Maclaurin series for $f(z)$ and $g(z)$. With the aid of the formula for the nth derivative of the product of two functions, we can see that

$$(3) \quad f(z)g(z) = a_0 b_0 + (a_0 b_1 + a_1 b_0)z + (a_0 b_2 + a_1 b_1 + a_2 b_0)z^2 + \cdots$$
$$+ \left(\sum_{k=0}^{n} a_k b_{n-k} \right) z^n + \cdots \qquad (|z| < r_0).$$

The series (3) is the same as the series obtained by multiplying the two series (1) together term by term and collecting the terms in like powers of z; it is the *Cauchy product* of the two given series. Thus we can state the following theorem:

Theorem. *The product of two power series converges to the product of their sums at all points interior to both their circles of convergence.*

If $g(z) \neq 0$ in some neighborhood of the origin, the quotient $f(z)/g(z)$ is an analytic function there. It therefore has a Maclaurin series expansion

$$(4) \qquad q(z) = \frac{f(z)}{g(z)} = \sum_{n=0}^{\infty} \gamma_n z^n,$$

where $\gamma_0 = q(0)$, $\gamma_1 = q'(0)$, $\gamma_2 = q''(0)/2!$, etc. The first few of these coefficients can be found in terms of the coefficients a_n and b_n by differentiating the quotient $f(z)/g(z)$ successively. The results are the same as those obtained by carrying out the division of the first of series (1) by the second. This method identifies the first few terms of the quotient of two power series with the power series that represents the quotient. This is generally the result that is needed in the applications, although it can be shown that the series are entirely identical.

The addition of two power series term by term is always valid within their common region of convergence. This follows from the definition of the sum of the series. Multiplication by a constant is a special **case** of the above theorem on the multiplication of two series; consequently, two power series can be subtracted term by term.

65. Examples. As an illustration of the use of the results found in the preceding sections, let us find the two Laurent series expansions, in powers of z, of the function

$$f(z) = \frac{1}{z(1+z^2)}.$$

The singular points of this function are $z = 0$ and $z = \pm i$. When $0 < |z| < 1$, we can write

$$f(z) = \frac{1}{z}(1 - z^2 + z^4 - z^6 + \cdots).$$

Hence

(1) $$\frac{1}{z(1+z^2)} = \frac{1}{z} + \sum_{n=1}^{\infty} (-1)^n z^{2n-1} \qquad (0 < |z| < 1).$$

This series is the Laurent series representation of $f(z)$ in powers of z in the region indicated here, since it is a series in positive and negative powers of z that converges to $f(z)$ in that region.

When $|z| > 1$, we can write

$$f(z) = \frac{1}{z^3}\frac{1}{1+z^{-2}} = \frac{1}{z^3}\sum_{n=0}^{\infty}(-1)^n z^{-2n},$$

and hence the Laurent series representation is

(2) $$\frac{1}{z(1+z^2)} = \sum_{n=0}^{\infty}(-1)^n \frac{1}{z^{2n+3}} \qquad (|z| > 1).$$

EXERCISES

1. Obtain the Maclaurin series expansion

$$\frac{z+1}{z-1} = -1 - 2\sum_{n=1}^{\infty} z^n \qquad (|z| < 1).$$

2. Obtain the Maclaurin series expansion

$$z \cosh(z^2) = z + \sum_{n=1}^{\infty}\frac{1}{(2n)!}z^{4n+1} \qquad (|z| < \infty).$$

3. Obtain the Taylor series expansion

$$\frac{z-1}{z^2} = \sum_{n=0}^{\infty}(-1)^n(n+1)(z-1)^{n+1} \qquad (|z-1| < 1).$$

4. Obtain the Laurent series expansion

$$\frac{\sinh z}{z^2} = \frac{1}{z} + \sum_{n=1}^{\infty} \frac{1}{(2n+1)!} z^{2n-1} \qquad (|z| > 0).$$

5. Obtain the first four terms of the Laurent series expansion

$$\frac{e^z}{z(z^2+1)} = \frac{1}{z} + 1 - \frac{1}{2} z - \frac{5}{6} z^2 + \cdots \qquad (0 < |z| < 1).$$

6. Obtain the first few terms of the Laurent series expansion

$$\csc z = \frac{1}{z} + \frac{1}{3!} z - \left[\frac{1}{5!} - \frac{1}{(3!)^2} \right] z^3 + \cdots \qquad (0 < |z| < \pi).$$

7. Give two Laurent series expansions, in powers of z, for the function

$$f(z) = \frac{1}{z^2(1-z)}$$

and specify the regions in which those expansions are valid.

$$Ans. \sum_{n=0}^{\infty} z^{n-2}, \ (0 < |z| < 1); \ -\sum_{n=0}^{\infty} z^{-n-3} \qquad (|z| > 1).$$

8. Expand the function $f(z) = z/(1 + z^3)$, (a) in a series of positive powers of z; (b) in a series of negative powers of z. In each case specify the region in which the expansion is valid.

9. Find the Maclaurin series representation of the function $(1 - z)^{-2}$ by differentiating the Maclaurin series for the function $(1 - z)^{-1}$.

10. Expand the function $1/z$ in powers of $(z - 1)$, and then obtain by differentiation the expansion of z^{-2} in powers of $(z - 1)$.

11. Show that if $z - 1 = \rho \exp i\phi$, then $1 - z = \rho \exp [i(\phi + \pi)]$ and Log $(1 - z)$ is single-valued and analytic in the region $|z| < 1$. By integrating the Maclaurin series for $(1 - z)^{-1}$ from zero to z, show that

$$\text{Log } (1 - z) = -\sum_{n=1}^{\infty} \frac{z^n}{n} \qquad (|z| < 1).$$

12. Write the Laurent series expansion of the function $(z - k)^{-1}$ in the region $|z| > k$, where k is real and $k^2 < 1$. Then set $z = e^{i\theta}$ to obtain the following sums of series of sines and cosines:

$$\sum_{n=0}^{\infty} k^n \sin [(n+1)\theta] = \frac{\sin \theta}{1 + k^2 - 2k \cos \theta},$$

$$\sum_{n=0}^{\infty} k^n \cos [(n+1)\theta] = \frac{\cos \theta - k}{1 + k^2 - 2k \cos \theta}.$$

13. Let $F(r,\theta)$ denote a function of $z = re^{i\theta}$ that is analytic in some annulus about the origin that includes the circle $r = 1$. Take that circle as the curve C in the formula for the coefficients A_n in the Laurent expansion of $F(r,\theta)$ in powers of z, and show that

$$F(1,\theta) = \frac{1}{2\pi} \int_0^{2\pi} F(1,\theta')\, d\theta' + \frac{1}{\pi} \sum_{n=1}^{\infty} \int_0^{2\pi} F(1,\theta')\, \cos\,[n(\theta - \theta')]\, d\theta'.$$

This is the Fourier series expansion of the complex function $F(1,\theta)$ of the real variable θ on the unit circle. If $u(\theta)$ and $v(\theta)$ denote the real and imaginary components of $F(1,\theta)$, show that the above expansion is true when F is replaced everywhere by u, or everywhere by v. The restrictions on the real functions u and v here, however, are much more severe than they need be in order that these real functions be represented by their Fourier series.*

* For other sufficient conditions see, for instance, the author's book "Fourier Series and Boundary Value Problems," pp. 70, 86.

CHAPTER VII

RESIDUES AND POLES

66. Residues. If there is some neighborhood of a singular point z_0 of a function $f(z)$ throughout which $f(z)$ is analytic, except at the point itself, then z_0 is called an *isolated singular point* of $f(z)$. As before, $f(z)$ here denotes a single-valued function in the region considered.

The function $1/z$ furnishes a simple example. It is analytic except at $z = 0$; hence the origin is an isolated singular point of that function. The function

$$\frac{z + 1}{z^3(z^2 + 1)}$$

has three isolated singular points, one at $z = 0$, one at $z = i$, and one at $z = -i$.

As another example, the function

$$\frac{1}{\sin (\pi/z)}$$

has an infinite number of isolated singular points all lying on the segment of the real axis from $z = -1$ to $z = 1$, namely, $z = \pm 1$, $z = \pm\frac{1}{2}$, $z = \pm\frac{1}{3}$, etc. But the origin $z = 0$ is also a singular point; it is not isolated, since every neighborhood of the origin contains other singular points of the function.

Again, the function $\text{Log } z$ has a singular point at the origin that is not isolated, because each neighborhood of the origin includes points on the negative real axis where $\text{Log } z$ is not continuous and hence not analytic.

When z_0 is an isolated singular point of $f(z)$, a positive number r_1 exists such that the function is analytic at each point z for which $0 < |z - z_0| \leqq r_1$. In that region the function is represented by the Laurent series

$$(1) \qquad f(z) = \sum_{n=0}^{\infty} a_n(z - z_0)^n + \frac{b_1}{z - z_0} + \frac{b_2}{(z - z_0)^2} + \cdots ,$$

where the coefficients a_n and b_n are given by formulas (2) and (3), or (5), of Sec. 59. In particular,

$$(2) \qquad b_1 = \frac{1}{2\pi i} \int_{C_2} f(z') \, dz',$$

where C_2 is any circle $|z - z_0| = r_2$ for which $r_2 \leqq r_1$, described in the positive sense.

The series of negative powers of $(z - z_0)$ in formula (1) is called the *principal part* of $f(z)$ at the isolated singular point z_0. It is the part that will show the character of the singularity.

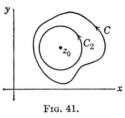

FIG. 41.

But the value of the integral in equation (2) is not changed if C_2 is replaced by any closed curve C around z_0 such that $f(z)$ is analytic on and inside C, except at the point z_0 itself (Fig. 41). For according to the Cauchy-Goursat theorem, on p.82 & took

$$\int_C f(z')\, dz' - \int_{C_2} f(z')\, dz' = 0.$$

Note that the curve C may extend outside the circle $|z - z_0| = r_1$. Thus

$$(3) \qquad b_1 = \frac{1}{2\pi i} \int_C f(z')\, dz',$$

where the integral is taken counterclockwise.

The coefficient b_1 is called the *residue* of $f(z)$ at the isolated singular point z_0. According to this definition, every function has a residue at each of its isolated singular points, since the Laurent expansion about such a point exists and is valid in a neighborhood of the point, except at the point itself. The value of the residue may, of course, be zero. We have noted that *the residue is the value of the integral of $f(z)/(2\pi i)$ taken counterclockwise around any curve enclosing z_0 and no other singular point of $f(z)$.*

We now have a powerful method of evaluating certain integrals around closed curves. For example, to evaluate the integral of the function $z^{-3} \cos z$ around any closed curve C containing the origin, which is the only singular point of that function in the finite plane, we may use the Maclaurin series for $\cos z$ to write

$$\frac{\cos z}{z^3} = \frac{1}{z^3} - \frac{1}{2}\frac{1}{z} + \frac{1}{4!}z - \frac{1}{6!}z^3 + \cdots,$$

when $|z| > 0$. From this Laurent series we see that b_1, the residue of our function at $z = 0$, is $-\frac{1}{2}$. It follows at once that

$$(4) \qquad \frac{1}{2\pi i} \int_C \frac{\cos z}{z^3}\, dz = -\frac{1}{2},$$

where the integral is taken counterclockwise.

As another example, consider the integral

$$(5) \qquad \int_C \exp\left(\frac{1}{z^2}\right) dz$$

where C is again any closed curve about the origin. Since $1/z^2$ is analytic except at $z = 0$, the integrand here also has that character. With the aid of the Maclaurin series for e^z, we can write

$$e^{1/z^2} = 1 + \frac{1}{z^2} + \frac{1}{2!}\frac{1}{z^4} + \frac{1}{3!}\frac{1}{z^6} + \cdots \qquad (z \neq 0).$$

The residue of the integrand at $z = 0$ is therefore zero, and hence the value of the integral (5) is zero.

The last example again illustrates the fact that the condition that the integrand be analytic within and on a closed curve C is not a necessary condition for the vanishing of the integral around C. The Cauchy-Goursat theorem shows that the condition is a sufficient one. Earlier we noted some simpler cases in which integrals around singular points vanish; namely,

$$(6) \qquad \int_C \frac{dz}{(z - z_0)^n} = 0 \qquad (n = 2,3,4, \cdots),$$

where C is a closed curve around the point z_0. In each case here, the integrand is discontinuous at a point inside C, so that Morera's theorem (Sec. 54) does not apply.

67. The Residue Theorem. If a function has only a finite number of singular points in some finite region, then those singular points are necessarily isolated.

Theorem. *Let C be a closed curve within and on which $f(z)$ is analytic except for a finite number of singular points $z_1, z_2, \cdots, z_n$, inside of C. If $K_1, K_2, \cdots, K_n$, denote the residues of $f(z)$ at those points, then*

$$(1) \qquad \int_C f(z)\, dz = 2\pi i(K_1 + K_2 + \cdots + K_n),$$

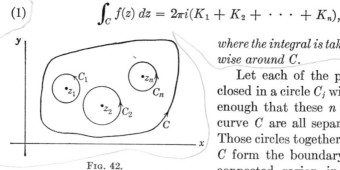

FIG. 42.

where the integral is taken counterclockwise around C.

Let each of the points z_j be enclosed in a circle C_j with radius small enough that these n circles and the curve C are all separated (Fig. 42). Those circles together with the curve C form the boundary of a multiply connected region in which $f(z)$ is analytic. According to the Cauchy-Goursat theorem, then

$$\int_C f(z)\, dz = \int_{C_1} f(z)\, dz + \int_{C_2} f(z)\, dz + \cdots + \int_{C_n} f(z)\, dz.$$

This reduces to formula (1), because

$$K_j = \frac{1}{2\pi i} \int_{C_j} f(z)\, dz \qquad (j = 1, 2, \cdots, n),$$

and so the theorem is proved.

As an example, let us evaluate the integral

(2)
$$\int_C \frac{5z - 2}{z(z - 1)}\, dz,$$

where C is the circle $|z| = 2$, described counterclockwise. The two singularities, $z = 0$ and $z = 1$, of the integrand lie inside C. To find the residue K_1 at $z = 0$, we may write

$$\frac{5z - 2}{z(z - 1)} = \left(5 - \frac{2}{z}\right)\left(\frac{-1}{1 - z}\right) = \left(-5 + \frac{2}{z}\right)(1 + z + z^2 + \cdots)$$
$$= \frac{2}{z} - 3 - 3z - 3z^2 - \cdots,$$

when $0 < |z| < 1$. Hence $K_1 = 2$.

To find the residue K_2 at $z = 1$, we may use the Taylor series

$$\frac{1}{z} = 1 - (z - 1) + (z - 1)^2 - \cdots \qquad (|z - 1| < 1)$$

in order to find the coefficients in the Laurent expansion of the integrand about the point $z = 1$. Thus

$$\frac{5z - 2}{z(z - 1)} = \left(5 + \frac{3}{z - 1}\right)\frac{1}{z}$$
$$= \left(5 + \frac{3}{z - 1}\right)\left[1 - (z - 1) + (z - 1)^2 - \cdots\right],$$

when $0 < |z - 1| < 1$. The coefficient of $(z - 1)^{-1}$ in this product is 3; that is, $K_2 = 3$. Therefore,

$$\int_C \frac{5z - 2}{z(z - 1)}\, dz = 2\pi i(K_1 + K_2) = 10\pi i.$$

In this example it is simpler to write the integrand as the sum of its partial fractions. Then

$$\int_C \frac{5z - 2}{z(z - 1)}\, dz = \int_C \frac{2}{z}\, dz + \int_C \frac{3}{z - 1}\, dz = 2\pi i(2 + 3) = 10\pi i.$$

In the following sections we shall note still simpler ways of finding residues of certain types of functions.

As still another method of evaluating the integral (2), we can note that the integral divided by $2\pi i$ is the coefficient b_1 of the Laurent expansion of the integrand about the origin in the region *outside* the circle $|z| = 1$, according to formula (3) of Sec. 59. That expansion is easily written as follows.   If $|z| > 1$,

$$\frac{5z - 2}{z(z - 1)} = \frac{5z - 2}{z^2} \frac{1}{1 - (1/z)} = (5z - 2) \sum_{n=0}^{\infty} \frac{1}{z^{n+2}}.$$

The coefficient b_1 of $1/z$ in this product is 5.   Hence the value of the integral is $10\pi i$.

68. Poles.   We have observed that a function can always be represented by its Laurent series in a neighborhood of an isolated singular point z_0.   Suppose an integer m exists such that the coefficients b_{m+1}, $b_{m+2}, \cdots$ all vanish, but b_m itself is not zero.   That is, the principal part of the function $f(z)$ at $z = z_0$ has a finite number of terms, and

$$(1) \quad f(z) = \frac{b_1}{z - z_0} + \frac{b_2}{(z - z_0)^2} + \cdots + \frac{b_m}{(z - z_0)^m} + \sum_{n=0}^{\infty} a_n(z - z_0)^n,$$

when $0 < |z - z_0| < r_1$, for some positive number r_1, where $b_m \neq 0$. The isolated singular point z_0 is then called a *pole of order m* of the function $f(z)$.

A pole of order $m = 1$ is called a *simple pole.*

When the principal part of $f(z)$ at the point z_0 has an infinite number of terms, the point is called an *essential singular* point of the function. The function

$$\frac{z^2 - 2z + 3}{z - 2} = \frac{3}{z - 2} + 2 + (z - 2),$$

for example, has a simple pole at $z = 2$.   Its residue there is 3.

As another example, the function

$$\frac{\sinh z}{z^4} = \frac{1}{z^3} + \frac{1}{3!}\frac{1}{z} + \frac{1}{5!}z + \frac{1}{7!}z^3 + \cdots \qquad (|z| > 0)$$

has a pole of order 3 at $z = 0$, with a residue there of $\frac{1}{6}$.   But the function

$$\cosh \frac{1}{z} = 1 + \sum_{n=1}^{\infty} \frac{1}{(2n)!}\frac{1}{z^{2n}} \qquad (|z| > 0)$$

has an essential singular point at $z = 0$.   Its residue there is 0.

When $f(z)$ has a pole at z_0, $f(z_0)$ is not defined. Now let us write

$$\phi(z) = (z - z_0)^m f(z);$$

this equation defines the function $\phi(z)$ except at $z = z_0$. According to equation (1), when $0 < |z - z_0| < r_1$, we can write

$$(2) \quad \phi(z) = b_1(z - z_0)^{m-1} + b_2(z - z_0)^{m-2} + \cdots$$

$$+ b_m + \sum_{n=0}^{\infty} a_n(z - z_0)^{n+m},$$

where $b_m \neq 0$. We now define $\phi(z)$ at $z = z_0$ to be the number b_m,

$$\phi(z_0) = b_m.$$

Then the representation (2) is valid throughout a neighborhood of z_0, including that point itself. Since the series in equation (2) is a convergent power series, the function $\phi(z)$ is analytic at z_0.

Our definition of $\phi(z_0)$ can now be written

$$(3) \qquad \phi(z_0) = \lim_{z \to z_0} (z - z_0)^m f(z) = b_m.$$

Since this limit exists and $b_m \neq 0$, it follows that $|f(z)|$ *always becomes infinite as z approaches a pole z_0.*

A function that is not analytic at a point z_0, but that can be made analytic there merely by assigning some value to the function at that point, is said to have a *removable singularity* at z_0.

We have now shown that when a function $f(z)$ has a pole of order m at $z = z_0$, then the function

$$(4) \qquad \phi(z) = (z - z_0)^m f(z)$$

has a removable singularity at z_0, and that $\phi(z_0) \neq 0$. Moreover equation (2) is the expansion of $\phi(z)$ in Taylor's series about the point z_0, so that

$$(5) \qquad\qquad b_1 = \frac{\phi^{(m-1)}(z_0)}{(m-1)!}.$$

When $m = 1$, this formula for the residue of $f(z)$ at z_0 can be written, according to equation (3), as

$$(6) \qquad b_1 = \phi(z_0) = \lim_{z \to z_0} (z - z_0)f(z).$$

Conversely, suppose $f(z)$ is a function such that the product

$$(z - z_0)^m f(z)$$

can be so defined at z_0 that it is analytic there. As before, m is a positive integer. Let $\phi(z)$ denote that product. Then in some neighborhood of z_0 it is true that

$$\phi(z) = (z - z_0)^m f(z) = \phi(z_0) + \phi'(z_0)(z - z_0) + \cdots$$
$$+ \frac{\phi^{(m)}(z_0)}{m!}(z - z_0)^m + \cdots.$$

Therefore at each point in the neighborhood except z_0 it is true that

$$f(z) = \frac{\phi(z_0)}{(z - z_0)^m} + \frac{\phi'(z_0)}{(z - z_0)^{m-1}} + \cdots + \frac{\phi^{(m-1)}(z_0)}{(m - 1)!}\frac{1}{z - z_0}$$
$$+ \sum_{n=m}^{\infty} \frac{\phi^{(n)}(z_0)}{n!}(z - z_0)^{n-m},$$

and if $\phi(z_0) \neq 0$, it follows that $f(z)$ has a pole of order m at z_0 with the residue given by equation (5) there. We can state this test for poles as follows:

Theorem. *Let a single-valued function $f(z)$ satisfy these conditions. For some positive integer m a value $\phi(z_0)$ exists such that the function*

$$\phi(z) = (z - z_0)^m f(z)$$

is analytic at z_0, and $\phi(z_0) \neq 0$. Then $f(z)$ has a pole of order m at z_0. Its residue there is $\phi^{(m-1)}(z_0)/(m - 1)!$.

69. Computation of Residues at Poles. In the applications of the theory of residues, it often happens that a function whose residue at a point z_0 is to be computed has the fractional form

$$(1) \qquad\qquad f(z) = \frac{p(z)}{q(z)},$$

where the functions $p(z)$ and $q(z)$ are both analytic at z_0 and $p(z_0) \neq 0$. Then

$$(2) \qquad f(z) = \frac{p(z_0) + p'(z_0)(z - z_0) + p''(z_0)(z - z_0)^2/2! + \cdots}{q(z_0) + q'(z_0)(z - z_0) + q''(z_0)(z - z_0)^2/2! + \cdots}.$$

If $f(z)$ has a simple pole at z_0, then $q(z_0) = 0$ and $q'(z_0) \neq 0$, and conversely. The reader can supply the proof of this statement. Then

$$(z - z_0)f(z) = \frac{p(z_0) + p'(z_0)(z - z_0) + \cdots}{q'(z_0) + q''(z_0)(z - z_0)/2! + \cdots},$$

and, according to formula (6) of the preceding section, the residue of $f(z)$ is given by the formula

$$(3) \qquad\qquad b_1 = \frac{p(z_0)}{q'(z_0)}$$

at the simple pole z_0.

If the pole z_0 is of order 2, then $q(z_0) = q'(z_0) = 0$ and $q''(z_0) \neq 0$, and conversely. Similarly for poles of higher order.

When $f(z)$ has the fractional form (1) and its pole at z_0 is one of order $m = 2$ or higher, a formula corresponding to (3) can be written for the residue there. When $m = 2$, for instance, *the residue is*

$$(4) \qquad b_1 = \frac{2}{3[q''(z_0)]^2} [3p'(z_0)q''(z_0) - p(z_0)q'''(z_0)],$$

as we can show by carrying out two steps of the division indicated in equation (2), with $q(z_0) = 0$ and $q'(z_0) = 0$. But when $m > 2$, the formula is even more complicated. It is generally simpler to calculate the residues at poles of order greater than one from the Laurent series for $f(z)$, or by using formula (5) of the preceding section.

A special case of formula (3) for the residue at a simple pole should be noted. When

$$(5) \qquad f(z) = \frac{p(z)}{z - z_0},$$

where the function $p(z)$ is analytic at the point z_0 and $p(z_0) \neq 0$, then z_0 is a simple pole of $f(z)$. The residue of $f(z)$ at that pole is given by the formula

$$(6) \qquad b_1 = p(z_0).$$

In the applications of this formula the function $p(z)$ itself often has a fractional form.

The function

$$\frac{e^z}{z^2 + \pi^2} = \frac{e^z}{(z - \pi i)(z + \pi i)},$$

for example, has simple poles at $z = \pi i$ and $z = -\pi i$. The residues at those poles are, respectively,

$$K_1 = \frac{e^{\pi i}}{2\pi i} = \frac{i}{2\pi}, \qquad K_2 = \frac{e^{-\pi i}}{-2\pi i} = -\frac{i}{2\pi}.$$

The function

$$\cot z = \frac{\cos z}{\sin z}$$

has the singular points $z = 0$, $z = \pm n\pi$ $(n = 1,2, \cdots)$. The derivative of the denominator, $q'(z) = \cos z$, does not vanish at any of those points. Since $p(z)$ and $q(z)$ are analytic and $p(z)$ does not vanish at those points, it follows that those points are all simple poles. According to formula (3), the residue at each pole z_0 here is

$$K = \frac{p(z_0)}{q'(z_0)} = \frac{\cos z_0}{\cos z_0} = 1;$$

that is, the residues of cot z at all its poles $z = 0, z = \pm n\pi$, are the same. As another example, consider the function

$$f(z) = \frac{1}{z(e^z - 1)} = \frac{1}{z^2} \frac{1}{1 + (z/2!) + (z^2/3!) + \cdots}.$$

The singular point $z = 0$ is a pole of order 2 since $z^2 f(z)$ has a removable singularity there. Carrying out two steps of the last division indicated here, we find that

$$\frac{1}{z(e^z - 1)} = \frac{1}{z^2}\left(1 - \frac{1}{2}z + \cdots\right).$$

The residue of this function at the origin is therefore $-\frac{1}{2}$. This residue can also be found by using formula (4).

EXERCISES

1. Show that all singular points in the finite z plane of each of the following functions are poles. Determine the order of each pole and the value of the residue of the function there.

(a) $\dfrac{z+1}{z^2 - 2z}$;   *Ans.* $m = 1, K = -\dfrac{1}{2}, \dfrac{3}{2}$.

(b) $\dfrac{z^2 + 1}{z^3 + 3z^2 + 2z}$;

(c) $\tanh z$;   *Ans.* $m = 1, K = 1$.

(d) $\dfrac{1}{z^3 - z^2}$;

(e) $\dfrac{1 - e^{2z}}{z^4}$;   *Ans.* $m = 3, K = -\dfrac{4}{3}$.

(f) $\dfrac{z}{\cos z}$;

(g) $\dfrac{e^{2z}}{(z - 1)^2}$;   *Ans.* $m = 2, K = 2e^2$.

2. Find the residue at $z = 0$ of the function

$$\frac{1 + e^z}{\sin z + z \cos z}.$$

3. Find the residue of $\csc^2 z$ at $z = 0$. *Suggestion:* Write

$$2 \sin^2 z = 1 - \cos 2z.$$

4. Determine the nature of the singular points of the function

$$\frac{\exp(1/z)}{z(1 + z)^2}.$$

5. Find the value of

$$\int_C \tan z \, dz,$$

where C is the circle $|z| = 2$ described in the positive sense.   *Ans.* $-4\pi i$.

6. Find the value of

$$\int_C \frac{dz}{\sinh z},$$

where C is the circle $|z| = 4$ described in the positive sense.   *Ans.* $-2\pi i$.

7. Find the value of

$$\int_C \frac{3z^3 + 2}{(z - 1)(z^2 + 9)} \, dz$$

taken counterclockwise around the circle (a) $|z - 2| = 2$; (b) $|z| = 4$.

Ans. (a) πi; (b) $6\pi i$.

8. Find the value of

$$\int_C \frac{\cosh \pi z}{z(z^2 + 1)} \, dz$$

taken counterclockwise around the circle $|z| = 2$.

9. Find the value of the integral

$$\int_C \frac{dz}{z^3(z + 4)}$$

taken counterclockwise around the circle (a) $|z| = 2$; (b) $|z + 2| = 3$.

Ans. (a) $\pi i/32$; (b) 0.

10. If C is the unit circle about the origin, described in the positive sense, evaluate the integrals

(a) $\displaystyle\int_C \frac{e^{-z}}{z^2} \, dz;$ *Ans.* $-2\pi i$.

(b) $\displaystyle\int_C \frac{dz}{z \sin z};$ *Ans.* 0.

(c) $\displaystyle\int_C \frac{dz}{z^2 \sin z};$ *Ans.* $\pi i/3$.

(d) $\displaystyle\int_C z e^{1/z} \, dz;$ *Ans.* πi.

70. Evaluation of Real Infinite Integrals. One of the important applications of the theory of residues consists in the evaluation of certain types of real definite integrals. These integrals often arise in physical problems, especially in the solution of boundary value problems in partial differential equations. Sometimes they appear as integrals in the complex plane, even though they are reducible to real definite integrals. The examples treated here and in the following sections will illustrate methods that are often useful. To illustrate fully the power of the method of residues, we should have to introduce examples that arise in such fields as partial differential equations.*

Real integrals of the type

$$(1) \qquad \int_{-\infty}^{\infty} \frac{p(x)}{q(x)} \, dx,$$

where $p(x)$ and $q(x)$ are polynomials, can be evaluated quite easily by using the theory of residues if the factors of $q(x)$ can be determined. We assume that $q(x)$ has no real zeros; for if $q(x)$ contains a factor $(x - x_0)^k$, where $k = 1, 2, \cdots$, then at the point $x = x_0$ the integrand is infinite and of such an order that the improper integral

$$\int_{a}^{x_0} \frac{p(x)}{q(x)} \, dx,$$

where a is any real constant, does not converge.

The value of the integral (1) exists when and only when the degree of $q(x)$ is at least two greater than the degree of $p(x)$, and $q(x)$ has no real zeros. The method of partial fractions, which can also be used to evaluate integrals of this type, is closely related to the method of residues.

As our first example, let us use residues to find the value of the elementary integral

$$(2) \qquad I = \int_{0}^{\infty} \frac{dx}{x^2 + 1} = \frac{1}{2} \int_{-\infty}^{\infty} \frac{dx}{x^2 + 1}.$$

The second integral represents an integration, along the entire length of the real axis, of the function

$$(3) \qquad f(z) = \frac{1}{z^2 + 1},$$

a function with simple poles at the points $z = i$ and $z = -i$.

Let C_R denote the upper half of a circle $|z| = R$, where $R > 1$ (Fig. 43). Integrating $f(z)$ counterclockwise around the boundary of the semicircular region, we have

$$\int_{-R}^{R} f(x) \, dx + \int_{C_R} f(z) \, dz = 2\pi i K_1,$$

where K_1 is the residue of $f(z)$ at the pole $z = i$. From the expression

* See, for instance, Chaps. VI–VIII of the author's book "Modern Operational Mathematics in Engineering."

(3) for $f(z)$ we see that

$$K_1 = \frac{1}{z + i}\Bigg]_{z=i} = \frac{1}{2i}.$$

Therefore,

(4) $$\int_{-R}^{R} \frac{dx}{x^2 + 1} = \pi - \int_{C_R} \frac{dz}{z^2 + 1}$$

for every $R > 1$.

Now $|z| = R$ when z is on C_R, and

$$|z^2 + 1| \geq |z^2| - 1 = R^2 - 1.$$

Consequently,

$$\left|\int_{C_R} \frac{dz}{z^2 + 1}\right| \leq \int_{C_R} \frac{|dz|}{R^2 - 1} = \frac{\pi R}{R^2 - 1},$$

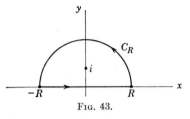

FIG. 43.

and this quantity approaches zero as R tends to infinity. It follows from equation (4) that

(5) $$\lim_{R \to \infty} \int_{-R}^{R} \frac{dx}{x^2 + 1} = \pi;$$

therefore,

(6) $$I = \frac{1}{2}\int_{-\infty}^{\infty} \frac{dx}{x^2 + 1} = \frac{\pi}{2}.$$

The limit (5) is called the *Cauchy principal value* of the integral in equation (6). In general,

(7) $$\lim_{R \to \infty} \int_{-R}^{R} f(x)\, dx = \text{P.V.} \int_{-\infty}^{\infty} f(x)\, dx.$$

Whenever each of the integrals

$$\int_{-\infty}^{0} f(x)\, dx, \qquad \int_{0}^{\infty} f(x)\, dx$$

has a value, as is the case here, the principal value (7) is the same as the integral. But if $f(x) = x$, for instance, the principal value of the integral is zero, whereas the value of the integral itself does not exist.

71. Another Example. Let us find the value of the integral

(1) $$I = \int_{0}^{\infty} \frac{x^2\, dx}{(x^2 + 9)(x^2 + 4)^2} = \frac{1}{2}\int_{-\infty}^{\infty} \frac{x^2\, dx}{(x^2 + 9)(x^2 + 4)^2},$$

which again is of the type discussed in the foregoing section.

Following the same method as before, we note that the singular points of the function

(2)
$$f(z) = \frac{z^2}{(z^2 + 9)(z^2 + 4)^2}$$

consist of simple poles at the points $z = \pm 3i$ and poles of the second order at $z = \pm 2i$. The residue K_1 at the pole $z = 3i$ is, according to formula (6) of Sec. 69,

$$K_1 = \frac{z^2}{(z + 3i)(z^2 + 4)^2}\bigg]_{z=3i} = -\frac{3}{50i}.$$

To find the residue K_2 at $z = 2i$, we write

$$\phi(z) = (z - 2i)^2 f(z) = \frac{z^2}{(z^2 + 9)(z + 2i)^2}.$$

Then $K_2 = \phi'(2i)$, according to formula (5) of Sec. 68; that is,

$$K_2 = \frac{(-4 + 9)(2i + 2i)^2(4i) - (2i)^2[5(2)(4i) + (4i)^2(4i)]}{5^2(4i)^4},$$

which reduces to

$$K_2 = -\frac{13i}{200}.$$

Let C_R again denote the upper half of the circle $|z| = R$, where $R > 3$ now. Integrating counterclockwise around the boundary of the semicircle, we have

(3)
$$\int_{-R}^{R} f(x)\, dx + \int_{C_R} f(z)\, dz = 2\pi i(K_1 + K_2) = \frac{\pi}{100}.$$

But when z is on C_R, we see from formula (2) that

$$|f(z)| \leq \frac{R^2}{(R^2 - 9)(R^2 - 4)^2},$$

and it follows as before that the limit, as R tends to infinity, of the second integral in equation (3) is zero. Therefore,

$$\int_{-\infty}^{\infty} f(x)\, dx = \frac{\pi}{100},$$

or in view of equation (1), $I = \pi/200$.

72. Infinite Integrals Involving Trigonometric Functions. As an example of another type of integral that can be evaluated by means of contour integrals and residue theory, consider the integral

(1)
$$\int_{0}^{\infty} \frac{\cos x\, dx}{x^2 + 1} = \frac{1}{2}\int_{-\infty}^{\infty} \frac{\cos x\, dx}{x^2 + 1}.$$

Since $|\cos z|$ increases like e^y as y tends to infinity, the method used above does not apply here without some modifications.

Now $\cos x$ is the real part of exp ix; therefore,

(2)
$$\int_0^\infty \frac{\cos x \, dx}{x^2 + 1} = \frac{1}{2} \Re \int_{-\infty}^\infty \frac{e^{ix} \, dx}{x^2 + 1}.$$

We write

$$f(z) = \frac{e^{iz}}{z^2 + 1}$$

and note that

(3)
$$|e^{iz}| = e^{-y} \leq 1 \qquad\qquad \text{when } y \geq 0.$$

The singularities of our function $f(z)$ are the simple poles $z = \pm i$. At $z = i$ the residue of $f(z)$ is

$$K_1 = \frac{e^{iz}}{z + i}\bigg]_{z=i} = \frac{1}{2ei},$$

and therefore,

(4)
$$\int_{-R}^R \frac{e^{ix} \, dx}{x^2 + 1} + \int_{C_R} \frac{e^{iz} \, dz}{z^2 + 1} = 2\pi i K_1 = \frac{\pi}{e},$$

where C_R is the upper half of the circle $|z| = R$ $(R > 1)$. In view of the inequality (3) it follows as before that the second integral in equation (4) approaches zero as R tends to infinity, so that

$$\int_{-\infty}^\infty \frac{e^{ix} \, dx}{x^2 + 1} = \frac{\pi}{e}.$$

The real part of this integral is therefore the same as the value of the integral itself. According to equation (2), then

$$\int_0^\infty \frac{\cos x \, dx}{x^2 + 1} = \frac{\pi}{2e}.$$

EXERCISES

Use the residue theory to show that

1. $\displaystyle\int_0^\infty \frac{x^2 \, dx}{(x^2 + 1)(x^2 + 4)} = \frac{\pi}{6}.$

2. $\displaystyle\int_0^\infty \frac{dx}{x^4 + 1} = \frac{\pi \sqrt{2}}{4}.$

3. $\displaystyle\int_0^\infty \frac{x^2 \, dx}{x^6 + 1} = \frac{\pi}{6}.$

4. $\displaystyle\int_0^\infty \frac{x^6 \, dx}{(x^4 + 1)^2} = \frac{3}{16} \pi \sqrt{2}.$

5. $\displaystyle\int_0^\infty \frac{\cos ax}{x^2+1}\,dx = \frac{\pi}{2}e^{-a}$ $\quad (a \geq 0).$

6. $\displaystyle\int_0^\infty \frac{\cos x\,dx}{(x^2+1)^2} = \frac{\pi}{2e}.$

7. $\displaystyle\int_{-\infty}^\infty \frac{\cos x\,dx}{(x^2+a^2)(x^2+b^2)} = \frac{\pi}{a^2-b^2}\left(\frac{e^{-b}}{b}-\frac{e^{-a}}{a}\right)$ $\quad (a>b>0).$

8. $\displaystyle\int_0^\infty \frac{\cos ax}{(x^2+b^2)^2}\,dx = \frac{\pi}{4b^3}(1+ab)e^{-ab}$ $\quad (a>0,\, b>0).$

9. $\displaystyle\int_0^\infty \frac{\cos ax}{x^4+4}\,dx = \frac{\pi}{8}(\cos a + \sin a)e^{-a}$ $\quad (a>0).$

Use residues to find the values of the following integrals.

10. $\displaystyle\int_{-\infty}^\infty \frac{dx}{x^2+2x+2}.$

11. $\displaystyle\int_{-\infty}^\infty \frac{x\,dx}{(x^2+1)(x^2+2x+2)}.$ $\qquad Ans. -\frac{\pi}{5}$

12. $\displaystyle\int_0^\infty \frac{x^2\,dx}{(x^2+1)^2}.$

13. $\displaystyle\int_0^\infty \frac{x \sin x\,dx}{(x^2+1)(x^2+4)}.$

14. $\displaystyle\int_{-\infty}^\infty \frac{\sin x\,dx}{x^2+4x+5}.$ $\qquad Ans. -\frac{\pi}{e}\sin 2.$

15. $\displaystyle\int_{-\infty}^\infty \frac{\cos x\,dx}{(x+a)^2+b^2}.$

73. Definite Integrals of Trigonometric Functions. The method of residues is useful in the evaluation of definite integrals of the type

(1) $$\int_0^{2\pi} F(\sin\theta,\,\cos\theta)\,d\theta,$$

where F is a quotient of polynomials in $\sin\theta$ and $\cos\theta$. If we consider θ as the argument of z on the unit circle $z = e^{i\theta}$, then we can write

(2) $\quad \sin\theta = \dfrac{z-z^{-1}}{2i}, \qquad \cos\theta = \dfrac{z+z^{-1}}{2}, \qquad dz = ie^{i\theta}\,d\theta = iz\,d\theta,$

and the integral (1) then represents the integral of a rational function of z around the unit circle. The latter integral can be evaluated by the residue theorem if we can find the zeros of the polynomial in the denominator.

As an example, we compute the value of the integral

$$I = \int_0^{2\pi} \frac{d\theta}{\frac{5}{4}+\sin\theta}.$$

Note that the denominator of the integrand is never zero.   According to equations (2), we can write

$$I = \int_C \frac{dz}{iz\left(\frac{5}{4} + \frac{z - z^{-1}}{2i}\right)} = \int_C \frac{4\,dz}{2z^2 + 5iz - 2},$$

where C is the unit circle $|z| = 1$ (Fig. 44).   The last integrand can be written

$$\frac{4}{2z^2 + 5iz - 2} = \frac{2}{(z + 2i)(z + \frac{1}{2}i)};$$

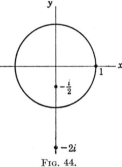

FIG. 44.

thus its only singularity inside C is the simple pole $z = -\frac{1}{2}i$, and the residue of the integrand there is $2/(-\frac{1}{2}i + 2i)$ or $4/(3i)$.   Hence, according to the residue theorem,

$$I = 2\pi i \frac{4}{3i} = \frac{8}{3}\pi.$$

74. Integration around a Branch Point.

The following example illustrates a method that is useful when the integrand of the complex integral is single-valued and analytic except along a branch cut.

Let us find the value of the real integral

$$I = \int_0^\infty \frac{x^{-k}}{x + 1}\,dx,$$

where k is a real constant and $0 < k < 1$.   It can be shown that this integral represents the product $\Gamma(k)\Gamma(1 - k)$ of gamma functions.*
We may consider I as a limit of the line integral of the function

$$f(z) = \frac{z^{-k}}{z + 1}$$

as the path of integration approaches the positive real axis.   We make the function z^{-k} single-valued and analytic everywhere except on the positive real axis and at the origin by writing

$$z^{-k} = \exp\left(-k \log z\right),$$

where $\log z = \operatorname{Log} r + i\theta$ and $0 < \theta < 2\pi, r > 0$.   Then

(1) $z^{-k} = \exp\left(-k \operatorname{Log} r\right) \exp\left(-ik\theta\right) = r^{-k}e^{-ik\theta}$ $(0 < \theta < 2\pi, r > 0)$,

and when θ approaches zero, z^{-k} becomes r^{-k}, which is the same as x^{-k}.

* See, for instance, Titchmarsh, "Theory of Functions," p. 106.

Except for the simple pole $z = -1$, the function $f(z)$ is analytic inside the region bounded by the closed curve consisting of the open circles C_0 and C and the segments L_1 and L_2 of the two rays shown in Fig. 45. These rays make angles $\pm\epsilon$ with the x axis. The residue of $f(z)$ at the pole is the value of z^{-k} when $z = -1$; that is, $e^{-k\pi i}$, in view of our definition (1). Therefore

$$(2)\qquad \int_{L_1} f(z)\ dz + \int_C f(z)\ dz + \int_{L_2} f(z)\ dz + \int_{C_0} f(z)\ dz = 2\pi i e^{-k\pi i}.$$

We are interested here in finding the limits of these integrals as ϵ and r_0 tend to zero and R tends to infinity, since the first of these integrals then approaches our real integral I.

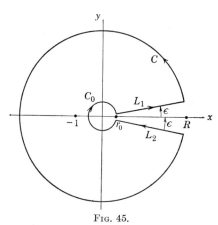

Fig. 45.

The integrals over the two circles approach zero. On C, $z = Re^{i\theta}$ and $|dz| = R\ d\theta$, so that

$$\left|\int_C \frac{z^{-k}\ dz}{z + 1}\right|$$
$$\leqq R^{-k}\left(\frac{R}{R - 1}\right)(2\pi - 2\epsilon);$$

but $k > 0$, and hence the right-hand member here vanishes as R becomes infinite for every $\epsilon(\epsilon \geqq 0)$.

Similarly on C_0,

$$\left|\int_{C_0} \frac{z^{-k}\ dz}{z + 1}\right| \leqq \frac{r_0^{1-k}}{1 - r_0}(2\pi - 2\epsilon),$$

and since $1 - k > 0$, this vanishes as r_0 tends to zero for every ϵ. It follows from equation (2) that, for every $\epsilon(\epsilon \geqq 0)$,

$$(3)\qquad \lim_{\substack{r_0 \to 0 \\ R \to \infty}} \left[\int_{L_1} f(z)\ dz + \int_{L_2} f(z)\ dz\right] = 2\pi i e^{-k\pi i}.$$

On the line segment L_1

$$z = re^{i\epsilon},\qquad dz = e^{i\epsilon}\ dr,$$

and on L_2

$$z = re^{i(2\pi-\epsilon)} = re^{-i\epsilon},\qquad dz = e^{-i\epsilon}\ dr.$$

In view of our formula (1) for z^{-k}, therefore, we can write the sum of the two integrals in equation (3) as

$$e^{-ik\epsilon}e^{i\epsilon} \int_{r_0}^{R} \frac{r^{-k}\,dr}{re^{i\epsilon}+1} + e^{-ik(2\pi-\epsilon)}e^{-i\epsilon}\int_{R}^{r_0}\frac{r^{-k}\,dr}{re^{-i\epsilon}+1}.$$

Since the limit given by formula (3) is independent of ϵ, we shall set $\epsilon = 0$ here and then let r_0 tend to zero and R tend to infinity; thus we find that

$$\int_{0}^{\infty}\frac{r^{-k}\,dr}{r+1} + e^{-2k\pi i}\int_{\infty}^{0}\frac{r^{-k}\,dr}{r+1} = 2\pi i e^{-k\pi i},$$

or

$$(1 - e^{-2k\pi i})\int_{0}^{\infty}\frac{r^{-k}\,dr}{r+1} = 2\pi i e^{-k\pi i}.$$

The integral here is our integral I, and it follows that

$$I = 2\pi i \frac{e^{-k\pi i}}{1 - e^{-2k\pi i}} = \frac{2\pi i}{e^{k\pi i} - e^{-k\pi i}} = \frac{\pi}{\sin \pi k}.$$

EXERCISES

Use residues to evaluate the integrals in Exercises 1–6.

1. $\displaystyle\int_{0}^{2\pi} \frac{d\theta}{5 + 3\cos\theta} = \frac{\pi}{2}.$

2. $\displaystyle\int_{0}^{2\pi} \frac{\cos^2 3\theta\,d\theta}{5 - 4\cos 2\theta} = \frac{3}{8}\pi.$

3. $\displaystyle\int_{0}^{2\pi} \frac{d\theta}{1 + a\cos\theta} = \int_{0}^{2\pi}\frac{d\theta}{1 + a\sin\theta} = \frac{2\pi}{\sqrt{1 - a^2}} \qquad (a^2 < 1).$

4. $\displaystyle\int_{0}^{\pi} \frac{\cos 2\theta\,d\theta}{1 - 2a\cos\theta + a^2} = \frac{\pi a^2}{1 - a^2} \qquad (a^2 < 1).$

5. $\displaystyle\int_{0}^{\pi} \frac{d\theta}{(a + \cos\theta)^2} = \frac{\pi a}{(a^2 - 1)^{\frac{3}{2}}} \qquad (a > 1).$

6. $\displaystyle\int_{0}^{2\pi} \frac{\sin n\theta\,d\theta}{1 + 2a\cos\theta + a^2} \qquad (a^2 < 1, \; n = 1,2, \cdots).$

7. Given that

$$\int_{0}^{\infty} e^{-x^2}\,dx = \frac{\sqrt{\pi}}{2},$$

integrate the function $\exp(-z^2)$ around the boundary of the rectangle $-a \leqq x \leqq a$, $0 \leqq y \leqq b$, and let a tend to infinity to prove that

$$\int_{0}^{\infty} e^{-x^2}\cos(2bx)\,dx = \frac{\sqrt{\pi}}{2}e^{-b^2}.$$

8. When $0 < k < 1$, show that

$$\int_{-\infty}^{\infty} \frac{e^{kx}\,dx}{1 + e^x} = \frac{\pi}{\sin \pi k}.$$

by integrating the function $e^{kz}/(1 + e^z)$ around the rectangular path along the lines $y = 0$, $x = \pm a$, and $y = 2\pi$ (Fig. 46), and letting a tend to infinity.

9. Given that

$$\int_0^\infty e^{-x^2}\, dx = \frac{\sqrt{\pi}}{2},$$

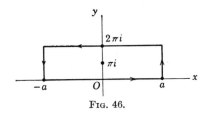

FIG. 46.

integrate the function $\exp(-z^2)$ around the boundary of the circular sector $0 \leq \theta \leq \pi/4$, $0 \leq r \leq r_0$, and let r_0 tend to infinity to show that

$$\int_0^\infty \cos(x^2)\, dx = \int_0^\infty \sin(x^2)\, dx = \frac{\sqrt{2\pi}}{4}.$$

Note: To show that the integral over the circular arc tends to zero, show that its absolute value is less than I where

$$I = r_0 \int_0^{\pi/4} \exp(-r_0^2 \cos 2\theta)\, d\theta,$$

and then that

$$I = \frac{r_0}{2} \int_0^{\pi/2} \exp(-r_0^2 \sin \phi)\, d\phi < \frac{r_0}{2} \int_0^{\pi/2} e^{-2r_0^2\phi/\pi}\, d\phi;$$

for it is clear from the graph of the sine curve that

$$\sin \phi \geq 2\phi/\pi \text{ when } 0 \leq \phi \leq \pi/2.$$

Carry out the integration in the last member of the inequality to show that this member approaches zero as r_0 tends to infinity.

10. Show that

$$\int_0^\infty \frac{\sin x}{x}\, dx = \frac{\pi}{2}$$

by integrating the function $z^{-1}e^{iz}$ around the indented contour shown in Fig. 47, consisting of the semicircles C_0 and C, with radii r_0 and R, and the segments L_1 and L_2 of the x axis, and then letting r_0 tend to zero and R tend to infinity. (See

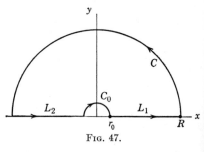

FIG. 47.

the note in Exercise 9 for a method of showing that the integral over C tends to zero as R tends to infinity.)

CHAPTER VIII

CONFORMAL MAPPING

75. Rotation of Tangents. We first examine the change in direction of curves at a point z_0 under a transformation $w = f(z)$, where the function $f(z)$ is analytic at that point.

The derivative of the function at z_0,

$$(1) \qquad f'(z_0) = \lim_{\Delta z \to 0} \frac{\Delta w}{\Delta z},$$

exists and is independent of the manner in which Δz approaches zero. Thus the absolute value of the complex variable $\Delta w / \Delta z$ must approach the absolute value of $f'(z_0)$:

$$(2) \qquad \lim_{\Delta z \to 0} \left| \frac{\Delta w}{\Delta z} \right| = |f'(z_0)|.$$

If $f'(z_0) \ne 0$, its argument ψ_0 $(0 \le \psi_0 < 2\pi)$ in the polar representation

$$(3) \qquad f'(z_0) = R_0 e^{i\psi_0}$$

has a unique value. Then it follows from equation (1) that

$$(4) \qquad \lim_{\Delta z \to 0} \arg \left(\frac{\Delta w}{\Delta z} \right) = \arg f'(z_0) = \psi_0,$$

where the argument of $\Delta w / \Delta z$ also has the range from zero to 2π.

Now let C be some curve through z_0 and S be its image under the transformation $w = f(z)$ (Fig. 48). If a positive sense of motion along C

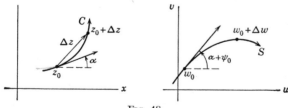

FIG. 48.

is prescribed, a corresponding positive sense along S is determined by the function $f(z)$. When $z_0 + \Delta z$ is a point on C in the positive sense from z_0, the limit of the argument of Δz as Δz approaches zero is the angle of

135

inclination of the tangent to C at z_0 drawn in the positive sense. Similarly, the argument of Δw approaches the angle of inclination of the tangent to S at w_0, where $w_0 = f(z_0)$. Equation (4) can be written

$$\lim_{\Delta z \to 0} \arg \Delta w - \lim_{\Delta z \to 0} \arg \Delta z = \psi_0.$$

It follows that if α is the angle of inclination of the curve C at z_0, then the angle of inclination of S at w_0 is

$$\lim_{\Delta w \to 0} \arg \Delta w = \alpha + \psi_0.$$

Thus the directed tangent to a curve C at z_0 is rotated through the angle

$$\psi_0 = \arg f'(z_0)$$

by the transformation $w = f(z)$, provided $f(z)$ is analytic at z_0 and $f'(z_0) \neq 0$.

76. Conformal Mapping. The angle ψ_0 is the same for all curves through z_0; it is determined by the function $f(z)$ and the point z_0. Consequently, any two curves C_1 and C_2 through z_0 are turned through the same angle by the transformation. To state it more precisely, the angle γ at z_0 from C_1 to C_2 is the same, both in magnitude and sense, as the angle at w_0 from S_1 to S_2, where the curves S_1 and S_2 are the images of C_1 and C_2 (Fig. 49).

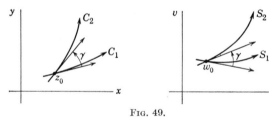

FIG. 49.

A mapping or transformation that preserves angles in this manner between every pair of curves through a point is said to be *conformal* at the point. We have therefore established the following theorem:

Theorem.   *At each point where a function $f(z)$ is analytic and $f'(z) \neq 0$, the mapping $w = f(z)$ is conformal.*

Henceforth the terms *conformal mapping* and *conformal transformation* will be used here to signify transformations by means of analytic functions.

According to equation (2) of the preceding section,

$$\lim_{\Delta z \to 0} \frac{|\Delta w|}{|\Delta z|} = |f'(z_0)| = R_0.$$

mapping op transformation

Therefore the transformation magnifies the lengths of short lines by approximately the factor R_0. The image of each small figure near the point *conforms* to the original figure in the sense that it has approximately the same shape. The coefficient of magnification R_0, as well as the angle of rotation ψ_0 varies from point to point. Large figures may transform into figures that bear no resemblance to the original.

A point at which $f'(z) = 0$ is called a *critical point* of the transformation.

The point $z = 0$ is a critical point of the transformation

$$w = z^2.$$

Here

$$w = \rho e^{i\phi} = r^2 e^{2i\theta},$$

so it is clear that each line $\theta = c$ through $z = 0$ transforms into a line $\phi = 2c$ in the w plane. Thus the angle between any two lines through the critical point $z = 0$ is doubled by this transformation.

By using the representation by power series of the analytic function $f(z)$, it can be shown* that if the first $n - 1$ derivatives of the function vanish at z_0 while $f^{(n)}(z_0) \neq 0$, then all angles at z_0 are multiplied by n under the transformation $w = f(z)$.

A transformation that preserves the magnitudes of angles but not necessarily the sense is called *isogonal*. Thus the transformation $w = \bar{z}$, a reflection in the real axis, is isogonal but not conformal. If this is followed by a conformal transformation, the resulting transformation $w = f(\bar{z})$ is also isogonal but not conformal.

77. Examples. Since the elementary functions used in Chap. IV are analytic, the mapping discussed there is conformal except at singular points and critical points.

Every conformal transformation must map orthogonal curves into orthogonal curves. In particular, if $f(z)$ is analytic and $f'(z) \neq 0$ at a point, the transformation

$$u + iv = f(x + iy)$$

maps the curves $u(x,y) = c_1$, $v(x,y) = c_2$ that intersect at that point into the lines $u = c_1$, $v = c_2$ in the w plane. Since the lines are orthogonal, *the curve $u(x,y) = c_1$ is orthogonal to the curve $v(x,y) = c_2$.*

As another illustration, the transformation

$$w = z^2 = x^2 - y^2 + 2ixy$$

maps the line $y = x$ into the line $u = 0$, and the line $x = 1$ into the

* See, for instance, the proof in Burkhardt-Rasor, "Theory of Functions of a Complex Variable," p. 396.

parabola whose parametric equations are

$$u = 1 - y^2, \qquad v = 2y;$$

this is the parabola $v^2 = -4(u - 1)$ (Fig. 50).   If the direction of increas-

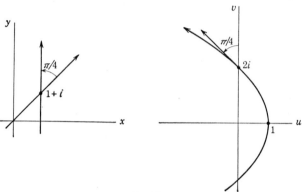

FIG. 50.

ing y is taken as the positive sense on the two lines in the z plane, the angle from the first to the second is $\pi/4$.   When y increases along the line $y = x$, v increases along the line $u = 0$, since $v = 2y^2$, and so the positive sense of the first image is upward.   This is also true for the parabola, as we see from the second parametric equation $v = 2y$.   It is readily verified that the angle from the first image to the second at the point $w = 2i$, which is the image of the point $z = 1 + i$, is $\pi/4$ as required by the conformality of the mapping.

The argument of the derivative of the function $w = z^2$ at the point $z = 1 + i$ is

$$\psi_0 = \arg 2z = \arg (2 + 2i) = \frac{\pi}{4}.$$

This is the angle through which the tangent to each curve at that point is turned by the transformation.   The coefficient of magnification $|f'(z_0)|$ of distances at that point is $2\sqrt{2}$.

EXERCISES

1. Show that the transformation $w = z^2$ changes directions of curves at the point $z = 2 + i$ by the angle $\arctan \frac{1}{2}$.   Illustrate this by using some particular curve.   Show that the coefficient of magnification of distances at that point is $2\sqrt{5}$.

2. Show that the transformation $w = z^n$ changes directions at the point $z = r_0 \exp i\theta_0$ by the angle $(n - 1)\theta_0$, when $r_0 > 0$ and $n > 0$.   What is the coefficient of magnification of distances at the point?   *Ans.* nr_0^{n-1}.

3. What change of directions is produced by the transformation $w = 1/z$ (a) at the point $z = 1$; (b) at the point $z = i$?

Ans. (a) A change in sense only; (b) none.

4. Prove that the transformation $w = z^2$ maps the two families of lines $x = c$ and $y = c$ into two families of parabolas with axes along the u axis, the parabolas of the two families opening in opposite directions. Show the mapping graphically and note the conformality of the mapping.

5. Under the transformation $w = 1/z$, show that the line $y = x - 1$ maps into the circle $u^2 + v^2 - u - v = 0$, and the line $y = 0$ into the line $v = 0$. Show graphically and note the conformality of the mapping at $z = 1$. Also show that the angular region between the half lines $y = x - 1$, $x \geq 1$ and $y = 0$, $x \geq 1$ maps into the segment of the circle lying below the u axis.

6. Show that under the transformation $w = z^n$ the angle between any two lines through the point $z = 0$ is multiplied by n, where $n = 1, 2, \cdots$.

78. Conjugate Harmonic Functions. We noted in Sec. 22 that the real and imaginary coefficients of every analytic function of a complex variable z are harmonic functions of x and y. That is, they satisfy Laplace's partial differential equation

$$(1) \qquad \frac{\partial^2 u}{\partial x^2} + \frac{\partial^2 u}{\partial y^2} = 0,$$

and their partial derivatives of the second order are continuous functions of x and y.

The functions $u(x,y)$ and $v(x,y)$ are conjugate harmonic functions when $u + iv$ is an analytic function of z. Then, in view of the Cauchy-Riemann conditions, the differential of v can be written

$$(2) \qquad dv = \frac{\partial v}{\partial x} dx + \frac{\partial v}{\partial y} dy = -\frac{\partial u}{\partial y} dx + \frac{\partial u}{\partial x} dy.$$

Now suppose that $u(x,y)$ is a given harmonic function in some simply connected region R. We can show that its harmonic conjugate $v(x,y)$ exists, and we can write an explicit formula for $v(x,y)$.

The last member of equation (2) is an exact differential if

$$\frac{\partial}{\partial y}\left(-\frac{\partial u}{\partial y}\right) = \frac{\partial}{\partial x}\left(\frac{\partial u}{\partial x}\right);$$

this condition is true because the function u satisfies Laplace's equation (1). It follows that the value of the line integral

$$\int_{(x_0,y_0)}^{(x,y)} \left(-\frac{\partial u}{\partial y} dx + \frac{\partial u}{\partial x} dy\right)$$

is independent of the path joining the fixed point (x_0,y_0) to the variable point (x,y), as long as the path is inside the region R. The integral thus represents a single-valued function of x and y; its value is changed by an additive constant when the fixed point is changed.

Let us write

$$(3) \qquad v(x,y) = \int_{(x_0,y_0)}^{(x,y)} \left(-\frac{\partial u}{\partial y}\, dx + \frac{\partial u}{\partial x}\, dy \right) + c,$$

where c is an arbitrary constant. It follows from the formulas for the derivatives of such line integrals, derived in advanced calculus, that

$$(4) \qquad \frac{\partial v}{\partial x} = -\frac{\partial u}{\partial y}, \qquad \frac{\partial v}{\partial y} = \frac{\partial u}{\partial x}.$$

These are the Cauchy-Riemann conditions. Since the partial derivatives of u of the second order are continuous, it is evident from equations (4) that the second-order partial derivatives of v are continuous. It follows from our theorem in Sec. 19 that the function

$$u(x,y) + iv(x,y)$$

is an analytic function of z in R; hence v is the harmonic conjugate of u.

The function $u = xy$, for example, is harmonic in every region. According to formula (3),

$$v = \int_{(0,0)}^{(x,y)} (-x'\, dx' + y'\, dy') + c.$$

The integration here may be carried out by inspection; also it is easily done by first integrating along the line $y' = 0$ from the origin to the point $(x,0)$ and then along the line $x' = x$ to the point (x,y). The result is

$$v = -\tfrac{1}{2}x^2 + \tfrac{1}{2}y^2 + c;$$

this is the harmonic conjugate of the function $u = xy$. Here the analytic function is

$$w = xy + \tfrac{1}{2}(y^2 - x^2)i + ic = -\tfrac{1}{2}iz^2 + ic.$$

79. Inverse Functions. In earlier chapters we showed that the inverses of several of the elementary functions are analytic. The inverse of the function $w = \exp z$, for example, is the function

$$z = \log w = \operatorname{Log} \rho + i\phi,$$

and the range of ϕ can be prescribed so as to make this function single valued and analytic in any simply connected region that does not include the point $w = 0$. Moreover,

$$\frac{dz}{dw} = \frac{1}{w} = \frac{1}{e^z} = \frac{1}{dw/dz}.$$

At this time it is convenient to note the corresponding general properties of inverses of analytic functions.

Theorem.   *Let the function $f(z)$ be analytic at a point $z = z_0$ where $f'(z_0) \neq 0$; also let w_0 denote the number $f(z_0)$.   Then there exists a neighborhood of the point w_0 in the w plane in which the function*

(1) $$w = f(z)$$

has a unique inverse

(2) $$z = F(w),$$

in the sense that the function $F(w)$ is single-valued and analytic there and $F(w_0) = z_0$ and that $w = f[F(w)]$; moreover,

(3) $$F'(w) = \frac{1}{f'(z)}$$

Equation (1) can be written in the form

(4) $$u = u(x,y), \qquad v = v(x,y).$$

Since w is analytic at the point $z_0 = x_0 + iy_0$, it is analytic in some neighborhood of that point.   The functions u and v and all their partial derivatives are continuous in that neighborhood.   The real function

$$|f'(z)| = \sqrt{\left(\frac{\partial u}{\partial x}\right)^2 + \left(\frac{\partial v}{\partial x}\right)^2}$$

is continuous in that neighborhood; it is positive at the point (x_0,y_0), since $f'(z_0) \neq 0$.   Then from the definition of a limit of a real function, it follows that there is some neighborhood of (x_0,y_0) throughout which this function is positive; thus $f'(z) \neq 0$ in that neighborhood.

In addition to the continuity of the functions $u(x,y)$ and $v(x,y)$ and their derivatives, the further condition under which the simultaneous equations (4) have unique solutions for x and y as continuous functions of u and v, is that the Jacobian of the functions u and v,

$$\begin{vmatrix} \dfrac{\partial u}{\partial x} & \dfrac{\partial u}{\partial y} \\[2mm] \dfrac{\partial v}{\partial x} & \dfrac{\partial v}{\partial y} \end{vmatrix}$$

be different from zero at the point (x_0,y_0).*   In view of the Cauchy-Riemann conditions the value of this determinant can be written

$$\left(\frac{\partial u}{\partial x}\right)^2 + \left(\frac{\partial v}{\partial x}\right)^2 = |f'(z)|^2,$$

---

* See, for instance, Goursat-Hedrick, "Mathematical Analysis," Vol. I, p. 45.

and by hypothesis this is not equal to zero at the point z_0. Thus it is established that one and only one pair of continuous functions $x(u,v)$, $y(u,v)$ exists in a neighborhood of the point $w_0 = u_0 + iv_0$ such that the functions

(5) $x = x(u,v), \qquad y = y(u,v)$

satisfy equations (4), and such that

$$x_0 = x(u_0,v_0), \qquad y_0 = y(u_0,v_0).$$

Equations (5) can be written in the complex form

$$z = F(w),$$

where $F(w)$ is a continuous function.   To show that its derivative exists, we write

(6) $$\frac{\Delta z}{\Delta w} = \frac{1}{\Delta w/\Delta z}.$$

Since w is an analytic function of z, it is continuous, and since z is a continuous function of w, it follows that when Δw approaches zero, Δz approaches zero, and conversely.   Now dw/dz exists and is different from zero; hence it follows from equation (6) that

$$\frac{dz}{dw} = \lim_{\Delta w \to 0} \frac{\Delta z}{\Delta w} = \lim_{\Delta z \to 0} \frac{1}{\Delta w/\Delta z} = \frac{1}{dw/dz}.$$

This is the same as equation (3).

Since $F'(w)$ exists in a neighborhood of w_0, the function $F(w)$ is analytic there.

Formula (3) could have been used to obtain the differentiation formulas for the inverses of our elementary functions.

Let us return to the example used at the beginning of this section, using the function $w = \exp z$.   If $z_0 = 0$ here, then $w_0 = \exp (0) = 1$. According to the theorem, there is a unique inverse corresponding to these points.   Now we know that the multiple-valued function

$$z = \log w = \text{Log } \rho + i(\phi + 2n\pi),$$

where $-\pi < \phi < \pi$, is an inverse of the function $\exp z$.   But if

$$F(w_0) = z_0$$

as stated in the theorem, then $\log 1 = 0$.   Since $\phi = 0$ and $\rho = 1$ when $w = 1$, it follows that $n = 0$ in the above formula for $\log w$.   Thus the unique inverse prescribed here is the function

$$F(w) = \text{Log } \rho + i\phi \qquad\qquad (-\pi < \phi < \pi).$$

80. Transformation of Harmonic Functions.   Each analytic function generates a pair of harmonic functions.   Since the function exp iz, for example, is analytic, its real and imaginary coefficients

$$e^{-y} \cos x, \qquad e^{-y} \sin x$$

are harmonic.

The problem of finding a function that is harmonic in a specified region and satisfies prescribed conditions on the boundary of the region is one of the oldest and most prominent types of boundary value problems in partial differential equations.

We have just noted that the function

$$H(x,y) = e^{-y} \sin x$$

is everywhere harmonic.   It satisfies, for instance, the boundary conditions

$$H(0,y) = 0, \qquad H(\pi,y) = 0,$$
$$H(x,0) = \sin x, \qquad \lim_{y \to \infty} H(x,y) = 0.$$

Thus this function is harmonic in the semiinfinite strip $0 \leqq x \leqq \pi, y \geqq 0$; it vanishes on the two parallel sides, and it assumes the values $\sin x$ along the base $y = 0$.   It vanishes as y tends to infinity.   The same function satisfies other boundary conditions for other regions, of course; for instance, its normal derivative $\partial H / \partial x$ on the line $x = \pi/2$ is zero.

Sometimes the solution of a given problem can be discovered by this method of conjugate functions.   But the success of this procedure will depend on the simplicity of the problem and on our familiarity with the real and imaginary parts of several analytic functions.   An important additional aid in solving such problems will now be noted.

Let H denote any harmonic function of the independent variables x and y, and let new independent variables u and v be introduced such that the complex variable $z = x + iy$ is an analytic function of $w = u + iv$,

$$z = f(w).$$

We have seen that, corresponding to the given harmonic function $H(x,y)$, a conjugate harmonic function $G(x,y)$ exists; $H + iG$ is an analytic function of z.   Since z is an analytic function of w, the function $H + iG$ is also an analytic function of w, and therefore H is a harmonic function of u and v.   Our result can be stated as follows:

Theorem.   *Every harmonic function of x and y transforms into a harmonic function of u and v under the change of variables*

$$x + iy = f(u + iv),$$

where f is an analytic function.

As a consequence, a harmonic function $H(x,y)$ remains harmonic under a change of variables arising from a conformal transformation

$$w = F(z),$$

where $F(z)$ is analytic and $F'(z) \neq 0$, in the region considered. For we have shown in Sec. 79 that the inverse function $z = f(w)$ is analytic.

As an illustration of the theorem, the function $H = e^{-y} \sin x$ is harmonic in any region of the xy plane. Under the transformation

$$z = w^2,$$

we have $x = u^2 - v^2$, $y = 2uv$, and hence the function

$$H = e^{-2uv} \sin (u^2 - v^2)$$

is harmonic in the corresponding region of the uv plane; that is,

$$\frac{\partial^2 H}{\partial u^2} + \frac{\partial^2 H}{\partial v^2} = 0$$

throughout that region.

81. Transformation of Boundary Conditions. The conditions that the harmonic function $H(x,y)$ or its normal derivative be a prescribed constant along portions of the boundary of a region are the most common although not the only important types of boundary conditions. Some of those conditions remain unaltered under the change of variables involved in conformal transformations.

A curve along which a function $H(x,y)$ is constant is called a *contour curve* of the function. Under the change in variables a contour curve $H(x,y) = c$ in the xy plane transforms into the contour curve

$$H[x(u,v), y(u,v)] = c$$

in the uv plane. In particular then, any portion of the boundary of a region in the xy plane upon which H has a constant value transforms into a corresponding curve in the uv plane along which H has the same constant value. That is, a boundary condition $H = c$ in the original problem carries over to the transformed problem.

If the normal derivative of $H(x,y)$ vanishes along some curve in the xy plane, then the normal derivative of H expressed as a function of u and v also vanishes along the corresponding curve in the uv plane.

To see that this is so, let us first recall that the gradient of a function $H(x,y)$ is a vector whose direction is that along which the directional derivative of H has its maximum value at the point considered. The magnitude of the gradient is the value of that maximum rate of change. It is shown in advanced calculus that the projection of that vector upon any direction is the directional derivative of the function H in that direction. In particular, the projection of the gradient on the x axis is $\partial H/\partial x$, and on the y axis is $\partial H/\partial y$. Thus the gradient vector is represented by the formula

$$\text{grad } H = \frac{\partial H}{\partial x} + i\,\frac{\partial H}{\partial y}.$$

The gradient is perpendicular to the contour curve $H(x,y) = c$ at each point.

Suppose that the normal derivative of $H(x,y)$ vanishes, $dH/dn = 0$, along some curve C (Fig. 51). Since dH/dn is the projection of the gradient on the normal, the normal to C must be perpendicular to the

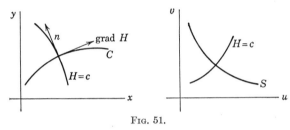

FIG. 51.

gradient of H at each point. The tangent to C therefore coincides with the gradient, and C is orthogonal to the contour curves $H(x,y) = c$. The image S of C, under a conformal transformation, is therefore orthogonal to the contour curves

$$H[x(u,v),\, y(u,v)] = c,$$

which are the images of $H(x,y) = c$. Therefore the normal derivative of H as a function of u and v, along the curve S, must also vanish.

A boundary condition that is not of the type $H = c$ or $dH/dn = 0$ may transform into a condition that is substantially different from the original one. Boundary conditions for the transformed problem may, of course, be obtained from the particular transformation in any case. It is of some interest to note that under a conformal transformation the ratio of a directional derivative of H in the z plane to the directional derivative of H in the corresponding direction in the w plane can be shown to be $|dw/dz|$. This ratio is not generally constant along a curve (see Exercises 3 and 5 below).

EXERCISES

1. The harmonic function

$$H = 2 - x + \frac{x}{x^2 + y^2}$$

assumes the value 2 on the circle $x^2 + y^2 = 1$. Under the change of variables $z = e^w$, find H as a function of u and v, and show directly that $H = 2$ on the image $u = 0$ of the circle, thus verifying one of the results of the preceding section for this special case.

2. The normal derivative of the harmonic function

$$H = e^{-x} \cos y$$

is zero along the line $y = 0$; that is, $\partial H / \partial y = 0$ on that line. Find H in terms of u and v under the change of variables $z = w^2$, and show directly that the normal derivatives of H along the images $u = 0$ and $v = 0$ of the line $y = 0$ also vanish.

3. The normal derivative of the harmonic function

$$H = 2y + e^{-x} \cos y$$

is constant, $\partial H / \partial y = 2$, along the line $y = 0$. Under the change of variables $z = w^2$, show that the normal derivative is not constant along the image of that line, but that $\partial H / \partial u = 4v$ along $u = 0$ and $\partial H / \partial v = 4u$ along $v = 0$.

4. Use partial differentiation under a change of variables to show that

$$\frac{\partial^2 H}{\partial x^2} + \frac{\partial^2 H}{\partial y^2} = \left(\frac{\partial^2 H}{\partial u^2} + \frac{\partial^2 H}{\partial v^2} \right) \left| \frac{dw}{dz} \right|^2,$$

where $w = u + iv$ is an analytic function of $z = x + iy$ and $dw/dz \neq 0$. Note that it follows from this formula for the transformation of the Laplacian that a harmonic function H remains harmonic under the change of variables.

5. (a) Under the change of variables described in Exercise 4, show that

$$|\text{grad } H(x,y)| = |\text{grad } H[u,v]| \left| \frac{dw}{dz} \right|.$$

(b) Why is the angle at a point in the xy plane between a curve C and the vector grad H equal to the angle at the image point in the uv plane between the image S of C and grad H? (c) If σ is distance along C and s is distance along S, use the results of parts (a) and (b) to show that the directional derivative transforms as follows:

$$\frac{dH}{d\sigma} = \frac{dH}{ds} \left| \frac{dw}{dz} \right|.$$

CHAPTER IX

APPLICATIONS OF CONFORMAL MAPPING

We shall now use conformal mapping to solve a number of physical problems involving Laplace's equation in two independent variables. Problems in the conduction of heat, electrostatic potential, and the flow of fluids will be treated. Since they are intended to illustrate methods, the problems will be kept on a fairly elementary level.

82. Steady Temperatures. Let K denote the thermal conductivity of the material in a solid body. Then the flux of heat by conduction across any surface within the solid is

$$-K \frac{dT}{dn},$$

where T denotes the temperature and n the distance normal to the surface. The flux is the rate of flow of heat per unit time per unit area. It is therefore measured in such units as calories per second per square centimeter.

We consider only cases in which the temperature is a function of x and y, because the use of analytic functions and conformal mapping is limited to this case. Since the temperature T does not vary with time, the flow of heat is in a steady state, and since T does not vary with the coordinate perpendicular to the xy plane, the flow is two dimensional, parallel to the xy plane.

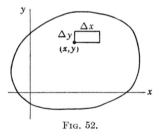

FIG. 52.

Consider an interior element of the solid, the element having the shape of a prism of unit length perpendicular to the xy plane, with a rectangular base Δx by Δy in that plane (Fig. 52). The time rate of flow of heat toward the right across the left-hand face is $-K \Delta y \, \partial T/\partial x$. If K is a constant, the difference between that rate and the rate of flow across the right-hand face is

$$-K \Delta y \frac{\partial^2 T}{\partial x^2} \Delta x,$$

which is the resultant rate of loss of heat from the element through those two faces. The expressions here are approximations whose accuracy increases as Δx and Δy are made smaller.

Similarly, the resultant rate of loss from the upper and lower faces of the element is

$$-K \, \Delta x \, \frac{\partial^2 T}{\partial y^2} \, \Delta y.$$

Heat enters or leaves the element only through those four faces, and the temperatures within the element are steady. Hence the sum of the resultants is zero; that is,

(1) $$\frac{\partial^2 T}{\partial x^2} + \frac{\partial^2 T}{\partial y^2} = 0.$$

Since Δx and Δy can be taken as small as we please, we have a brief demonstration here that the temperature function must satisfy Laplace's equation at each interior point of the solid.

Suppose that the point (x,y) moves through the position (x_0,y_0), both points being interior to the solid in which K is a constant. A sudden jump at (x_0,y_0) in the value of the flux in some specified direction, or in the value of the directional derivative of the flux in some specified direction, would correspond to a source of heat at (x_0,y_0). We suppose that no heat is being generated within the solid, that no sources or sinks are present interior to the solid.   Then the partial derivatives of T up to the second order are continuous functions of x and y interior to the solid, and in view of equation (1), $T(x,y)$ *is a harmonic function.*

The surfaces $T(x,y) = c$, where c is any constant, are the *isotherms.* They can also be considered as curves in the xy plane, for the function $T(x,y)$ can be interpreted as the temperature in a thin sheet of the material in that plane with the faces of the sheet thermally insulated. The isotherms are the contour curves of the function T.   The gradient of T is perpendicular to the isotherm at each point, and the current of heat, that is, the maximum flux, is in the direction of the gradient.   If $S(x,y)$ is a conjugate harmonic of the function $T(x,y)$, then the curves $S(x,y) = c$ have the gradient vectors as their tangents; those curves are the lines of flow.

If the normal derivative dT/dn is zero along any part of the boundary of the solid sheet, the flux of heat across that part is zero.   That is, the part is thermally insulated; it is therefore a line of flow.

The function T may also denote the concentration of a substance that is diffusing through a solid.   In this case, the constant K is the diffusion constant.   The above discussion and derivation applies as well to steady-state diffusion as to the conduction of heat.

83. Steady Temperatures in a Wall. Let us find the formula for the steady temperatures $T(x,y)$ in a semiinfinite slab bounded by the planes $x = \pi/2$, $x = -\pi/2$, and $y = 0$ when the first two boundaries are kept at temperature zero and the last at temperature $T = 1$ (Fig. 53). The function $T(x,y)$ is to be bounded at all points in this region, in particular, as y tends to infinity. This condition is natural if we consider the slab as a limiting case of a slab of finite height whose upper boundary is kept at a fixed temperature as the height is increased.

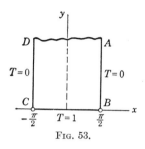

Fig. 53.

The problem is also that of finding the temperatures in a plate having the form of a semi-infinite strip, where the faces of the plate are perfectly insulated.

The boundary value problem to be solved here can be written

$$(1) \qquad \frac{\partial^2 T}{\partial x^2} + \frac{\partial^2 T}{\partial y^2} = 0 \qquad \left(-\frac{\pi}{2} < x < \frac{\pi}{2},\, y > 0\right),$$

$$(2) \qquad T\left(-\frac{\pi}{2},y\right) = T\left(\frac{\pi}{2},y\right) = 0 \qquad (y > 0),$$

$$(3) \qquad T(x,0) = 1 \qquad \left(-\frac{\pi}{2} < x < \frac{\pi}{2}\right);$$

also $|T(x,y)| < M$ where M is some constant, a condition that could be replaced by the condition that T is to approach zero as y tends to infinity. Note that the boundary conditions (2) and (3) are all of the type $T = c$.

The transformation $z' = \sin z$ transforms the strip into the upper half of the z' plane, as noted in Fig. 9 of Appendix II. As indicated in Fig. 54, the image of the base of the strip is the segment of the x' axis

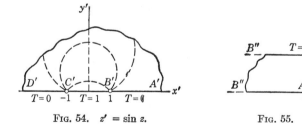

Fig. 54. $z' = \sin z$.   Fig. 55. $w = \log \dfrac{z' - 1}{z' + 1}$.

between the points $z' = -1$ and $z' = 1$, and the images of the sides are the remaining parts of the x' axis. We note in Fig. 19, Appendix II, that this half plane is transformed into the infinite strip between the lines $v = 0$ and $v = \pi$ by the transformation

$$w = \text{Log}\,\frac{z' - 1}{z' + 1}.$$

As indicated in Figs. 54 and 55, the segment of the x' axis between $z' = -1$ and $z' = 1$ maps into the upper side of the strip, and the rest of that axis into the lower side.

A harmonic function of u and v that is zero on the side $v = 0$ of the strip and unity on the side $v = \pi$ is clearly

$$(4) \qquad\qquad T = \frac{1}{\pi} v,$$

for this is the imaginary coefficient of the analytic function $f(w) = w/\pi$. Changing to the coordinates x' and y' by means of the transformation

$$(5) \qquad w = \text{Log} \frac{z' - 1}{z' + 1} = \text{Log} \left| \frac{z' - 1}{z' + 1} \right| + i \arg \frac{z' - 1}{z' + 1},$$

we find that

$$v = \arg \left(\frac{x' - 1 + iy'}{x' + 1 + iy'} \right) = \arg \left[\frac{x'^2 + y'^2 - 1 + 2iy'}{(x' + 1)^2 + y'^2} \right],$$

or

$$v = \arctan \left(\frac{2y'}{x'^2 + y'^2 - 1} \right),$$

where the arctangent function has the range 0 to π since

$$\arg \frac{z' - 1}{z' + 1} = \theta_1 - \theta_2,$$

and the angles here are those indicated under Fig. 19, Appendix II.

The function T given by equation (4) therefore becomes

$$(6) \qquad\qquad T = \frac{1}{\pi} \arctan \left(\frac{2y'}{x'^2 + y'^2 - 1} \right).$$

The function used in the transformation (5) is analytic in the upper half plane $y' > 0$. Since the function (4) is harmonic in the strip, the function (6) must be a harmonic function of x' and y' in the half plane. The boundary conditions for the two functions must be the same on corresponding parts of the boundaries. It can, of course, be verified directly that the function (6) satisfies Laplace's equation and approaches the values indicated in Fig. 54 as the point approaches the x' axis from above.

The function represents the steady temperatures in the semiinfinite plate $y \geq 0$ with a section $(-1 < x' < 1)$ of its boundary $y = 0$ kept at the temperature $T = 1$ and the rest at temperature zero.   The isotherms $T = c$ are the circles

$$x'^2 + y'^2 - \frac{2}{\tan \pi c} y' - 1 = 0,$$

each of which passes through the points $(\pm 1, 0)$.   They are represented by the broken lines in Fig. 54.   By noting the conjugate harmonic of the function T from equation (5), one can see that the lines of flow are circles with centers on the x' axis.

We proceed now to the solution of the original problem represented by equations (1) to (3).   Under the transformation

(7) $z' = \sin z,$

the change of variables can be written

$$x' = \sin x \cosh y, \qquad y' = \cos x \sinh y,$$

and the harmonic function (6) becomes

$$T = \frac{1}{\pi} \arctan \left(\frac{2 \cos x \sinh y}{\sin^2 x \cosh^2 y + \cos^2 x \sinh^2 y - 1} \right).$$

The denominator here reduces to $\sinh^2 y - \cos^2 x$, and the fraction can be written

$$\frac{2 \cos x \sinh y}{\sinh^2 y - \cos^2 x} = \frac{2 \cos x / \sinh y}{1 - (\cos x / \sinh y)^2} = \tan 2\alpha,$$

where $\tan \alpha = \cos x / \sinh y$.   Our formula for T therefore reduces to

(8) $T = \frac{2}{\pi} \arctan \left(\frac{\cos x}{\sinh y} \right).$

The arctangent function here has the range 0 to $\pi/2$, its argument being nonnegative.

Since $\sin z$ is analytic, the transformation (7) ensures that the function (8) will be harmonic in the strip $-\pi/2 < x < \pi/2$, $y > 0$, into which the half plane maps, and it must satisfy the boundary conditions (2) and (3).   Moreover $|T(x,y)| \leq 1$ throughout the strip.   Formula (8) is therefore the temperature formula sought.

The isotherms $T = c$ are the curves

$$\cos x = \tan \frac{\pi c}{2} \sinh y,$$

each of which passes through the points $(\pm \pi/2, 0)$.   If K is the thermal conductivity, the flux of heat into the wall through its base is

$$-K \frac{\partial T}{\partial y} \bigg]_{y=0} = \frac{2K}{\pi \cos x} \qquad \left(-\frac{\pi}{2} < x < \frac{\pi}{2} \right),$$

and the flux outward through the plane $x = \pi/2$ is

$$-K \frac{\partial T}{\partial x}\bigg]_{x=\pi/2} = \frac{2K}{\pi \sinh y} \qquad (y > 0).$$

The product of a harmonic function by a constant is also harmonic. The function

$$T = \frac{2A}{\pi} \arctan\left(\frac{\cos x}{\sinh y}\right)$$

represents the steady temperatures in the above slab when the base is kept at temperature A and the sides at zero.

The boundary value problem given by equations (1) to (3) can also be solved with the aid of Fourier series. That method is more direct, but it gives the solution in the form of an infinite series.*

84. Temperatures in a Quadrant with Part of One Boundary Insulated. Let us find the steady temperatures in a plate having the form of a quadrant if a segment at the end of one edge is insulated, if the rest of that edge is kept at a fixed temperature and if the second edge is kept at another fixed temperature. The faces are insulated so that the problem is two dimensional.

The temperature scale and the unit of length can be so chosen that the boundary value problem in the temperature function $T(x,y)$ becomes

(1) $$\frac{\partial^2 T}{\partial x^2} + \frac{\partial^2 T}{\partial y^2} = 0 \qquad (x > 0, y > 0);$$

(2) $$\frac{\partial T}{\partial y}\bigg]_{y=0} = 0 \qquad (0 < x < 1);$$
$$T(x,0) = 1 \qquad (x > 1);$$
(3) $$T(0,y) = 0 \qquad (y > 0),$$

where $T(x,y)$ is bounded for all positive x and y. The plate and its boundary conditions are shown in Fig. 56.

Conditions (2) prescribe the value of the normal derivative of the function T over a part of a boundary line and the value of the function itself over the rest of that line. The Fourier method mentioned above, which would call for the use of a Fourier integral in this case, is not adapted to problems with such different types of conditions on the same boundary line.

As indicated in Fig. 10 of Appendix II, the transformation

(4) $$z = \sin w$$

---

* See for instance the author's "Fourier Series and Boundary Value Problems," Probs. 8 and 9, p. 116.

maps the quadrant $x \geqq 0, y \geqq 0$ into the strip $0 \leqq u \leqq \pi/2, v \geqq 0$. The insulated segment of the x axis maps into the base of the strip and the rest of the boundary into the sides of the strip, as shown in Fig. 57.

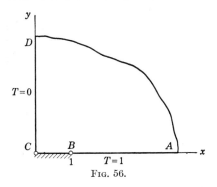

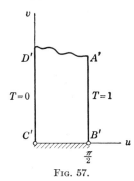

FIG. 56.   FIG. 57.

The corresponding boundary conditions on the function T of u and v are indicated in that figure. The function T here is clearly

$$(5) \qquad T = \frac{2}{\pi} u,$$

for this is a harmonic function of u and v such that $T = 0$ when $u = 0$, $T = 1$ when $u = \pi/2$; also $\partial T/\partial v = 0$ everywhere, along the u axis in particular. The required temperature function for the quadrant is obtained by writing T in terms of x and y.

In order to obtain u in terms of x and y, we may first note, according to equation (4), that

$$x = \sin u \cosh v, \qquad y = \cos u \sinh v;$$

therefore

$$(6) \qquad \frac{x^2}{\sin^2 u} - \frac{y^2}{\cos^2 u} = 1.$$

In solving for u it is convenient to observe that for each fixed u the point (x,y), which is in the first quadrant, lies on the hyperbola (6) with foci at the points $(\pm 1,0)$ and with a transverse axis of length $2 \sin u$. The difference of its distances from the foci is therefore $2 \sin u$,

$$\sqrt{(x + 1)^2 + y^2} - \sqrt{(x - 1)^2 + y^2} = 2 \sin u.$$

According to equation (5), the required temperature function is therefore

$$(7) \qquad T = \frac{2}{\pi} \arcsin \frac{1}{2} \left[\sqrt{(x + 1)^2 + y^2} - \sqrt{(x - 1)^2 + y^2} \right].$$

If we wish to verify that this function satisfies the boundary conditions (2), we must remember that the square roots here are positive, so that $\sqrt{(x-1)^2}$ denotes $x-1$ when $x>1$ and $1-x$ when $x<1$.

It can be seen from equation (5) that the isotherms $T=c$ are the parts of the confocal hyperbolas (6), with $u=\pi c/2$, which lie in the first quadrant. The lines of flow are quarters of the confocal ellipses obtained by holding v constant, since the function $2v/\pi$ is a harmonic conjugate of the function (5). The temperature along the insulated part of the lower edge is

$$T(x,0) = \frac{2}{\pi} \arcsin x.$$

Since $T = 2u/\pi$, the real part of $2w/\pi$, and $\sin w = z$, our temperature formula (7) can be written

$$T(x,y) = \frac{2}{\pi} \Re (\sin^{-1} z).$$

85. Electric Potential. The electrostatic potential at a point is a function of the coordinates of the point whose directional derivative in each direction is the component of the electric force in that direction. The potential can also be defined as the work done by the electric force upon a unit charge when that charge is brought up to the point from a fixed reference position.

The electric force of attraction or repulsion between two stationary charged particles in space is inversely proportional to the square of the distance between them and directly proportional to the product of their charges. Starting from this inverse-square law for the force, it can be seen that the potential due to a single particle in space is inversely proportional to the first power of the distance from the point to the particle. The potential due to any distribution of charges, at a point free from electric charges, can then be shown to satisfy Laplace's equation in the three-dimensional space.

When conditions are such that the potential V is the same in all planes parallel to the xy plane, then V is a harmonic function of the two variables x and y:

$$\frac{\partial^2 V}{\partial x^2} + \frac{\partial^2 V}{\partial y^2} = 0.$$

The intensity of the electric field of force at each point, that is, the force that would be exerted on a unit positive charge placed at the point, is then a vector parallel to the xy plane with components $-\partial V/\partial x$ and

$-\partial V/\partial y$ parallel to the coordinate axes. Thus the electric intensity is represented by a vector that is the negative of the gradient of V.

A surface along which V is constant is an equipotential surface. The force tangent to a conducting surface is zero in the static case, since charges are free to move on such a surface under an electric force along it. Thus V is constant along the surface of a conductor, and that surface is an equipotential.

If $U(x,y)$ is a harmonic conjugate of $V(x,y)$, the curves $U = c$ in the xy plane are called the *flux lines*. These curves are orthogonal to the equipotential surfaces or curves. The electric force has the direction of the flux line at each point.

As in the case of steady temperatures, the methods of complex variables are limited to problems in the two-dimensional potential $V(x,y)$, sometimes called the *logarithmic potential*. Such potentials may arise from a distribution of charges that is uniform along every line perpendicular to the xy plane. The electric force at a point (x,y) due to a single uniformly charged line turns out to be inversely proportional to the first power of the distance from the point to the line.

Boundary value problems in the potential V are the same mathematical problems as those in steady temperatures T. In fact, the temperature is the potential for the flow of heat by conduction.

The problem in Sec. 83 (Fig. 53), for instance, can be interpreted as the problem of finding the two-dimensional electrostatic potential in the empty space bounded by the conducting planes $x = \pm\pi/2$ and $y = 0$, insulated at their intersections, when the planes at the sides are kept at potential zero and the base at the potential $V = 1$. Problems of this type arise in electronics. If the space charge inside a vacuum tube is small, the space is sometimes considered free of charge, as an approximation; then the potential can be assumed to satisfy Laplace's equation.

The potential in the steady flow of electricity in a plane conducting sheet is also a harmonic function at points free from sources or sinks. Magnetic potential and gravitational potential are further examples of harmonic functions in physics.

86. Potential in a Cylindrical Space. A long circular cylinder is made out of a thin sheet of conducting material, and the cylinder is split along two of its elements to form two equal parts. Those parts are separated by slender strips of insulating material and used as electrodes, one of which is grounded and the other kept at some other fixed potential. We take the coordinate axes and units of length and potential difference as indicated in Fig. 58. The electrostatic potential $V(x,y)$ over any cross section of the enclosed space that is distant from the ends of the cylinder is a harmonic function inside the circle $x^2 + y^2 = 1$; also, $V = 0$ on the upper half of the circle and $V = 1$ on the lower half.

To determine the function V, we may note that the linear fractional transformation, a special case of equation (6) on page 62,

$$(1) \qquad z = \frac{i - w}{i + w}$$

maps the region inside the unit circle $|z| = 1$ upon the upper half of the w plane (Fig. 13, Appendix II). The lower semicircle maps into the left-hand half of the u axis, and the upper one into the right-hand half, as shown in Fig. 59.

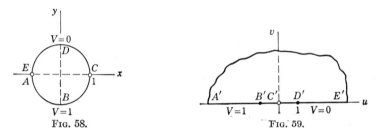

FIG. 58.   FIG. 59.

The problem of determining the potential V in this half plane can be reduced to a still simpler one by using the transformation $w = e^{z'}$. But the second transformation is unnecessary if we observe that the imaginary coefficient of the function

$$(2) \qquad \frac{1}{\pi} \log w = \frac{1}{\pi} \operatorname{Log} \rho + \frac{i}{\pi} \phi \qquad (0 \leq \phi \leq \pi)$$

is a bounded function of u and v that assumes the required values on the two parts $\phi = 0$ and $\phi = \pi$ of the u axis. The required harmonic function for the half plane is therefore

$$(3) \qquad V = \frac{1}{\pi} \arctan \frac{v}{u}.$$

Equation (1) can be written in the form

$$(4) \qquad w = i \frac{1 - z}{1 + z},$$

from which u and v can be seen as functions of x and y. The function (3) then becomes

$$(5) \qquad V = \frac{1}{\pi} \arctan \left(\frac{1 - x^2 - y^2}{2y} \right),$$

where $0 \leqq \arctan t \leqq \pi$ and therefore

$$\lim_{t \to +0} \arctan t = 0, \qquad \lim_{t \to -0} \arctan t = \pi.$$

The function (5) is the potential function for the space enclosed by the cylindrical electrodes, since it must be harmonic in the circle and it must assume the required values on the semicircles, which are the images of the half lines $\phi = 0$ and $\phi = \pi$ in the w plane. A direct verification of all conditions from formula (5) is not difficult.

The equipotentials $V = c$ in the circular region are arcs of the circles

$$x^2 + y^2 + 2y \tan \pi c = 1,$$

each of which passes through the points $(\pm 1,0)$. Also, the segment of the x axis between those points is the equipotential $V = \frac{1}{2}$. The conjugate harmonic U of V is $(1/\pi) \operatorname{Log} \rho$, according to equation (2). In view of equation (4),

$$U = \frac{1}{\pi} \operatorname{Log} \frac{|1 - z|}{|1 + z|}.$$

From this equation it can be seen that the flux lines $U = c$ are arcs of circles with centers on the x axis. The segment of the y axis between the electrodes is also a flux line.

In those exercises given below which involve unbounded regions, the condition that the required function be bounded throughout the region is tacitly assumed. It can be shown that such conditions are necessary if the problems are to have unique solutions; this is illustrated in Exercises 9 and 10.

EXERCISES

1. Find the formula for the steady temperatures $T(x,y)$ in a plate in the form of a quadrant $x \geqq 0$, $y \geqq 0$, if its flat faces are perfectly insulated and if $T(x,0) = 0$ and $T(0,y) = 1$ (Fig. 60). What curves represent the isotherms and the lines of flow in the plate? Draw some of these curves.

$$Ans. \ T = \frac{2}{\pi} \arctan \frac{y}{x}.$$

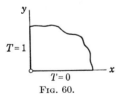

Fig. 60.

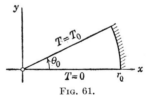

Fig. 61.

2. Find the steady temperatures in a solid in the shape of a long cylindrical wedge if its boundary planes $\theta = 0$ and $\theta = \theta_0$ are kept at constant temperatures zero and T_0, respectively, and its surface $r = r_0$ is perfectly insulated (Fig. 61).

$$Ans. \ T = \frac{T_0}{\theta_0} \arctan \frac{y}{x}.$$

3. Find the electrostatic potential $V(x,y)$ in the space between two coaxial conducting cylindrical surfaces $x^2 + y^2 = 1$ and $x^2 + y^2 = r_0^2$ when $V = 0$ on the first surface and $V = 1$ on the second. $\qquad$ *Ans.* $V = \dfrac{\text{Log }(x^2 + y^2)}{2 \text{ Log } r_0}.$

4. Find the electrostatic potential $V(x,y)$ in the space above an infinite conducting plane $y = 0$ one strip $(-a < x < a)$ of which is insulated from the rest and kept at potential $V = 1$, while $V = 0$ on the rest, as indicated in Fig. 62.

$$Ans. \ V = \frac{1}{\pi} \arctan\left(\frac{2ay}{x^2 + y^2 - a^2}\right) \qquad (0 \leqq \arctan t \leqq \pi).$$

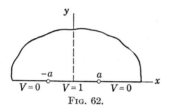

FIG. 62.

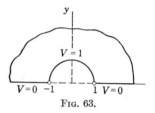

FIG. 63.

5. Derive a formula for the electrostatic potential in the space indicated in Fig. 63, bounded below by two half planes and half a cylinder, if $V = 1$ on the cylinder and $V = 0$ on the half planes. $\qquad$ *Ans.* $V = \dfrac{2}{\pi} \arctan\left(\dfrac{2y}{x^2 + y^2 - 1}\right).$

6. Find the steady temperatures $T(x,y)$ in the semiinfinite solid $y \geqq 0$, if $T = 0$ on the part $x < -1$ of the boundary, $T = 1$ on the part $x > 1$, and if the strip $-1 < x < 1$ of the boundary is insulated (Fig. 64).

$$Ans. \ T = \frac{1}{2} + \frac{1}{\pi} \arcsin\frac{1}{2}\left[\sqrt{(x+1)^2 + y^2} - \sqrt{(x-1)^2 + y^2}\right]$$

$$\left(-\frac{\pi}{2} \leqq \arcsin t \leqq \frac{\pi}{2}\right).$$

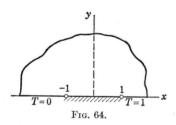

FIG. 64.

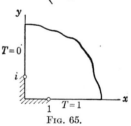

FIG. 65.

7. Find the steady temperatures in a quadrant when the boundary planes are kept at fixed temperatures except for strips of equal width at the corner that are insulated, as shown in Fig. 65.

$$Ans. \ T = \frac{1}{2} + \frac{1}{\pi} \arcsin\frac{1}{2}\left[\sqrt{(x^2 - y^2 + 1)^2 + 4x^2y^2}\right.$$

$$\left. - \sqrt{(x^2 - y^2 - 1)^2 + 4x^2y^2}\right] \qquad \left(-\frac{\pi}{2} \leqq \arcsin t \leqq \frac{\pi}{2}\right).$$

8. Obtain the formula

$$T = \frac{1}{2} - \frac{1}{\pi}\arcsin\frac{1}{2}\left(\sqrt{1 + r^{\frac{4}{3}} + 2r^{\frac{2}{3}}\cos\frac{2\theta}{3}} - \sqrt{1 + r^{\frac{4}{3}} - 2r^{\frac{2}{3}}\cos\frac{2\theta}{3}}\right),$$

where $-\pi/2 \leqq \arcsin t \leqq \pi/2$, for the steady temperatures in a solid extending over the infinite region $0 \leqq \theta \leqq 3\pi/2$, if strips of the boundary planes one unit wide at the corner are insulated, and if $T = 0$ on the rest of the plane $\theta = 0$ and $T = 1$ on the rest of the plane $\theta = 3\pi/2$ (Fig. 66).

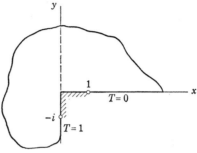

FIG. 66.

9. Suppose that the condition $|T(x,y)| < M$ were omitted from the boundary value problem of temperatures in a semiinfinite slab (Sec. 83, Fig. 53). Show that an infinite number of solutions would then be possible by noting the effect of adding to the solution found there the imaginary coefficient of the function $A\sin z$, where A is an arbitrary real constant.

10. The harmonic function (3) of Sec. 86 is bounded in the half plane $v \geqq 0$ and satisfies the boundary conditions indicated in Fig. 59. Show that if the imaginary coefficient of Ae^w is added to that function, where A is any real constant, the resulting function satisfies all requirements except the boundedness condition. Also show that the resulting function transforms under equation (4), Sec. 86, into a function of x and y that is not bounded in a neighborhood of the point $z = -1$, a point on the circle in Fig. 58.

11. Find the electrostatic potential in the space bounded by the planes $\theta = 0$ and $\theta = \pi/4$ and the cylinder $r = 1$ if $V = 0$ on the planes and $V = 1$ on the cylinder (Fig. 67).   *Ans.* $V = 1 - \dfrac{2}{\pi}\arctan\left(\dfrac{1 - r^8}{2r^4\sin 4\theta}\right).$

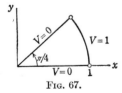

FIG. 67.

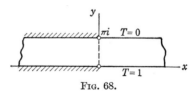

FIG. 68.

12. The part $x < 0$ of each of the two boundary planes of an infinite slab $0 \leqq y \leqq \pi$ is thermally insulated. On the parts $x > 0$ the conditions $T(x,0) = 1$ and $T(x,\pi) = 0$ are maintained (Fig. 68). Find the steady temperatures $T(x,y)$ in the slab. (This problem can be transformed into the one in Exercise 6.)

13. Find the electrostatic potential $V(x,y)$ in the space between the planes $y = 0$ and $y = \pi$ if $V = 0$ on the part $x > 0$ of each of those planes and $V = 1$

on the part $x < 0$ of each (Fig. 69).   Find the equipotential surfaces.

$$Ans. \; V = \frac{1}{\pi} \arctan \left(\frac{\sin y}{\sinh x} \right) \qquad (0 \le \arctan t \le \pi).$$

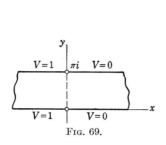

Fig. 69.

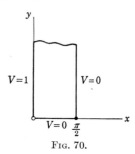

Fig. 70.

14. Solve the boundary value problem (Fig. 70)

$$\frac{\partial^2 V}{\partial x^2} + \frac{\partial^2 V}{\partial y^2} = 0 \qquad \left(0 < x < \frac{\pi}{2}, y > 0 \right),$$

$$V(x,0) = 0, \qquad V(0,y) = 1, \qquad V\left(\frac{\pi}{2}, y \right) = 0.$$

$$Ans. \; V = \frac{2}{\pi} \arctan \left(\frac{\tanh y}{\tan x} \right).$$

15. Find the temperatures $T(x,y)$ in a semicircular plate if $T = 1$ along one of the two radii on the boundary and $T = 0$ on the rest of the boundary, the flat faces being insulated (note Exercise 14).

16. Find the steady temperatures in a plate in the form of a segment of a circle (Fig. 20, Appendix II) with its flat faces insulated, when $T = 0$ on the circular part of its boundary and $T = 1$ on the base.

17. A plate with insulated flat faces has the form of the semiellipse shown in Fig. 11, Appendix II.   The temperature of the elliptical part of its boundary is $T = 1$; $T = 0$ on the segment $-1 < x < 1$ of its base, and the rest of its base is insulated.   Find the steady temperatures in the plate and the lines of flow of heat.

18. The boundary value problem

$$\frac{\partial^2 V}{\partial x^2} + \frac{\partial^2 V}{\partial y^2} = 0 \qquad (0 < x < a, 0 < y < b),$$

$$V(0,y) = V(a,y) = V(x,0) = 0, \qquad V(x,b) = 1,$$

for $V(x,y)$ in a rectangle (Fig. 71) can be solved with the aid of the Fourier sine series.*   The solution turns out to be

$$V = \frac{4}{\pi} \sum_{n=1}^{\infty} \frac{\sinh (n'\pi y/a)}{n' \sinh (n'\pi b/a)} \sin \frac{n'\pi x}{a} \qquad (n' = 2n - 1).$$

* See "Fourier Series and Boundary Value Problems," p. 114.

Accepting this formula as correct, find the potential function $V(r,\theta)$ in the space $1 \leq r \leq r_0, 0 \leq \theta \leq \pi$, if $V = 1$ on the boundary $\theta = \pi$ and $V = 0$ on the rest of the boundary (Fig. 72).

$$Ans. \quad V = \frac{4}{\pi} \sum_{n=1}^{\infty} \frac{\sinh N\theta}{\sinh N\pi} \frac{\sin (N \operatorname{Log} r)}{2n - 1} \qquad \left(N = \frac{(2n - 1)\pi}{\operatorname{Log} r_0} \right).$$

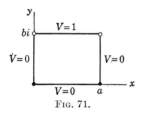

Fig. 71.

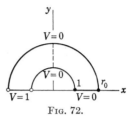

Fig. 72.

19. With the aid of the formula for $V(x,y)$ in a rectangle, given in Exercise 18, find the potential function $V(r,\theta)$ for the region $1 \leq r \leq r_0, 0 \leq \theta \leq \pi$, if $V = 1$ on the boundary $r = r_0$ and $V = 0$ on the rest of the boundary (Fig. 73).

$$Ans. \quad V = \frac{4}{\pi} \sum_{n=1}^{\infty} \frac{r^{n'} - r^{-n'}}{r_0^{n'} - r_0^{-n'}} \frac{\sin n'\theta}{n'} \qquad (n' = 2n - 1).$$

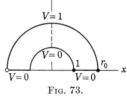

Fig. 73.

20. With the aid of the formula given in Exercise 18, show that the formula for the potential in the rectangular region of Fig. 11, Appendix II, with $V = 1$ on the side $y = k$ and $V = 0$ on the other three sides can be written

$$V = \frac{4}{\pi} \sum_{n=1}^{\infty} \frac{(-1)^{n-1}}{2n - 1} \frac{\sinh n'y}{\sinh n'k} \cos n'x \qquad (n' = 2n - 1).$$

Find the potential $V(u,v)$ in the semielliptical region shown in that figure when $V = 0$ on the base $v = 0$ and $V = 1$ on the elliptical boundary.

21. Derive the formula for the electrostatic potential $V(r,\theta)$ inside a long cylinder $r = 1$ if $V = 1$ on one quadrant, $0 < \theta < \pi/2$, of the cylinder and $V = 0$ on the rest.

22. Apply the transformation $w = i/z$ to the problem on temperatures in a quadrant solved in Sec. 84 (Fig. 56). State the new problem on temperatures in a quadrant of the uv plane and write the temperature formula. Then use the transformation $w = \sin z'$ in that new problem and state the resulting problem on temperatures in a semiinfinite strip in the z' plane.

87. Two-dimensional Fluid Flow. Harmonic functions play an important role in hydrodynamics and aerodynamics. Again, we consider only the two-dimensional steady-state type of flow. That is, the motion of the fluid is assumed to be the same in all planes parallel to the xy plane, the velocity being parallel to that plane and independent of the time. It is then sufficient to consider the motion of a sheet of the fluid in the xy plane.

Let the vector that represents the complex variable

$$q = q_1 + iq_2$$

denote the velocity of a particle of the fluid at any point (x,y), so that the real variables q_1 and q_2 are the x and y components of the velocity. If the real variable q_t denotes the component of the velocity tangent to a given curve C at each point on C, and if s is arc length along C, the line integral

(1)
$$\int_C q_t \, ds$$

is called the *circulation* of the fluid along C. When the circulation is divided by the length of the curve, the quotient represents the mean velocity along the curve.

Let C be a closed curve and let $x + iy$ be any point on C. The complex number $dx + i\,dy$ represents a vector tangent to C and of length ds. Now $q_t\,ds$ is the product of the lengths of the vectors q and $dx + i\,dy$ by the cosine of the angle between them; that is, $q_t\,ds$ is the scalar product of those two vectors. It can be written

$$q_t\,ds = q_1\,dx + q_2\,dy.$$

With the aid of Green's theorem, the circulation around C can be written

(2)
$$\int_C (q_1\,dx + q_2\,dy) = \int\int_R \left(\frac{\partial q_2}{\partial x} - \frac{\partial q_1}{\partial y} \right) dx\,dy,$$

where R is the region bounded by C.

In order to see a physical interpretation of the integrand of the last integral, let C be a circle $|z - z_0| = r_0$. The mean velocity v_0 along C is then found by dividing the circulation by $2\pi r_0$, and the mean angular velocity ω_0 of the fluid about the axis of the circle is v_0/r_0; thus

$$\omega_0 = \frac{1}{\pi r_0^2} \int\int_R \frac{1}{2} \left(\frac{\partial q_2}{\partial x} - \frac{\partial q_1}{\partial y} \right) dx\,dy.$$

The member on the right represents the mean value of the function

(3)
$$\omega = \frac{1}{2} \left(\frac{\partial q_2}{\partial x} - \frac{\partial q_1}{\partial y} \right)$$

over the circular region R. Its limit as r_0 tends to zero is the value of ω at the point z_0. Hence the function $\omega(x,y)$, called the *rotation* of the fluid, represents the limiting angular velocity of a circular element of the fluid as the circle shrinks to the point (x,y).

If $\omega = 0$ at all points in some region, the flow is *irrotational* in the region. We consider only such irrotational flows. We also assume that the fluid is *incompressible* and *free from viscosity*.

Let R be a simply connected region in which the flow is irrotational. If C is any closed curve in R, it follows from equation (2) that the circulation around C is zero,

$$\int_C (q_1\, dx + q_2\, dy) = 0.$$

As a consequence, if (x_0, y_0) is a fixed point in R, the equation

(4) $$\phi(x,y) = \int_{(x_0,y_0)}^{(x,y)} [q_1(x',y')\, dx' + q_2(x', y')\, dy']$$

defines a function of the point (x,y) in R that is independent of the path of integration between the limits, as long as the path lies in R, for the integral along one path C_1 (Fig. 74) minus the integral along another path C_2 is the integral along a closed path C, which must be zero.

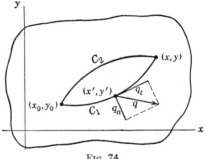

Fig. 74.

Since the line integral (4) is independent of the path, it follows that its integrand is an exact differential, the differential of the function $\phi(x,y)$. Hence

(5) $$q_1 = \frac{\partial\phi}{\partial x}, \qquad q_2 = \frac{\partial\phi}{\partial y};$$

that is, the vector q is the gradient of ϕ,

(6) $$q = \frac{\partial\phi}{\partial x} + i\,\frac{\partial\phi}{\partial y},$$

and the directional derivative of ϕ in any direction represents the component of the velocity of flow in that direction.

The function $\phi(x,y)$ is called the *velocity potential*. It follows from equation (4) that $\phi(x,y)$ changes by an additive constant when the reference point z_0 is changed.

The curves $\phi(x,y) = c$ are called *equipotentials*. They are the contour curves of the function ϕ. The velocity vectors at all points are normal to them, since q is the gradient of ϕ.

Just as in the case of the flow of heat, the condition of continuity of flow, that is, the condition that fluid enters or leaves an element of the region only by flowing through the boundaries of the element, requires that the function ϕ be harmonic; thus Laplace's equation

(7)
$$\frac{\partial^2 \phi}{\partial x^2} + \frac{\partial^2 \phi}{\partial y^2} = 0$$

is satisfied in every region that is free from sources or sinks of the fluid.

88. The Stream Function. If $\psi(x,y)$ is a conjugate harmonic of the function $\phi(x,y)$, then the velocity vectors are tangent to the curves

(1)
$$\psi(x,y) = c.$$

These curves are called the *streamlines* of the flow; the function ψ is the *stream function*. In particular, a boundary across which fluid cannot flow is a streamline of flow for nonviscous fluids.

The analytic function

$$F(z) = \phi(x,y) + i\psi(x,y)$$

is called the *complex potential* of the flow. Now

$$F'(z) = \frac{\partial \phi}{\partial x} + i\frac{\partial \psi}{\partial x} = \frac{\partial \phi}{\partial x} - i\frac{\partial \phi}{\partial y},$$

since ϕ and ψ satisfy the Cauchy-Riemann conditions. In view of equation (6), Sec. 87, it follows that the conjugate of the derivative of the complex potential function is the velocity

(2)
$$q = \overline{F'(z)}.$$

The speed, or magnitude of the velocity, is given by the formula

(3)
$$|q| = |F'(z)|.$$

The function ψ has a physical interpretation. Since the fluid is incompressible, its density is uniform, and thus the mass of any part of it bears a constant ratio to the volume of that part. In Fig. 74 let q_n denote the component of q normal to the curve C_1. Then the integral

$$\int_{C_1} q_n \, ds$$

represents the time rate of flow of fluid, by volume, across C_1. It is independent of the path from z_0 to z, since the rate of flow across C_2 is the same as that across C_1. The product of ds by the projection of q on the normal is the scalar product of the vector q by the vector $-i \, dz$ normal to dz and of length ds; hence

$$q_n \, ds = q_1 \, dy - q_2 \, dx.$$

The integral represents the stream function

(4) $$\psi(x,y) = \int_{C_1} q_n\, ds = \int_{(x_0,y_0)}^{(x,y)} (-q_2\, dx + q_1\, dy),$$

because it satisfies the Cauchy-Riemann conditions with the function ϕ:

$$\frac{\partial \psi}{\partial x} = -q_2 = -\frac{\partial \phi}{\partial y}, \qquad \frac{\partial \psi}{\partial y} = q_1 = \frac{\partial \phi}{\partial x}.$$

The value of ψ changes by an additive constant when the position of z_0 is changed.

Since ϕ and ψ are harmonic functions, the properties noted earlier apply to them. For instance, a streamline $\psi = c$ in the xy plane transforms into a streamline $\psi = c$ in the uv plane under a conformal transformation. The function ψ is the principal one in boundary value problems in the flow of fluids since natural boundaries of the region of flow are curves $\psi = c$.

89. Flow around a Corner. When the complex potential is the function

(1) $$F(z) = Az,$$

where A is a positive real constant, then

(2) $$\phi(x,y) = Ax, \qquad \psi(x,y) = Ay.$$

The streamlines $\psi = c$ are the horizontal lines $y = c/A$, and the velocity of the fluid is the vector

$$q = \overline{F'(z)} = A.$$

The flow is a uniform flow to the right (Fig. 75). It can be interpreted as the uniform flow in the upper half plane bounded by the x axis, or as the uniform flow between two parallel lines $y = y_1$ and $y = y_2$.

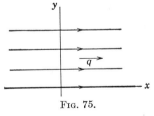

FIG. 75.

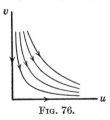

FIG. 76.

To determine the flow in a quadrant $u \geqq 0$, $v \geqq 0$, we note that the boundary is mapped into the entire x axis by the transformation

(3) $$z = w^2 = u^2 - v^2 + 2uvi,$$

and the quadrant is mapped into the upper half of the xy plane. The stream function $\psi = Ay$ for the flow in the half plane transforms into the stream function

$$(4) \qquad\qquad \psi = 2Auv$$

for the flow in the quadrant.   That is, this function ψ must be harmonic in the quadrant and reduce to zero on the boundaries.

The streamlines $\psi = c$ in the quadrant are branches of the rectangular hyperbolas (Fig. 76)

$$2Auv = c.$$

The complex potential is the function $F = Aw^2$, and the velocity of the fluid is

$$q = \overline{F'(w)} = 2A(u - iv).$$

The speed

$$|q| = 2A\sqrt{u^2 + v^2}$$

is directly proportional to the distance of the particle from the origin The value of the stream function (4) can be interpreted here as the rate of flow across a line segment extending from the origin to the point (u,v).

In such problems it is simplest to write first the complex potential as a function of the complex variable in the new region.   The stream function and the velocity can be obtained from that potential function.

The function ψ characterizes a definite flow in the region.   The question as to whether just one function exists corresponding to a given region, except possibly for a constant factor or an additive constant, cannot be adequately examined here.   In some of the examples to follow, in which the velocity is uniform far from the obstruction, the physical situation indicates that the flow is uniquely determined by the conditions given in the problem.*

It may be noted that a harmonic function is not always uniquely determined, even up to a constant factor, by simply prescribing its values on the boundary of an infinite region.   We noted above, for example, that $\psi = Ay$ is harmonic in the half plane $y \geqq 0$ and vanishes on the boundary.   The function $\psi_1 = Be^x \sin y$ also satisfies those conditions. However, the streamline $\psi_1 = 0$ consists not only of the line $y = 0$ but also of the lines $y = n\pi$, which are interior to the region.   Here the function $F_1 = Be^z$ is the complex potential for the flow in the strip between the lines $y = 0$ and $y = \pi$, both boundaries of which make up the streamline $\psi_1 = 0$; the fluid flows to the right along the lower boundary and to the left along the upper one.

---

* Also, see the examples and exercises given in Chap. X, in which the description of the problem includes a consideration of sources and sinks.

90. Flow around a Cylinder. Let a long circular cylinder of unit radius be placed in a large body of fluid flowing with a uniform velocity, with its axis perpendicular to the direction of flow. To determine the steady flow around the cylinder, we can represent the cylinder by the circle $x^2 + y^2 = 1$ and let the flow distant from it be parallel to the x axis (Fig. 77). The symmetry shows that the part of the x axis exterior to the circle may be treated as a boundary so that we need consider only the upper part of the figure as the region of flow.

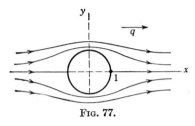

FIG. 77.

The boundary of this region of flow, consisting of the upper semicircle and the two parts of the x axis, is mapped into the entire u axis by the transformation

$$w = z + \frac{1}{z}.$$

The region is mapped into the half plane $v \geqq 0$ (Fig. 17, Appendix II). The complex potential for a uniform flow in the half plane is

$$F = Aw,$$

where A is a real constant. Hence the complex potential for the region about the circle is

$$F = A \left(z + \frac{1}{z} \right).$$

The velocity

$$q = A \left(1 - \frac{1}{z^2} \right)$$

approaches A as $|z|$ increases; that is, the flow is nearly uniform and parallel to the x axis at points distant from the circle. This result also follows by observing that the derivative of the mapping function $w = z + 1/z$ used here approaches unity as $|z|$ increases, and hence directions and lengths are only slightly changed by the transformation, at points far from the origin $z = 0$ (Secs. 75 and 76).

According to the formula for F, the stream function is, in polar coordinates,

$$\psi = A \left(r - \frac{1}{r} \right) \sin \theta.$$

The streamlines

$$A \left(r - \frac{1}{r} \right) \sin \theta = c,$$

are symmetric to the y axis and have asymptotes parallel to the x axis. Note that when $c = 0$ the streamline consists of the circle and the x axis.

EXERCISES*

1. Show that the speed of the fluid at the boundary of the cylinder in the last example above is $2A|\sin \theta|$. Note the points where this has its maximum and minimum values.

2. Write the complex potential for the flow around a cylinder $r = r_0$ when the velocity q approaches a real constant A as the point recedes from the cylinder.

3. If the flow at an infinite distance from the cylinder of unit radius is uniform in a direction making an angle α with the x axis, that is, if

$$\lim_{|z| \to \infty} q = Ae^{i\alpha},$$

find the complex potential.   *Ans.* $F = A[ze^{-i\alpha} + (e^{i\alpha}/z)]$.

4. The transformation $z = w + 1/w$ maps the circle $|w| = 1$ into the line

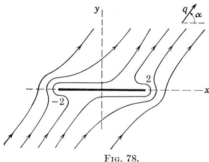

segment between the points $z = -2$ and $z = 2$, and the region outside the circle into the entire z plane. Show that it also leaves directions unchanged at points infinitely far from the origin. Using the result of Exercise 3, find the complex potential for the flow around that line segment when the velocity at infinity is $q = Ae^{i\alpha}$. This is the problem of steady flow around a long plate inserted in a large body of fluid with a uniform flow (Fig. 78).

FIG. 78.

Ans. $F(z) = A[z \cos \alpha - i(z^2 - 4)^{\frac{1}{2}} \sin \alpha]$.

5. If $\sin \alpha \neq 0$ in the flow considered in Exercise 4, show that the speed of the fluid along the line segment is infinite at the ends, and equal to $A|\cos \alpha|$ at the mid-point.

6. Obtain the stream function $\psi = Ar^4 \sin 4\theta$ for a flow in the angular region $0 \leq \theta \leq \pi/4$ (Fig. 79), and trace one or two of the streamlines inside the region.

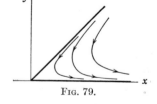

FIG. 79.

* Additional problems on fluid flow are presented in Chap. X. For further examples and problems see, for instance, L. M. Milne-Thomson, "Theoretical Hydrodynamics."

7. Obtain the complex potential $F = A \sin z$ for flow inside the semiinfinite region $-\pi/2 \leq x \leq \pi/2, y \geq 0$ (Fig. 80).   Write the equations of the streamlines.

8. Examine the flow when the complex potential is $F = A \log z$.   Show that the flow outside the circle $r = r_0$ is that due to a constant source of fluid supplied within that circle; that the rate of flow out through all circles concentric to that circle is the same.

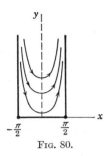
Fig. 80.

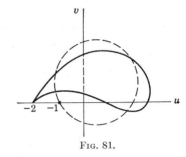
Fig. 81.

9. A circle through the point $z = -1$ enclosing the point $z = 1$ in its interior is to be mapped upon the w plane by means of the transformation $w = z + 1/z$. Individual points $z = re^{i\theta}$ can be mapped geometrically by adding the vector $(1/r)e^{-i\theta}$ to the vector z.   Show that the image of the circle is a profile of the type shown in Fig. 81.   This is an example of the *Joukowski airfoil.*

10. (a) Show that the mapping of the circle in Exercise 9 is conformal except at the point $z = -1$.

(b) The complex numbers

$$t = \lim_{\Delta z \to 0} \frac{\Delta z}{|\Delta z|}, \qquad \tau = \lim_{\Delta z \to 0} \frac{\Delta w}{|\Delta w|}$$

represent unit tangent vectors to a directed curve at $z = -1$ and its image under the transformation $w = z + 1/z$.   Show that $\tau = -t^2$ and hence that the above Joukowski profile has a cusp at the point $w = -2$, and that the angle between the tangents at the cusp is zero.

11. Indicate the method of obtaining the complex potential for the flow about the airfoil of Exercise 9 from the complex potential for the flow about a circle with center at the origin.

12. Describe the flow in the region $r \geq 1$ when the complex potential is $F_1(z) = -iB \log z$, where B is a real constant.   Show that when the complex potential is

$$F_2(z) = -iB \log z + A\left(z + \frac{1}{z}\right),$$

the flow consists of a streaming past the circle $r = 1$, combined with a circulation about the circle.

13. Note that under the transformation

$$w = e^z + z,$$

both the positive and negative parts of the line $y = \pi$ are mapped upon the half line $v = \pi$, $u \leqq -1$. Similarly $y = -\pi$ maps into $v = -\pi$, $u \leqq -1$, and the strip $-\pi \leqq y \leqq \pi$ maps into the w plane. Also note that the change of directions, arg (dw/dz), under this transformation approaches zero as $x \to -\infty$. Show

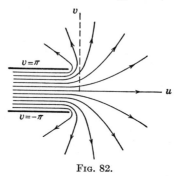

Fig. 82.

that the streamlines of a fluid flowing through the open channel formed by the half lines in the w plane (Fig. 82) are the images of the lines $y = c$ in the strip. These streamlines also represent the equipotentials of the electrostatic field near the edge of a parallel-plate condenser.

14. Determine the stream function for a flow in the region $r \geqq 1, 0 \leqq \theta \leqq \pi/2$.

CHAPTER X

THE SCHWARZ-CHRISTOFFEL TRANSFORMATION

91. The Transformation of the Real Axis into a Polygon. Let us consider first any conformal transformation $w = f(z)$. In order to examine the changes in direction along a curve S in the w plane as the point z moves along the image curve C in the z plane, it is convenient to introduce the complex variables t and τ, which represent vectors of unit length tangent to C and S at corresponding points. This was suggested earlier in Sec. 90, Exercise 10.

When the points z and $z + \Delta z$ are on C, the number Δz represents a secant vector and $\Delta z/|\Delta z|$ represents a secant vector of unit length. Thus

$$t = \lim_{\Delta z \to 0} \frac{\Delta z}{|\Delta z|};$$

similarly,

$$\tau = \lim_{\Delta w \to 0} \frac{\Delta w}{|\Delta w|}.$$

Since Δw tends to zero with Δz, we have the relation

$$f'(z) = \lim_{\Delta z \to 0} \left(\frac{\Delta w/|\Delta w|}{\Delta z/|\Delta z|} \frac{|\Delta w|}{|\Delta z|} \right) = \frac{\tau}{t} |f'(z)|;$$

that is,

$$(1) \qquad \tau = \frac{f'(z)}{|f'(z)|} t.$$

Now let C be the x axis, traversed in the positive direction. Then $t = 1$, and in view of equation (1),

$$\tau = \frac{f'(z)}{|f'(z)|};$$

hence

$$(2) \qquad \arg \tau = \arg f'(z).$$

If the image of the x axis is to be a polygon of n sides, it is therefore necessary that the argument of the derivative $f'(z)$ of the mapping function remain constant along the x axis except for abrupt changes at n points.

Let $x_1, x_2, \cdots, x_{n-1}$, and $z = \infty$ denote the values of z along the real

171

axis for which arg $f'(z)$ changes as the point z moves all the way along
that axis.   The notation is to be chosen so that

$$x_1 < x_2 < \cdots < x_{n-1}.$$

If w_n denotes the value of $f(z)$ as z tends to infinity and if $w_j = f(z_j)$
for $j = 1, 2, \cdots, n - 1$, the points $w_1, w_2, \cdots, w_n$ will be the vertices
of the polygon.

Now we can see that if $f(z)$ is chosen as a function such that

(3) $$f'(z) = A(z - x_1)^{-k_1}(z - x_2)^{-k_2} \cdots (z - x_{n-1})^{-k_{n-1}},$$

where A is a complex constant and each k_j is a real constant, the argument
of $f'(z)$ changes in the prescribed manner as z describes the real axis; for
the argument of the function (3) can be written

(4) $\arg f'(z) = \arg A - k_1 \arg (z - x_1) - k_2 \arg (z - x_2) - \cdots$
$$- k_{n-1} \arg (z - x_{n-1}).$$

When $z = x$ and $x < x_1$,

$$\arg (z - x_1) = \arg (z - x_2) = \cdots = \arg (z - x_{n-1}) = \pi,$$

provided we use arguments ranging from zero to π here.   When

$$x_1 < x < x_2,$$

the first of the above arguments is zero and each of the others is π.
According to equation (4) then, arg $f'(z)$ increases by the angle $k_1\pi$ as z
moves to the right through the point $z = x_1$.   It again increases, by
the angle $k_2\pi$, as z passes through the point $z = x_2$, etc.

Since arg $\tau = $ arg $f'(z)$, it follows that τ is constant as z moves along
any segment of the x axis between two of the points x_j; that is, the path
of the point w is a straight line.   But the direction of τ changes abruptly
at each of the points w_j corresponding to $z = z_j$; in fact, arg τ increases
by the angle $k_j\pi$ at those points (Fig. 83).

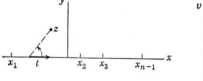 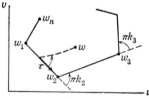

FIG. 83.

Under such a transformation $w = f(z)$, the image of the x axis is
therefore a polygon with exterior angles $k_j\pi$ at the vertices $w_j(j = 1,$
$2, \cdots, n - 1)$, provided we interpret the word **polygon** to mean a

figure consisting of segments of straight lines, whether or not they cross each other. The numbers k_j can be restricted to the range $-1 < k_j < 1$, since the exterior angles can be limited to angles between π and $-\pi$. It is then possible to show that $f(z)$, the integral of the right-hand member of equation (3), exists at $z = z_j$ and is continuous there in the region $y \geqq 0$. The vertices w_j then exist and actually connect the line segments.

The sum of the exterior angles of every closed polygon is 2π. Hence the exterior angle at the vertex w_n, which is the image of the point $z = \infty$, is given by the formula

(5) $$k_n\pi = 2\pi - (k_1 + k_2 + \cdots + k_{n-1})\pi.$$

In case

(6) $$k_1 + k_2 + \cdots + k_{n-1} = 2,$$

then $k_n = 0$; the last side and the first side of the polygon then have the same direction, and w_n is not a vertex but a point on the first side. In this case, the polygon has $n - 1$ sides.

92. The Schwarz-Christoffel Transformation. The derivative of a function $w = f(z)$ that maps the x axis into a polygon in the w plane is given by equation (3) of the preceding section. The function itself is therefore

(1) $$w = A\int(z - x_1)^{-k_1}(z - x_2)^{-k_2} \cdots (z - x_{n-1})^{-k_{n-1}}\, dz + B,$$

where the integral sign denotes any one of the indefinite integrals of the integrand and A and B are arbitrary constants. The transformation (1) is named in honor of the two German mathematicians H. S. Schwarz (1843–1921) and E. B. Christoffel (1829–1900), who discovered it independently.

Consider the region $y \geqq 0$. If the arguments of $z - x_j$ are chosen as angles between zero and π, the integrand in formula (1), and hence w itself, is a single-valued function of z in that upper half plane. The derivative of w exists and is different from zero except at the points $z = x_j$, and hence the transformation is conformal in the half plane $y \geqq 0$ except at those points. Interior points of the half plane lie on the left-hand side of the vector t along the boundary; that is, if z is an interior point and x_0 is any point on the boundary, where $x_0 \neq x_j$, then the angle from the vector t to the vector $z - x_0$ is positive and less than π (Fig. 83). The angle between the image of the vector $z - x_0$ and τ has the same value. Thus the image of the half plane is a region lying to the left of the vectors τ on the boundary of the polygon. If all k_j's are positive, that is, if the polygon is convex, the image of the half plane

$y > 0$ is interior to the polygon. A little further argument based on the continuity of the function w would show that the image of the half plane must consist of all points interior to the polygon if each $k_j > 0$.

If a transformation of a given polygon in the w plane into the upper half of the z plane can be made by means of one function $w = f(z)$, it can be made by many functions. For it can be shown from our discussion of the linear fractional transformation (Sec. 37), that there is an infinite number of ways of mapping the half plane into itself. Consequently, we can anticipate some freedom in the choice of the constants appearing in the Schwarz-Christoffel transformation, if that transformation is to map a prescribed polygon into the half plane.

Let us investigate the number of constants that must be determined in order to transform a prescribed polygon. Let n denote the number of sides and $k_j\pi(j = 1,2, \cdots ,n)$, the exterior angles of this polygon. The sum of the numbers k_j is 2. The exponents in formula (1) are now prescribed, while the $n - 1$ real constants x_j and the two complex constants A and B are as yet undetermined.

Our transformation (1) is the result of the successive transformations

$$(2) \qquad W = \int(z - x_1)^{-k_1}(z - x_2)^{-k_2} \cdots (z - x_{n-1})^{-k_{n-1}} \, dz$$

$$(3) \qquad\qquad\qquad w = AW + B.$$

The transformation (3) represents an arbitrary rotation, expansion or contraction, and translation.

The numbers k_j in the transformation (2) have been selected so that the image of the x axis is a polygon having the same angles as the prescribed one. That polygon will be similar to the prescribed polygon if $n - 2$ of its sides have a common ratio to the corresponding sides of the prescribed one, a condition that is expressed by means of $n - 3$ equations in the $n - 1$ real constants x_j. Thus *two of the numbers x_j, or two relations between them, can be chosen arbitrarily,* provided of course that those $n - 3$ simultaneous equations in the remaining $n - 3$ constants have real solutions.

The complex constants A and B in equation (3) can be determined in just one way so as to transform the similar polygon in the W plane into the prescribed polygon in the w plane, since a definite expansion or contraction, and a definite rotation and translation are needed to make the polygons coincide.

It follows from the preceding section that when a finite point $z = x_n$, instead of the infinite point, represents the image of the vertex w_n, the Schwarz-Christoffel transformation can be written in the form

$$(4) \qquad w = A\int(z - x_1)^{-k_1}(z - x_2)^{-k_2} \cdots (z - x_n)^{-k_n} \, dz + B,$$

where $k_1 + k_2 + \cdots + k_n = 2$. The exponents k_j are determined from the exterior angles of the given polygon. But in this case there are n real constants x_j, which must satisfy the $n - 3$ equations noted above. Thus in the transformation (4) *three of the numbers x_j, or three relations between them, can be chosen arbitrarily,* in the transformation of a given polygon into the x axis.

Here again the result is sound provided the $n - 3$ simultaneous equations have real solutions. We cannot investigate this matter here, but in particular applications we can verify that the transformation that is obtained actually maps the given polygon into the x axis.

93. Triangles and Rectangles. The Schwarz-Christoffel transformation is written in terms of the images x_j of the vertices of the polygon, not in terms of the vertices themselves. Not more than three of those images can be chosen arbitrarily, so that when the given polygon has more than three sides, some of the images must be determined in order to make the given polygon, or any polygon congruent to it, map into the real axis. The selection of conditions for the determination of those constants, conditions that are convenient to use, often requires ingenuity.

A more serious limitation in using the transformation, however, arises because of the integration that is involved. In most cases, the integral cannot be evaluated in terms of a finite number of elementary functions. In such cases, the transformation may still be highly useful, but the solution of problems by means of it can become quite involved.

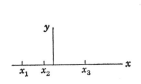

Fig. 84.

If the polygon is a triangle with vertices at the points w_1, w_2, and w_3 (Fig. 84), the transformation can be written

(1) $$w = A \int (z - x_1)^{-k_1}(z - x_2)^{-k_2}(z - x_3)^{-k_3} \, dz + B,$$

where $k_1 + k_2 + k_3 = 2$. In terms of the interior angles θ_j,

$$k_j = 1 - \frac{1}{\pi} \theta_j \qquad\qquad (j = 1,2,3).$$

Here we have taken all three images x_j as finite points on the x axis. Arbitrary values can be assigned to each of the three constants x_j. The complex constants A and B, associated with the size and position of the triangle, can be determined so that the given triangular region maps into the upper half plane.

If we take the image of the vertex w_3 as the infinite point, the transformation of the triangle becomes

$$(2) \qquad w = A \int (z - x_1)^{-k_1}(z - x_2)^{-k_2}\, dz + B,$$

where arbitrary real values can be assigned to x_1 and x_2.

The integrals in equations (1) and (2) do not represent elementary functions unless the triangle is degenerate, that is, unless one or two of its vertices are at infinity. The integral in equation (2) becomes an elliptic integral when the triangle is equilateral and when it is a right triangle with one of its angles equal to either $\pi/3$ or $\pi/4$. In these cases z is an elliptic function of w, but for other nondegenerate triangles the process of solving for z as a function of w involves further complications.*

When the polygon is a rectangle, $k_j = \tfrac{1}{2}$, and the transformation becomes

$$w = A \int [(z - x_1)(z - x_2)(z - x_3)(z - x_4)]^{-\frac{1}{2}}\, dz + B.$$

If we choose the points ± 1, $\pm 1/k$ as the images x_j of the four vertices, we can write this transformation in terms of an elliptic integral, as follows:

$$w = A' \int_0^z \frac{dz'}{\sqrt{(1 - z'^2)(1 - k^2 z'^2)}} + B.$$

Here the real constant k and the complex constants A' and B can be determined so that the given rectangle maps into the x axis.

94. Degenerate Polygons. We shall now apply the Schwarz-Christoffel transformation to some degenerate polygons for which the integrals represent elementary functions. For the purpose of illustration we can begin with some known transformations.

As our first example, let us map the semiinfinite strip

$$-\frac{\pi}{2} \leq u \leq \frac{\pi}{2}, \qquad v \geq 0$$

into the half plane $y \geq 0$. We consider this strip as the limiting form of a triangle with vertices w_1, w_2, and w_3 (Fig. 85) as the imaginary part of w_3 tends to infinity.

The limiting values of the exterior angles are

$$\pi k_1 = \pi k_2 = \frac{\pi}{2}, \qquad \pi k_3 = \pi.$$

---

* For proofs and further discussions of the functions involved when the polygon is nondegenerate, see A. R. Forsyth, "Theory of Functions of a Complex Variable," pp. 543 ff. and E. T. Copson, "Theory of Functions of a Complex Variable," pp. 198 ff.

We choose the images of the vertices as $x_1 = -1$, $x_2 = 1$, and, for w_3, $z = \infty$. Then the transformation becomes

$$w = A \int (z+1)^{-\frac{1}{2}}(z-1)^{-\frac{1}{2}} dz + B$$

$$= iA \int_0^z \frac{dz'}{\sqrt{1-z'^2}} + B,$$

$$w = iA \sin^{-1} z + B.$$

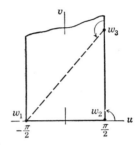
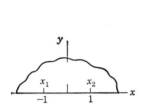

FIG. 85.

Since $w = -\pi/2$ when $z = -1$, and $w = \pi/2$ when $z = 1$, the constants A and B must satisfy the two conditions

$$-\frac{\pi}{2} = -iA \frac{\pi}{2} + B, \qquad \frac{\pi}{2} = iA \frac{\pi}{2} + B.$$

Consequently, $B = 0$ and $iA = 1$. Thus $w = \sin^{-1} z$, or

$$z = \sin w.$$

In Sec. 41 we showed that this transformation does map the strip into the half plane.

95. The Infinite Strip. Consider the strip $0 < v < \pi$ as the limiting form of a rhombus with vertices at w_1, $w_2 = 0$, w_3, $w_4 = \pi i$, as the points

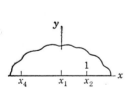
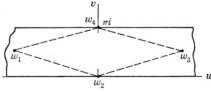

FIG. 86.

w_3 and w_1 are moved infinitely far to the right and left, respectively (Fig. 86). In the limit the exterior angles become

$$\pi k_1 = \pi, \qquad \pi k_2 = 0, \qquad \pi k_3 = \pi, \qquad \pi k_4 = 0.$$

Leave x_4 to be determined and take $x_1 = 0$, $x_2 = 1$, and $x_3 = \infty$; then the Schwarz-Christoffel transformation becomes

$$w = A \int z^{-1} (z - 1)^0 (z - x_4)^0 \, dz + B$$

$$= A \int \frac{dz}{z} + B = A \operatorname{Log} z + B.$$

Since $z = 1$ when $w = 0$, it follows that $B = 0$; thus

$$w = A \operatorname{Log} z.$$

The constant A must be real because the point w lies on the real axis when $z = x$ and $x > 0$. The image of the point $w = \pi i$ is $z = x_4$, where x_4 is a negative number; therefore

$$\pi i = A \operatorname{Log} x_4 = A \operatorname{Log} |x_4| + A\pi i.$$

By equating real and imaginary coefficients here, we see that $|x_4| = 1$ and $A = 1$. Hence the transformation becomes

$$w = \operatorname{Log} z;$$

also $x_4 = -1$. We have shown earlier (Sec. 40) that this transformation does map the strip into the half plane.

The method used here and in the preceding section is not a rigorous one since the limiting values of angles and coordinates were not introduced in an orderly way; in fact the limiting values were introduced wherever it seemed convenient to use them. But as long as we verify the mapping obtained, it is not essential that the steps in the derivation of the mapping function be justified. The formal method used here is shorter and less tedious than rigorous methods.

96. Fluid Flow in a Channel through a Slit. Let us present a further example of the idealized steady flow treated in Chap. IX, an example that will help to show how sources and sinks can be accounted for in problems of the flow of a fluid.

Consider the two-dimensional steady flow of fluid between two parallel

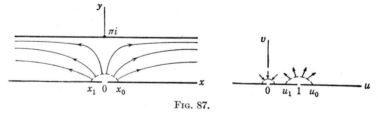

Fig. 87.

planes $y = 0$ and $y = \pi$, when the fluid is entering through a narrow slit along the line $x = 0$ in the first plane (Fig. 87). Let the rate of flow of fluid into the channel through the slit be Q units of volume per unit time for each unit of depth of the channel, where the depth is measured perpendicular to the xy plane.   Then the rate of flow out at either end is $\frac{1}{2}Q$.

We transform the strip into the upper half of the w plane by means of the transformation $z = \mathrm{Log}\ w$, derived in the preceding section; then

(1) $$w = e^z = e^x e^{iy}.$$

The image of the x axis is the positive half of the u axis, and the image of the line $y = \pi$ is the negative half of the u axis.   Thus the boundary of the cross section of the channel transforms into the boundary of the half plane.

The image of the point $z = 0$ is the point $w = 1$.   The image of a point $z = x_0$ such that $x_0 > 0$ is a point $w = u_0$ where $u_0 > 1$.   The rate of flow of fluid across a curve joining the point $z = x_0$ to a point (x,y) within the strip is a stream function $\psi(x,y)$ for the flow (Sec. 88).   If x_1 is a negative real number, then the rate of flow into the channel through the slit can be written

$$\psi(x_1,0) = Q.$$

Now under a conformal transformation, the function ψ is a function of u and v that represents the stream function for the flow in the region in the w plane; that is, the rate of flow is the same across corresponding curves in the two planes.   Since the image of the point $z = x_1$ is a point $w = u_1$ where $0 < u_1 < 1$, the rate of flow across any curve connecting the points $w = u_0$ and $w = u_1$ and lying in the upper half of the w plane is also equal to Q.   Thus there is a source at the point $w = 1$ equal to the source at $z = 0$.

The above argument applies in general to show that, *under a conformal transformation, a source or sink at a given point corresponds to an equal source or sink at the image of that point.*

As $x \to -\infty$, the image of the point z approaches the point $w = 0$. A sink of strength $\frac{1}{2}Q$ at the latter point corresponds to the sink infinitely far to the left in the strip.   To apply the above argument in this case, we consider the rate of flow across a curve connecting the boundaries $y = 0$ and $y = \pi$ of the left-hand part of the strip and the flow across the image of that curve in the w plane.

The sink at the right-hand end of the strip transforms into a sink at infinity in the w plane.

The stream function ψ for the flow in upper half of the w plane in this case must be a function that has a constant value along each of the three parts of the u axis.   Moreover its value must increase by Q when the point w moves around the point $w = 1$ from the position $w = u_0$ to the position $w = u_1$, and its value must decrease by $\frac{1}{2}Q$ when w moves about the origin in the corresponding manner. In terms of the polar coordinate angles θ_1 and θ_2 ranging from zero to π, where

$$w = r_1 \exp \theta_1, \qquad w - 1 = r_2 \exp \theta_2,$$

we see that the function

$$\psi = \frac{Q}{\pi}\left(\theta_2 - \frac{1}{2}\,\theta_1\right)$$

satisfies those requirements. Furthermore, this function is harmonic because it is the imaginary coefficient of the function

$$F = \frac{Q}{\pi}\left[\text{Log }(w - 1) - \frac{1}{2}\text{Log }w\right]$$

$$= \frac{Q}{\pi}\text{Log }(w^{\frac{1}{2}} - w^{-\frac{1}{2}}).$$

The function F is a complex potential for the flow in the w plane. Since $w = \exp z$, a complex potential for the flow in the channel is

$$F(z) = \frac{Q}{\pi}\text{Log }(e^{z/2} - e^{-z/2}).$$

By dropping an additive constant, the potential can be written

$$(2) \qquad\qquad F(z) = \frac{Q}{\pi}\text{Log sinh }\frac{z}{2}.$$

The velocity vector $\overline{F'(z)}$ is given by the formula

$$(3) \qquad\qquad q = \frac{Q}{2\pi}\text{coth }\frac{\bar{z}}{2}.$$

From this formula it can be seen that

$$\lim_{|x|\to\infty} q = \frac{Q}{2\pi}.$$

Also, the point $z = \pi i$ is a *stagnation point;* that is, the velocity is zero there. It can be shown that the fluid pressure at points along a stream-line increases as the magnitude of the velocity decreases.[*] Since the line $y = \pi$ is a streamline, it follows that the pressure along the upper wall of the channel is greatest at points opposite the slit.

The stream function $\psi(x,y)$ for the channel is the imaginary coef-

[*] Lamb, H., "Hydrodynamics," p. 21; Milne-Thomson, L. M., "Theoretical Hydrodynamics," p. 9.

ficient of the function $F(z)$ given by equation (2). The streamlines $\psi(x.y) = c$ are therefore curves

$$\frac{Q}{2\pi} \arg\left(\sinh\frac{z}{2}\right) = c,$$

an equation that reduces to

(4) $$\tan\frac{y}{2} = k \tanh\frac{x}{2},$$

where k is any real constant.   Some of these streamlines are indicated in Fig. 87.

97. Flow in a Channel with an Offset.   As a further example of the use of the Schwarz-Christoffel transformation, let us find the complex potential for the flow of a fluid in a channel with an abrupt change in its breadth (Fig. 88).   We take our unit of length such that the breadth of

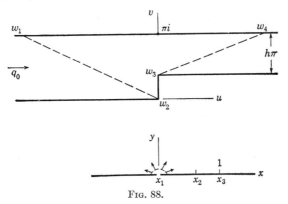

Fig. 88.

the wide part of the channel is π units; then $h\pi$ represents the breadth of the narrow part, where $0 < h < 1$.   Let the real constant q_0 denote the velocity of the fluid far from the offset in the wide part; more precisely, in Fig. 88,

$$\lim_{u \to -\infty} q = q_0,$$

where the complex variable q represents the velocity vector.   The rate of flow per unit depth through the channel, or the strength of the source on the left and of the sink on the right, is then

(1) $$Q = \pi q_0.$$

The cross section of the channel can be considered as the limiting case of the rectangle with the vertices w_1, w_2, w_3, and w_4 shown in the figure, as the first and last of these vertices are moved infinitely far to the left and to the right, respectively.   In the limit the exterior angles become

$$\pi k_1 = \pi, \qquad \pi k_2 = \frac{\pi}{2}, \qquad \pi k_3 = -\frac{\pi}{2}, \qquad \pi k_4 = \pi.$$

We take $x_1 = 0$, $x_3 = 1$, $x_4 = \infty$ and leave $x_2 (0 < x_2 < 1)$ to be determined.   Then the Schwarz-Christoffel transformation can be written

(2) $$\frac{dw}{dz} = Az^{-1}(z - x_2)^{-\frac{1}{2}}(z - 1)^{\frac{1}{2}}.$$

In order to simplify the determination of the constants A and x_2 here, let us proceed at once to the use of the complex potential of the flow. The source of the flow in the channel infinitely far to the left is transformed into an equal source at $z = 0$ (Sec. 96).   The entire boundary of the cross section of the channel has the x axis as its image.   In view of equation (1) then, the complex potential for the flow in the channel is transformed into the function

(3) $$F = q_0 \text{ Log } z = q_0 \text{ Log } r + iq_0\theta,$$

since this is the potential for the flow in the upper half of the z plane with the required source at the origin.   Note that the sink on the right of the channel must transform into a sink at infinity in the z plane.

The complex conjugate of the velocity q in the w plane can be written

$$\overline{q(w)} = \frac{dF}{dw} = \frac{dF}{dz}\frac{dz}{dw}.$$

Thus by referring to equations (2) and (3), we can write

(4) $$\overline{q(w)} = \frac{q_0}{A}\left(\frac{z - x_2}{z - 1}\right)^{\frac{1}{2}}.$$

At the limiting position of the point w_1, which corresponds to $z = 0$, the velocity is the real constant q_0.   Consequently, it follows from equation (4) that

$$q_0 = \frac{q_0}{A}\sqrt{x_2}.$$

At the limiting position of w_4, which corresponds to $z = \infty$, let the real number q_4 denote the velocity.   Now it seems plausible that q approaches q_4, at all points of a vertical line segment that spans the narrow part of the channel, as the segment is moved infinitely far to the right.   We could establish this conjecture as a fact by first finding w as a function of z from equation (2); but to shorten our discussion, we assume that this conjecture is true here.   Then since the flow is steady,

$$\pi h q_4 = \pi q_0 = Q,$$

or $q_4 = q_0/h$. Letting z tend to infinity in equation (4), we therefore find that

$$\frac{q_0}{h} = \frac{q_0}{A}.$$

Thus

(5) $$A = h, \qquad x_2 = h^2,$$

and

(6) $$\overline{q(w)} = \frac{q_0}{h}\left(\frac{z - h^2}{z - 1}\right)^{\frac{1}{2}}.$$

From equation (6) we can see that the magnitude $|q|$ of the velocity becomes infinite at the corner w_3 of the offset, since the image of that point is the point $z = 1$.   Also, the corner w_2 is a stagnation point, a point where $q = 0$.   Along the boundary of the channel, the fluid pressure is therefore greatest at w_2 and least at w_3 (Sec. 96).

In order to write the relation between the potential and the variable w, we must integrate equation (2), which can now be written

(7) $$\frac{dw}{dz} = \frac{h}{z}\left(\frac{z - 1}{z - h^2}\right)^{\frac{1}{2}}.$$

By substituting a new variable s here, where

$$\frac{z - h^2}{z - 1} = s^2,$$

it can be shown that equation (7) reduces to the equation

$$\frac{dw}{ds} = 2h\left(\frac{1}{1 - s^2} - \frac{1}{h^2 - s^2}\right).$$

Therefore

(8) $$w = h \, \mathrm{Log}\, \frac{1 + s}{1 - s} - \mathrm{Log}\, \frac{h + s}{h - s},$$

where the constant of integration is zero because when $z = h^2$, that is, when $s = 0$, $w = 0$.

In terms of s the potential (3) becomes

$$F = q_0 \, \mathrm{Log}\, \frac{h^2 - s^2}{1 - s^2};$$

consequently,

$$(9) \qquad s^2 = \frac{\exp \ (F/q_0) - h^2}{\exp \ (F/q_0) - 1}.$$

By substituting s from this equation into equation (8), we get an implicit relation between the potential $F(w)$ and w.

For a more satisfying treatment of the above problem, but one that would not be so brief, we could start with a prescribed source Q at the left-hand end of the channel, and, of course, an equal sink at the other end, and then from the potential $F(w)$ so obtained, deduce the values of the velocity q at infinite points.

98. Electrostatic Potential about an Edge of a Conducting Plate. Two parallel conducting plates of infinite extent are kept at the electro-

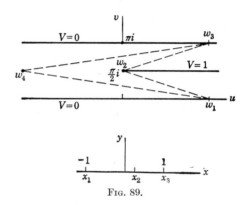

Fig. 89.

static potential $V = 0$, and a parallel semiinfinite plate, placed midway between them, is kept at the potential $V = 1$. The coordinate system and the unit of length are chosen so that the plates lie in the planes $v = 0$, $v = \pi$, and $v = \pi/2$ (Fig. 89). Let us determine the potential function $V(x,y)$ in the region between those plates.

The region has the limiting form of the quadrilateral bounded by the broken lines in the figure, as the points w_1 and w_3 move out to the right and w_4 to the left. In applying the Schwarz-Christoffel transformation here, we let the image x_4 of the vertex w_4 be infinity. We choose the images $x_1 = -1$, $x_3 = 1$ and leave x_2 to be determined. As before we proceed formally, using limiting values whenever it is convenient to do so. The final result can be verified as the required transformation.

The limiting values of the exterior angles of the quadrilateral are

$$\pi k_1 = \pi, \qquad \pi k_2 = -\pi, \qquad \pi k_3 = \pi k_4 = \pi.$$

Thus

$$\frac{dw}{dz} = A(z + 1)^{-1}(z - x_2)(z - 1)^{-1}$$

$$= A\frac{z - x_2}{z^2 - 1} = \frac{A}{2}\left(\frac{1 + x_2}{z + 1} + \frac{1 - x_2}{z - 1}\right),$$

so that the transformation of the divided strip in the w plane into the upper half of the z plane has the form

$$(1) \qquad w = \frac{A}{2}\left[(1 + x_2)\,\mathrm{Log}\,(z + 1) + (1 - x_2)\,\mathrm{Log}\,(z - 1)\right] + B.$$

Let A_1 A_2 and B_1, B_2 denote the real and imaginary components of the constants A and B. When $z = x$, the point w lies on the boundary of the divided strip, and according to equation (1),

$$(2) \quad u + iv = \tfrac{1}{2}(A_1 + iA_2)\{(1 + x_2)[\mathrm{Log}\,|x + 1| + i\,\arg\,(x + 1)] \\ + (1 - x_2)[\mathrm{Log}\,|x - 1| + i\,\arg\,(x - 1)]\} + B_1 + iB_2.$$

In order to determine the constants here, we first note that the limiting position of the line joining the points w_1 and w_4 is the u axis. The image of that line is the part of the x axis to the left of the point $x_1 = -1$, because the part $x > 1$ is the image of the line joining w_3 and w_4, and the remaining two segments of the x axis are the images of the other two sides of the quadrilateral. Hence when $v = 0$ and u tends to infinity through positive values, the image point x approaches the point $z = -1$ from the left; thus

$$\arg\,(x + 1) = \pi, \qquad \arg\,(x - 1) = \pi, \qquad \mathrm{Log}\,|x + 1| \to -\infty,$$

and since $-1 < x_2 < 1$, the real part of the quantity inside the braces in equation (2) tends to negative infinity. Since $v = 0$, it follows that $A_2 = 0$, otherwise the coefficient of the imaginary part on the right would become infinite. By equating imaginary coefficients on the two sides, we now see that

$$0 = \tfrac{1}{2}A_1[(1 + x_2)\pi + (1 - x_2)\pi] + B_2.$$

Hence

$$(3) \qquad\qquad -\pi A_1 = B_2, \qquad A_2 = 0.$$

The limiting position of the line joining the points w_1 and w_2 is the half line $v = \pi/2$, $u \geqq 0$. The images of points on that half line are the points $z = x$, where $-1 < x \leqq x_2$, and therefore

$$\arg\,(x + 1) = 0, \qquad \arg\,(x - 1) = \pi.$$

Identifying the imaginary parts of the two members of equation (2) for those points, we see that

$$(4) \qquad \frac{\pi}{2} = \frac{A_1}{2}(1 - x_2)\pi + B_2.$$

Finally, the limiting positions of points on the line joining w_3 to w_4 are the points $u + \pi i$, and their images are the points x where $x > 1$. By identifying the imaginary parts in equation (2) for those points, we find that

$$\pi = B_2.$$

Then in view of equations (3) and (4),

$$A_1 = -1, \qquad x_2 = 0.$$

Thus $x = 0$ when $w = \pi i/2$, and upon substituting these values into equation (2) and identifying real parts, we see that $B_1 = 0$.

The transformation (1) now becomes

$$(5) \qquad w = -\tfrac{1}{2}\operatorname{Log}(z^2 - 1) + \pi i,$$

or

$$(6) \qquad z^2 = 1 + e^{-2w}.$$

Under this transformation, the required harmonic function $V(u,v)$ becomes a harmonic function of x and y in the region $y > 0$, which satisfies the boundary conditions indicated in Fig. 90. Note that $x_2 = 0$ now. The harmonic function in that half plane that assumes those values on the boundary is the imaginary coefficient of the analytic function

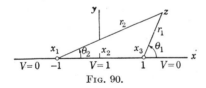

Fig. 90.

$$F(z) = \frac{1}{\pi}\operatorname{Log}\frac{z-1}{z+1} = \frac{1}{\pi}\operatorname{Log}\frac{r_1}{r_2} + \frac{i}{\pi}(\theta_1 - \theta_2),$$

where θ_1 and θ_2 range from zero to π. Writing the tangents of these angles as functions of x and y and simplifying, we find that the function V satisfies the equation

$$(7) \qquad \tan \pi V = \tan(\theta_1 - \theta_2) = \frac{2y}{x^2 + y^2 - 1}.$$

According to equation (6),

$$x^2 - y^2 = 1 + e^{-2u}\cos 2v, \qquad 2xy = -e^{-2u}\sin 2v.$$

By eliminating y and $x^2 + y^2$ between these equations and equation (7), we find that the relation between the potential V and the coordinates u and v can be written

(8)
$$\tan \pi V = \frac{1}{s} \sqrt{e^{-4u} - s^2},$$

where

$$s = -1 + \sqrt{1 + 2e^{-2u} \cos 2v + e^{-4u}}$$

EXERCISES

1. Use the Schwarz-Christoffel transformation to arrive at the transformation $w = z^m$, which maps the angular region $0 \leqq \arg w \leqq m\pi$ into the half plane $y \geqq 0$ and the point $w = 1$ into the point $z = 1$. Consider the angular region as the limiting case of the triangle shown in Fig. 91 as the angle α tends to zero.

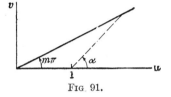

FIG. 91.

2. Give a formal derivation of the transformation presented in Fig. 22, Appendix II, using the Schwarz-Christoffel transformation.

3. Refer to Fig. 26, Appendix II. In traversing the boundary of the region in the w plane, a point w moves through A' and B', then through C' to D', and from D' through E'. This path might be considered as a degenerate triangle; at least the point is moving in the same direction on the right of E' as it is on the left of A', and the infinite ends of those parts of the path might be considered as a single point on the same side of the triangle. Proceed formally with the Schwarz-Christoffel transformation to obtain the mapping function given with the figure. Verify the formula as one that does produce the indicated mapping.

4. Derive the mapping function presented with Fig. 29, Appendix II, for the mapping shown there.

5. Complete the derivation of equation (4), Sec. 96.

6. Let $T(u,v)$ denote the steady temperatures in the strip with an offset, shown in Fig. 88, when $T(u,\pi) = 1$, and $T = 0$ on the rest of the boundary. Derive a formula that gives T implicitly as a function of u and v.

FIG. 92.

7. Show how the solution of the problem of flow in a channel with a semiinfinite rectangular obstruction (Fig. 92) is included in the solution of the problem treated in Sec. 97.

8. Derive formulas that give the complex potential $F(w)$ for the flow of fluid over a step in the bed of a deep stream indicated in Fig. 29, Appendix II.*

* Milne-Thomson, *op. cit.*, p. 266. The reader will find further examples of the use of the Schwarz-Christoffel transformation in several other books listed in Appendix I; for example, in the books by Green, Bateman, and Rothe, Ollendorff, and Pohlhausen.

CHAPTER XI

ANALYTIC CONTINUATION

The theory of analytic functions that was presented in several of the foregoing chapters was intended to be brief but self-contained. In following such a program many topics must be omitted, as long as their omission does not interfere with the continuity of the presentation. Some of those topics are of such general interest that they may well be included in an introductory course. We present several of them in these final chapters.

99. Analytic Continuation. For some given region R, suppose that a function $f(z)$ exists that is analytic throughout R and vanishes at every point on some arc within R. It will then follow that $f(z) = 0$ throughout the region.

Let A_0 denote the arc on which $f(z) = 0$. Then $f'(z) = 0$ on A_0, because $f(z)$ is analytic in R, and thus the value of the derivative $f'(z)$ is independent of the manner in which Δz tends to zero. When the point $z + \Delta z$, as well as z, is kept on A_0, the derivative is clearly zero. Since the function $f'(z) = 0$ at all points on A_0 and that function is analytic in R, its derivative $f''(z) = 0$ on A_0, etc. Thus if z_0 denotes some point on A_0, then

$$f(z_0) = 0, \qquad f^{(n)}(z_0) = 0 \qquad (n = 1,2,\ \cdot\ \cdot\ \cdot),$$

and it follows from the expansion of $f(z)$ by Taylor's series about the point z_0 that $f(z) = 0$ at all points interior to any circle having its center at z_0 and lying within the region R.

Now consider any other point Z in R. Let C denote a curve connecting z_0 and Z and lying interior to R (Fig. 93), and let d_0 denote the shortest distance between C and the boundary of R. Then $f(z) = 0$ at all points within the circle C_0 with center at z_0 and radius d_0.

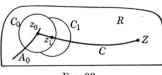

Fig. 93.

Let z_1 be a point on C between z_0 and Z but inside the circle C_0, and let C_1 be the circle with center at z_1 and radius d_0. Since

$$f(z_1) = 0 \qquad \text{and} \qquad f^{(n)}(z_1) = 0 \qquad (n = 1,2,\ \cdot\ \cdot\ \cdot),$$

it follows from the expansion of $f(z)$ by Taylor's series in powers of $z - z_1$ that $f(z) = 0$ everywhere inside C_1. The curve C can be covered in this way by a finite sequence of circles C_0, C_1, C_2, $\cdots$, C_m, each with the radius d_0; consequently $f(Z) = 0$.

Our result leads easily to the following theorem:

Theorem. *If a function is single-valued and analytic throughout a region, it is uniquely determined by its values over an arc, or throughout a subregion, within the given region.*

If two functions $f_1(z)$ and $f_2(z)$ were analytic throughout the given region R and assumed the same values on the given arc A_0, then their difference would be an analytic function in R that vanishes on A_0, and therefore

$$f_1(z) - f_2(z) = 0$$

throughout R.. That is, the two functions are identical in R.

In order to see an important consequence of the above theorem, suppose that $f_1(z)$ is a function that is analytic throughout a closed region R_1, and let R_2 be an adjoining closed region; let C denote the arc that is common to the boundaries of R_1 and R_2 (Fig. 94). A function $f_2(z)$ may exist that is analytic throughout R_2 and equal to $f_1(z)$ along C. The two functions could then be used to define a function $F(z)$

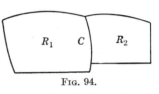

Fig. 94.

$$F(z) = f_1(z) \qquad \text{when } z \text{ is in } R_1,$$
$$= f_2(z) \qquad \text{when } z \text{ is in } R_2,$$

that is analytic in the larger region consisting of R_1 and R_2 together.

The function $f_2(z)$ is then called the *analytic continuation* of $f_1(z)$ into the region R_2. The functions $f_1(z)$ and $f_2(z)$ are called *elements* of the function $F(z)$. According to the above theorem, if an analytic continuation $f_2(z)$ of the function $f_1(z)$ across C into R_2 is possible, then it is unique, because the function $F(z)$ is uniquely determined by the values of $f_1(z)$.

100. Examples. Consider first the function $f_1(z)$ defined by the equation

(1)
$$f_1(z) = \sum_{n=0}^{\infty} z^n.$$

The power series here converges if and only if $|z| < 1$. It is the Maclaurin series expansion of the function $(1 - z)^{-1}$; thus

$$f_1(z) = \frac{1}{1 - z} \qquad \text{when } |z| < 1,$$

but $f_1(z)$ is not defined when $|z| \geq 1$.   Now the function

$$(2) \qquad\qquad F(z) = \frac{1}{1-z} \qquad\qquad (z \neq 1),$$

is defined and analytic everywhere except at the point $z = 1$.   Since it is identical to $f_1(z)$ in the interior of the circle $|z| = 1$, it represents the analytic continuation of $f_1(z)$ outside that region whenever $|z| \geq 1$ and $z \neq 1$.   This is the only possible analytic continuation of $f_1(z)$ beyond the unit circle, according to the results established in the preceding section. In this case $f_1(z)$ is an element of the function $F(z)$ defined by equation (2).

It is of interest to note that if we begin with the information that the power series

$$\sum_{n=0}^{\infty} z^n$$

converges and represents an analytic function of z when $|z| < 1$ and that its sum is $(1 - x)^{-1}$ when $z = x$, then we can conclude that its sum is $(1 - z)^{-1}$ whenever $|z| < 1$, because the function $(1 - z)^{-1}$ is the analytic function interior to the circle that assumes the values $(1 - x)^{-1}$ along the segment of the x axis inside the circle.

As another illustration of analytic continuation, consider the function

$$(3) \qquad\qquad g_1(z) = \int_0^{\infty} e^{-zt}\, dt.$$

Here the variable of integration, t, is real, whereas the parameter z is complex, and the integral can be described in terms of real integrals by writing

$$g_1(z) = \int_0^{\infty} e^{-xt} \cos yt\, dt - i \int_0^{\infty} e^{-xt} \sin yt\, dt.$$

As we would expect, the evaluation of these real integrals leads to the result we get by a formal evaluation of the integral (3), namely,

$$(4) \qquad\qquad g_1(z) = -\frac{1}{z} e^{-zt} \Big]_0^{\infty} = \frac{1}{z} \qquad\qquad \text{when } x > 0.$$

Thus $g_1(z)$ is defined in the half plane $x > 0$.

Now the function

$$G(z) = \frac{1}{z} \qquad\qquad (z \neq 0)$$

is analytic everywhere except at $z = 0$ and equal to $g_1(z)$ in the right half plane.   Thus the function

$$g_2(z) = \frac{1}{z} \qquad\qquad (x \leq 0,\ z \neq 0)$$

is the analytic continuation of $g_1(z)$ into the region on the left of that half plane. The functions $g_1(z)$ and $g_2(z)$ are elements of the function $G(z)$.

A further observation about analytic continuation can be made by means of the following example. The function

$$h_1(z) = z^{\frac{1}{2}} = \sqrt{r}\, e^{i\theta/2} \qquad (r > 0, 0 < \theta < 2\pi)$$

is single-valued and analytic throughout the z plane except at the origin and at points on the positive x axis. This function can be continued across the positive x axis, from the lower half plane, for instance, for the function

$$h_2(z) = \sqrt{r}\, e^{i\theta/2} \qquad (r > 0, \pi < \theta < 3\pi)$$

is single-valued and analytic except at the origin and along the negative x axis. At each point in the lower half plane $(\pi < \theta < 2\pi)$, $h_2(z) = h_1(z)$. Consequently, $h_2(z)$ is the desired analytic continuation of $h_1(z)$. Both functions are analytic in the half plane $y > 0$, but their values are not the same there. In fact, since $2\pi < \theta < 3\pi$ there in the definition of $h_2(z)$, we see that

$$f_2(z) = -f_1(z) \qquad\qquad \text{when } y > 0.$$

This last example illustrates the fact that in the process of analytic continuation from regions to adjacent regions the function and its continuation are not necessarily identical in all overlapping regions.

101. Natural Boundaries. Some analytic functions cannot be continued analytically across certain curves. Such a curve is called a *natural boundary* of the function.

As an example, the function

$$f(z) = 1 + \sum_{n=0}^{\infty} z^{2^n}$$

is analytic when $|z| < 1$, since the power series here converges when z is interior to that unit circle. But when p and q are any two positive integers, it can be shown that the limit of $f(z)$ does not exist as z approaches any one of the points $\exp(2\pi ip/2^q)$ from the interior of the circle.* Every arc of the circle, no matter how small its length, contains some of those points.

If an analytic continuation of $f(z)$ across the unit circle is possible, a function $F(z)$ must exist that is analytic throughout a neighborhood of

* See, for example, E. T. Copson, "Theory of Functions of a Complex Variable," p. 87. For another well-known example of a function that has a natural boundary, see E. C. Titchmarsh, "Theory of Functions," p. 159.

some point on the circle. However, $F(z)$ must be equal to $f(z)$ at all interior points of the unit circle that belong to that neighborhood. It follows that the limit of $F(z)$ as z approaches a point $\exp(2\pi i p/2^q)$ on the unit circle in that neighborhood could not exist. Therefore, $F(z)$ cannot be analytic throughout the neighborhood. Thus the unit circle is a natural boundary of the function $f(z)$.

102. The Principle of Reflection. In Chap. III we noted that some elementary functions $w = f(z)$ possess the property that $\bar{w} = f(\bar{z})$, and others do not. As examples of those that do, we can cite the functions

$$z, \qquad z^2 + 1, \qquad e^z, \qquad \sin z,$$

for when z is replaced by its conjugate, the value of each of these functions changes to the conjugate of the original value. On the other hand, the functions

$$iz, \qquad z^2 + i, \qquad e^{iz}, \qquad (1 + i)\sin z$$

do not satisfy this property that the reflection of z in the real axis corresponds to the reflection of w in the real axis.

The following theorem shows that an analytic function satisfies this *reflection principle* if and only if the function is real when z is real.

Theorem. *Let a function $w = f(z)$ be analytic in some region R that includes a segment of the x axis and is symmetric to the x axis. If $f(x)$ is real when x is a point of that segment, then*

$$f(\bar{z}) = \bar{w} \tag{1}$$

when z is a point in R. Conversely, if the condition (1) is satisfied then $f(x)$ is real.

Equation (1) represents the same condition on $f(z)$ as does the equation

$$\overline{f(\bar{z})} = f(z), \tag{2}$$

since the corresponding members of the two equations are the complex conjugates of each other. Now

$$\overline{f(\bar{z})} = u(x,-y) - iv(x,-y). \tag{3}$$

When condition (2) is satisfied at a point on the real axis, then

$$f(x) = u(x,0) + iv(x,0) = u(x,0) - iv(x,0);$$

consequently $v(x,0) = 0$ and $f(x)$ is real. The converse statement in the theorem is therefore true.

In order to prove the direct statement in the theorem, let us first show that the function $\overline{f(\bar{z})}$ is analytic throughout the region R. We write

$$F(z) = \overline{f(\bar{z})} = U(x,y) + iV(x,y).$$

Then, according to equation (3),

(4) $\qquad U(x,y) = u(x,\eta), \qquad V(x,y) = -v(x,\eta), \quad$ where $\eta = -y$.

Since $f(x + i\eta)$ is an analytic function of $x + i\eta$ in R, the functions $u(x,\eta)$, $v(x,\eta)$ and their partial derivatives are continuous and satisfy the Cauchy-Riemann conditions

$$\frac{\partial u}{\partial x} = \frac{\partial v}{\partial \eta}, \qquad \frac{\partial u}{\partial \eta} = -\frac{\partial v}{\partial x}$$

throughout R. Now in view of equations (4), we see that

$$\frac{\partial U}{\partial x} = \frac{\partial u}{\partial x}, \qquad \frac{\partial V}{\partial y} = -\frac{\partial v}{\partial \eta}\frac{\partial \eta}{\partial y} = \frac{\partial v}{\partial \eta},$$

and therefore $\partial U/\partial x = \partial V/\partial y$. Similarly we find that

$$\frac{\partial U}{\partial y} = -\frac{\partial V}{\partial x},$$

and it follows that the function $F(z)$ is analytic in the region R.

Since $f(x)$ is real, $v(x,0) = 0$, and therefore

$$F(x) = U(x,0) + iV(x,0) = u(x,0);$$

that is, $F(z) = f(z)$ when the point z is on the segment of the x axis within the region R. According to our theorem in Sec. 99, it follows that $F(z) = f(z)$ throughout R since both functions are analytic there. Thus $f(\bar{z}) = \overline{f(z)}$ in R, and the proof of the theorem is complete.

The following principle of reflection due to Schwarz and Riemann is closely related to the above one. Let a function $w = f(z)$ be analytic at all points of a closed region R that has a segment L of a straight line as a part of its boundary; also let $f(z)$ be such a function that the image of the segment L in the w plane, under the transformation $w = f(z)$, is a segment M of a straight line. Then if Z denotes the reflection of the point z in L, and W the reflection of w in M, the equation

$$W = f(Z)$$

represents the analytic continuation of $f(z)$ across L.

Proofs of this theorem will be found in several of the references listed in Appendix I.*

When L lies along the x axis and M along the u axis, this principle shows that the analyticity of $f(z)$ in a region above the x axis, together

---

* See, for example, Titchmarsh, *op. cit.*, p. 155. The condition of analyticity at all points in the closed region can be replaced by those of analyticity at interior points and continuity at points on L.

with the condition that $f(x)$ is real, leads to the conclusion that the function $\overline{f(\bar{z})}$ is the analytic continuation of $f(z)$ across the x axis into the reflected region.

103. The Zeros of Analytic Functions.   A zero of a function $f(z)$ is a number z_0 for which $f(z_0) = 0$.

If a function is analytic at a point z_0, there is a neighborhood of that point throughout which the function is represented by Taylor's series

$$(1) \qquad\qquad f(z) = a_0 + \sum_{n=1}^{\infty} a_n(z - z_0)^n,$$

where $a_0 = f(z_0)$ and $n!a_n = f^{(n)}(z_0)$.   When z_0 is a zero of $f(z)$, $a_0 = 0$. If, in addition to this,

$$(2) \qquad\qquad f'(z_0) = f''(z_0) = \cdots = f^{(m-1)}(z_0) = 0,$$

but $f^{(m)}(z_0) \neq 0$, then

$$(3) \qquad\qquad f(z) = (z - z_0)^m \sum_{n=0}^{\infty} a_{m+n}(z - z_0)^n \qquad (a_m \neq 0),$$

and z_0 is called a *zero of order m*.

Since the series (1) converges for all z in some neighborhood of z_0, the series

$$\sum_{n=0}^{\infty} a_{m+n}(z - z_0)^n = g(z)$$

converges there.   Note that $g(z_0) = a_m \neq 0$, and that if $m = 0$, then $g(z) = f(z)$ and z_0 is not a zero of $f(z)$.   It was shown in Sec. 61 that a convergent power series represents a continuous function.   Corresponding to each positive number ϵ, therefore, a positive number δ exists such that

$$|g(z) - a_m| < \epsilon \qquad\qquad \text{when } |z - z_0| < \delta.$$

If $\epsilon = |a_m|/2$ and δ_1 is the corresponding δ, we can write

$$||a_m| - |g(z)|| < \tfrac{1}{2}|a_m| \qquad\qquad \text{when } |z - z_0| < \delta_1.$$

It follows that $g(z) \neq 0$ at any point in the neighborhood $|z - z_0| < \delta_1$, otherwise the inequality here would be contradicted.   Thus we have established the following theorem:

Theorem.   *Unless a function is identically zero, about each point where the function is analytic there is a neighborhood throughout which the function is different from zero, except possibly at the point itself.*

The poles of a function were defined as particular kinds of isolated singular points.   The above theorem shows that *the zeros of an analytic function are isolated.* We have noted that the derivative of a quotient $p(z)/q(z)$ of two analytic functions exists at each point z_0 where $q(z_0) \neq 0$. It now follows that the derivative exists at all points in some neighborhood of that point, and thus the quotient is analytic at z_0. It also follows that if $q(z_0) = 0$, then z_0 is an isolated singular point of the quotient.

104. Essential Singular Points. When z_0 is a pole of order m of a function $f(z)$, then the function

$$(z - z_0)^m f(z)$$

has a removable singular point at z_0. It follows that $|f(z)|$ tends to infinity as z approaches z_0 in any manner.

The behavior of a function at an essential singular point is more complicated. We recall (Sec. 68) that an essential singularity z_0 is an isolated singular point such that the Laurent series representation of the function about that point in powers of $z - z_0$ contains an infinite number of negative power terms.* As z approaches z_0, the value of the function can be made to approach any prescribed complex number by a proper choice of the method of approach. This theorem, due to Weierstrass, can be stated more precisely as follows.

Theorem. *Let z_0 be an essential singular point of the function $f(z)$. Then for any given positive numbers ϵ and δ and for any given complex number w_1, there is a point z in the neighborhood $|z - z_0| < \delta$ at which $|f(z) - w_1| < \epsilon$.*

The reader can refer to references listed in Appendix I for the proof of this theorem of Weierstrass.†

EXERCISES

1. Give the analytic continuation of the function

$$f(z) = \sum_{n=0}^{\infty} (-1)^n z^{2n}$$

into the region beyond the interior of the unit circle $|z| = 1$.   *Ans.* $(1 + z^2)^{-1}$.

2. Show that the function z^{-2} represents the analytic continuation of the function

$$f(z) = \sum_{n=0}^{\infty} (n + 1)(z + 1)^n$$

beyond the region $|z + 1| < 1$.

---

* An *essential singular point* is often defined to be any singular point that is not a pole, whether or not it is an isolated singular point.

† See, for example, Titchmarsh, *op. cit.*, p. 93; K. Knopp, "Theory of Functions," Part 1, p. 124.

3. Find the analytic continuation of the function

$$f(z) = \int_0^\infty te^{-zt}\, dt$$

into the region on the left of the half plane $x > 0$.   *Ans.* z^{-2}.

4. If k is a real constant, show that the analytic continuation of the function

$$f(z) = \int_0^\infty e^{-zt} \sin kt\, dt \qquad\qquad (x > 0)$$

has simple poles at the points $z = \pm ik$.

5. In the theorem of Sec. 102, show that if the condition that $f(x)$ be real is replaced by the condition that $f(x)$ have pure imaginary values, the conclusion is changed to $\bar{w} = -f(\bar{z})$.

6. Show that the function $z^2 \sin z$ has a zero of order 3 at $z = 0$ and that its other zeros are of the first order.

7. If a function $f(z)$ has a zero of order m at z_0, prove that the function $1/f(z)$ has a pole of order m at z_0.

8. Let $f(z)$ and $g(z)$ be two functions that are analytic at a point z_0, and let $z_1, z_2, \cdots$ be an infinite set of points having z_0 as a limit point. Prove that if $f(z_n) = g(z_n)$ $(n = 1,2, \cdots)$, then $f(z) = g(z)$ at all points in some neighborhood of z_0. With the aid of this result, generalize the theorem in Sec. 99.

9. Write Cauchy's integral formula for an analytic function $f(z)$ when the curve C is the circle $z = r_0 e^{i\theta'}$, where $z = r e^{i\theta}$ is any point inside C. Note that when z is replaced by its inverse $z = r_1 e^{i\theta}$ with respect to the circle, where $r_1 r = r_0^2$, the integral in the formula vanishes. Subtract that integral from the integral in Cauchy's integral formula to derive the equation

$$f(re^{i\theta}) = \frac{1}{2\pi} \int_0^{2\pi} \frac{f(r_0 e^{i\theta'})(r_0^2 - r^2)d\theta'}{r_0^2 - 2r_0 r \cos(\theta' - \theta) + r^2}.$$

Identify real parts here to arrive at *Poisson's integral formula*

$$u(r,\theta) = \frac{1}{2\pi} \int_0^{2\pi} \frac{u(r_0,\theta')(r_0^2 - r^2)d\theta'}{r_0^2 - 2r_0 r \cos(\theta' - \theta) + r^2},$$

a formula that gives the values of a harmonic function $u(x,y)$ at points inside the circle in terms of the values of the function on the circle.

CHAPTER XII

RIEMANN SURFACES

A Riemann surface is a generalization of the z plane into a surface of more than one sheet such that a multiple-valued function has only one value corresponding to each point on that surface. Once such a surface is devised for a given function, that function is a single-valued function of points on the surface, and the theory of single-valued functions can be used in dealing with the function. The complexities arising because the function is multiple-valued are thus removed by means of a geometrical device; but the latter is not always easily devised, nor is it always a simple surface to describe.

We limit our treatment of Riemann surfaces to the discussion of several simple examples. For many functions, the arrangement of the proper connections between the sheets in order to describe a Riemann surface becomes quite involved and requires considerable ingenuity. The reader can refer to other books for a broader treatment of the subject.*

105. A Surface for the Function log z. Corresponding to each point other than the origin in the z plane, the function

$$(1) \qquad\qquad w = \log z = \operatorname{Log} r + i\theta$$

has infinitely many values. In order to describe this function as a single-valued function of a point, we may replace the z plane by a surface on which a new point is represented whenever the argument of the point z is increased or decreased by 2π.

Consider the z plane as a thin sheet R_0, which is cut along the positive half of the x axis. On that sheet let θ range from zero to 2π. Let a second sheet R_1 be cut in the same way and placed in front of the sheet R_0. The lower edge of the slit in R_0 is then joined to the upper edge of the slit in R_1. On R_1 the angle θ ranges from 2π to 4π, so that when z represents a point on R_1, the imaginary coefficient of log z has a value between 2π and 4π.

A sheet R_2 is then cut in the same way and placed in front of R_1, and the lower edge of the slit in R_1 is joined to the upper edge of the slit in this

---

* Forsyth, A. R., "Theory of Functions of a Complex Variable," Chaps. 15 and 16; Townsend, E. J., "Functions of a Complex Variable," Chap. 8; Knopp, K., "Theory of Functions," Part 2, Chaps. 4–6.

new sheet, and similarly for sheets R_3, R_4, $\cdots$. A sheet R_{-1} on which θ varies from zero to -2π is cut and placed behind R_0, with the lower edge of its slit connected to the upper edge of the slit in R_0; similarly for the sheet R_{-2}, etc. The coordinates r and θ of a point on any sheet can be taken as the polar coordinates of the projection of the point on the original z plane, except that the angular coordinate θ is restricted to a definite range of 2π radians on each sheet. The origin is a point common to all the sheets.

Consider any continuous curve on this connected surface of infinitely many sheets, a curve that does not pass through the origin. As a point

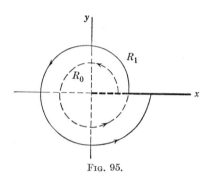

FIG. 95.

z moves over that curve, the values of the function log z vary continuously, since θ varies continuously, and the function assumes just one value corresponding to each point on the curve. As the point makes a complete cycle around the origin in the sheet R_0, for example, over the path indicated in Fig. 95, the angle changes from zero to 2π. As it moves across the line $\theta = 2\pi$, the point passes to the sheet R_1 of the surface. As the point completes a cycle in R_1, the angle θ varies from 2π to 4π, and as it crosses the line $\theta = 4\pi$, the point passes to the sheet R_2.

The surface described here is a Riemann surface for the function log z, a connected surface of more than one sheet so defined that this multiple-valued function of points in the z plane is a single-valued function of points on that surface.

The single-valued function $w = \text{Log } z$ maps the entire z plane upon the strip $-\pi < v \leqq \pi$ in the w plane, since $-\pi < \theta \leqq \pi$ for the principal value of the function (1). The multiple-valued function (1) maps all the sheets of the above Riemann surface upon the entire w plane, with a one-to-one correspondence between points on the

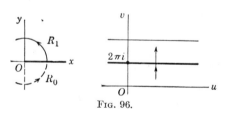

FIG. 96.

surface and points on the w plane. The image of the sheet R_0 is the strip $0 \leqq v \leqq 2\pi$. As the point z moves into the sheet R_1 over the arc shown in Fig. 96, its image w moves upward across the line $v = 2\pi$ as indicated in the figure.

Note that the function w in the strip $2\pi \leqq v \leqq 4\pi$ represents the analytic continuation of the single-valued analytic function

$$w = \operatorname{Log} r + i\theta \qquad\qquad (0 < \theta < 2\pi)$$

upward across the positive x axis. In this sense, the function (1) is not only a single-valued function of all points z on the Riemann surface, but it is also an analytic function at all points except the origin.

The sheets could, of course, be cut along the negative x axis, or along any other half line starting at the origin, and properly joined along the slits to form other Riemann surfaces for the function $\log z$.

106. A Surface for the Function $z^{\frac{1}{2}}$. The function

$$z^{\frac{1}{2}} = \sqrt{r}\left(\cos\frac{\theta}{2} + i \sin\frac{\theta}{2}\right)$$

has two values corresponding to each point, except the origin, in the z plane. Let the plane be replaced by two sheets R_0 and R_1, each of which is cut along the positive x axis, with R_1 placed in front of R_0. Join the lower edge of the slit in R_0 to the upper edge of the slit in R_1, and the lower edge of the slit in R_1 to the upper edge of the slit in R_0. The two sheets therefore cross each other at the cut.

As the point z describes a continuous circuit (Fig. 97) about the origin on that surface, the angle θ grows from zero to 2π, and then the point passes from the sheet R_0 to the sheet R_1, where θ grows from 2π to 4π. As the point moves still farther, it passes back to the sheet R_0 where the values of θ vary either from 4π to 6π or from zero to 2π, a choice that does not effect the value of the function $z^{\frac{1}{2}}$, etc. The function is a single-valued function of points on this surface except that some more artificial device is needed to distinguish between points of the two sheets along the cut.

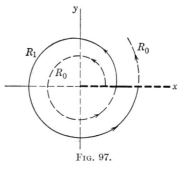

Fig. 97.

The image of the sheet R_0 of this Riemann surface for the function $z^{\frac{1}{2}}$ is the upper half of the w plane, since

$$w = \rho e^{i\phi} = \sqrt{r}\, e^{i\theta/2},$$

and $0 \leqq \theta/2 \leqq \pi$ on R_0. The image of the sheet R_1 is the lower half of the w plane. As defined on either sheet, the function is the analytic continuation across the cut of the function defined on the other sheet.

In this respect, this single-valued function $z^{\frac{1}{2}}$ of points on the Riemann surface is analytic at all points except the origin.

107. Other Irrational Functions. Let us describe a Riemann surface for the double-valued function

$$(1) \qquad f(z) = [(z-1)(z-3)]^{\frac{1}{2}} = \sqrt{\rho_1\rho_2} \exp\left(i\,\frac{\phi_1 + \phi_2}{2}\right)$$

discussed in Sec. 39. The polar coordinates are those indicated in Fig. 23. The points $z = 1$ and $z = 3$ are branch points of this function. As noted before, the line segment L joining those points is a branch cut for the branch of the function that is obtained by limiting the angles ϕ_1 and ϕ_2 to a range from zero to 2π. That branch of the function is single-valued and analytic everywhere except at points on L. As the point z crosses L, the angle ϕ_1 jumps in value by the amount 2π, and the angle ϕ_2 varies continuously so that the value of that branch of the function $f(z)$ changes sign; thus the branch is not continuous at points on L.

The Riemann surface for the function (1) must consist of two sheets R_0 and R_1. Let them both be cut along the line segment L, and let the lower edge of the slit in R_0 be joined to the upper edge of the slit in R_1, and the lower edge in R_1 to the upper edge in R_0. The two sheets of the continuous surface so formed cross each other along the segment L, so that a point can move continuously from one sheet to the other by crossing that segment, and only in that way.

Let the sheet R_0 be the one on which each of the angles ϕ_1 and ϕ_2 may have values Φ_1 and Φ_2 ranging from zero to 2π. However, at any point on R_0 the value of both angles simultaneously may be increased or decreased by 2π, since the function $f(z)$ will have the same value as before. That change in the angles corresponds to a movement of the point z from its original position around any curve enclosing the entire segment L and back to its original position. Likewise, the value of either ϕ_1 or ϕ_2 can be increased by 4π, if the other angle is left unchanged, without affecting the value of $f(z)$, a change that corresponds to moving the point z over a curve twice around just one of the branch points and back to its original position. In general, for each point on R_0, the angles ϕ_1 and ϕ_2 have the values

$$\phi_1 = \Phi_1 + 2\pi n_1, \qquad \phi_2 = \Phi_2 + 2\pi n_2,$$

where the positive or negative integers n_1 and n_2 are both even or both odd, so that their sum is an even integer. Here zero is to be included among the even integers.

If the integers n_1 and n_2 are not both even or both odd, the angles

$$\phi_1 = \Phi_1 + 2\pi n_1, \qquad \phi_2 = \Phi_2 + 2\pi n_2$$

are coordinates of points on the sheet R_1.   The point whose coordinates are $\phi_1 = \pi/4$, $\phi_2 = 5\pi/2$, for example, is a point on R_1.

The function (1) has just one value corresponding to each point on the Riemann surface consisting of the two sheets R_0 and R_1, except for points on the segment L.   Since the position of all points on R_0 can be described with the angles Φ_1 and Φ_2, whose range is from zero to 2π, the argument $(\phi_1 + \phi_2)/2$ of $f(z)$ ranges from zero to 2π, and so the transformation $w = f(z)$ maps that sheet into the entire w plane.   Similarly, it maps R_1 into the entire w plane.

As another example, consider the double-valued function

$$(2) \qquad g(z) = [z(z^2 - 1)]^{\frac{1}{2}} = \sqrt{r\rho_1\rho_2} \exp\left(i\,\frac{\theta + \phi_1 + \phi_2}{2}\right)$$

(Fig. 98).   The points $z = 0$, $z = \pm 1$ are branch points of this function.

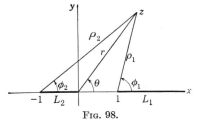

Fig. 98.

We note that if the point z describes a circuit that includes all three of those points, the argument of $g(z)$ changes by the angle 3π, and hence the value of the function changes. Therefore, a branch cut must be run from one of those branch points to infinity in order to describe a single-valued branch of $g(z)$.   Thus the infinite point is a branch point, as we can show also by writing $z = 1/Z$ and noting that $g(1/Z)$ has a branch point at $Z = 0$.

Let two sheets be cut along the line segment L_2 from $z = -1$ to $z = 0$ and along the part L_1 of the real axis on the right of the point $z = 1$. On the sheet R_0 we specify that each of the three angles θ, ϕ_1, and ϕ_2 may range from zero to 2π, and on R_1 from 2π to 4π; but we add the specification that the angles corresponding to a point on either sheet may be increased or diminished by multiples of 2π in such a way the sum of the three angles changes by a multiple of 4π, so that the value of the function $g(z)$ is not altered.

If we connect the edges of the slits along L_1 and L_2 crosswise, that is, if along L_1 we join the lower edge in R_0 to the upper edge in R_1, etc., so that whenever a point crosses either L_1 or L_2, it moves from one sheet to the other, a Riemann surface for the function $g(z)$ is formed.   The reader can verify with the aid of Fig. 98 that one branch of the function is represented by its values at points on R_0 and the other branch at points on R_1, and that the values change to those of the other branch when and only when the point crosses either L_1 or L_2.

EXERCISES

1. Describe a Riemann surface for the triple-valued function

$$w = (z - 1)^{\frac{1}{3}},$$

and point out which third of the w plane represents the image of each sheet of the surface.

2. Describe the image, on a Riemann surface, of the entire circle $|w| = 1$ under the transformation $w = z^{\frac{1}{3}}$.

3. It was pointed out in the preceding section that although a single value of the function

$$w = [(z - 1)(z - 3)]^{\frac{1}{2}}$$

corresponds to each point z on the Riemann surface, there are two points z corresponding to each value of w, in general. Show in another way why this is so.

4. Corresponding to each point on the Riemann surface described in the preceding section for the function $w = g(z)$, there is just one value of w. Show that corresponding to each value of w there are in general three points on the surface.

5. Describe a Riemann surface for the function

$$w = \left(\frac{z - 1}{z}\right)^{\frac{1}{2}}.$$

6. Let C denote the circle $|z - 2| = 1$ on the Riemann surface described in Sec. 106 for the function $z^{\frac{1}{2}}$, where the upper half of that circle lies in the sheet R_0 and the lower half in R_1. State why it is true that

$$\int_C z^{\frac{1}{2}} \, dz = 0.$$

Generalize this result to fit the case of other closed curves that cross from one sheet to another without enclosing the branch points, and generalize to other functions, thus extending the Cauchy-Goursat theorem to integrals of multiple-valued functions.

7. Describe a Riemann surface for the function $(z^2 - 1)^{\frac{1}{2}}$ with its sheets connected along the line segment L connecting the two branch points $z = \pm 1$, and note that this is also a Riemann surface for the function defined by either of the equations

$$w = z + (z^2 - 1)^{\frac{1}{2}}, \qquad z = \frac{1}{2}\left(w + \frac{1}{w}\right).$$

If $g_0(z)$ denotes the branch of $(z^2 - 1)^{\frac{1}{2}}$ defined on the sheet R_0, show that the branches w_0 and w_1 of w on the two sheets are given by the equations

$$w_0 = \frac{1}{w_1} = z + g_0(z).$$

Show that the transformation $z = \frac{1}{2}(w + 1/w)$ maps one sheet of the Riemann z surface into the region $|w| \geq 1$, the other into the region $|w| \leq 1$, and the segment L into the circle $|w| = 1$ (compare Exercise 9, Sec. 43).

APPENDIX I

BIBLIOGRAPHY

The following list of books on the theory of functions of complex variables and its various applications is far from exhaustive. Further references can be found in many of the books listed here.

Bateman, H.: "Partial Differential Equations of Mathematical Physics," Cambridge University Press, London, 1932, and Dover Publications, New York, 1944.

Bieberbach, L.: "Einführung in die konforme Abbildung," Walter De Gruyter & Company, Berlin, 1927.

Burkhardt, H.: "Theory of Functions of a Complex Variable," translated by S. E. Rasor, D. C. Heath and Company, Boston, 1913.

Caratheodory, C.: "Conformal Representation," Cambridge University Press, London, 1932.

Carslaw, H. S., and J. C. Jaeger: "Operational Methods in Applied Mathematics," Oxford University Press, New York, 1941.

————: "Conduction of Heat in Solids," Oxford University Press, New York, 1947.

Churchill, R. V.: "Modern Operational Mathematics in Engineering," McGraw-Hill Book Company, Inc., New York, 1944.

Copson, E. T.: "Theory of Functions of a Complex Variable," Oxford University Press, New York, 1935.

Curtiss, D. R.: "Analytic Functions of a Complex Variable," The Open Court Publishing Company, La Salle, Ill., 1926.

Forsyth, A. R.: "Theory of Functions of a Complex Variable," Cambridge University Press, London, 1893.

Glauert, H.: "Aerofoil and Airscrew Theory," Cambridge University Press, London, 1926.

Goursat, E.: "Mathematical Analysis," translated by E. R. Hedrick and O. Dunkel, Vol. II, Part 1, Ginn & Company, Boston, 1916.

Green, S. L.: "Theory and Use of the Complex Variable," Sir Isaac Pitman & Sons, Ltd., London, 1939.

————: "Hydro- and Aero-dynamics," Sir Isaac Pitman & Sons, Ltd., London, 1937.

Hurwitz, A., and R. Courant: "Vorlesungen über allgemeine Funktionentheorie und elliptische Funktionen," Verlag Julius Springer, Berlin, 1925.

Jeans, J. H.: "Mathematical Theory of Electricity and Magnetism," Cambridge University Press, London, 1925.

Kellogg, O. D.: "Foundations of Potential Theory," Verlag Julius Springer, Berlin, 1929.

Kober, H.: "Dictionary of Conformal Representations," Admiralty Computing Service, British Admiralty, London, 1945.

Knopp, K.: "Funktionentheorie," Parts 1 and 2, Sammlung Göschen Nr. 668 and 703; 1930, 1931. English translation by F. Bagemihl, Dover Publications, New York, 1947.

Lamb, H.: "Hydrodynamics," Cambridge University Press, 1932, and Dover Publications, 1945.

Love, A. E. H.: "Elasticity," Cambridge University Press, London, 1927.

McLachlan, N. W.: "Complex Variable and Operational Calculus with Technical Applications," Cambridge University Press, London, and The Macmillan Company, New York, 1942.

MacRobert, T. M.: "Functions of a Complex Variable," Macmillan & Co., Ltd., London, 1933.

Milne-Thomson, L. M.: "Theoretical Hydrodynamics," Macmillan & Co., Ltd., London, 1938.

Mises, R. v., and K. O. Friedrichs: "Fluid Dynamics," Brown University Notes, Providence, 1942.

Osgood, W. F.: "Functions of a Complex Variable," G. E. Stechert & Company, New York, 1938.

Phillips, E. G.: "Functions of a Complex Variable with Applications," Oliver and Boyd, Edinburgh, 1940; Interscience Publishers, Inc., New York, 1943.

Pierpont, J.: "Functions of a Complex Variable," Ginn & Company, Boston, 1914.

Rothe, R., F. Ollendorff, and K. Pohlhausen: "Theory of Functions as Applied to Engineering Problems," Technology Press, Massachusetts Institute of Technology, Cambridge, Mass., 1942.

Sokolnikoff, I. S., and R. D. Specht: "Mathematical Theory of Elasticity," McGraw-Hill Book Company, Inc., New York, 1946.

Sternberg, W. J., and T. L. Smith: "Theory of Potential and Spherical Harmonics," University of Toronto Press, Toronto, 1944.

Titchmarsh, E. C.: "Theory of Functions," Oxford University Press, New York, 1939.

Townsend, E. J.: "Functions of a Complex Variable," Henry Holt and Company, Incorporated, New York, 1915.

Walker, M.: "Conjugate Functions for Engineers," Oxford University Press, New York, 1933.

Whittaker, E. T., and G. N. Watson: "Modern Analysis," Cambridge University Press, London, 1927.

APPENDIX II

TABLE OF TRANSFORMATIONS OF REGIONS
(See Sec. 43)

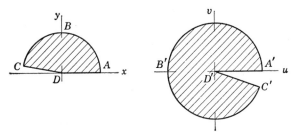

FIG. 1. $w = z^2$.

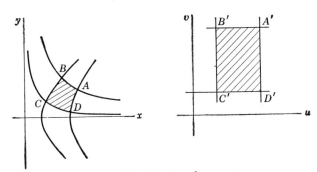

FIG. 2. $w = z^2$.

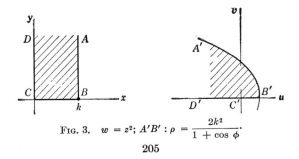

FIG. 3. $w = z^2$; $A'B' : \rho = \dfrac{2k^2}{1 + \cos \phi}$.

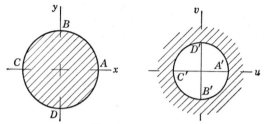

Fig. 4. $w = 1/z$.

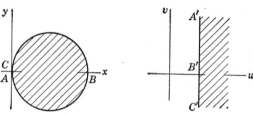

Fig. 5. $w = 1/z$.

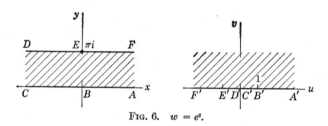

Fig. 6. $w = e^z$.

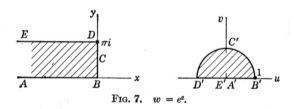

Fig. 7. $w = e^z$.

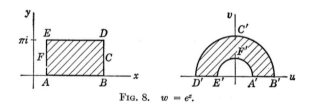

Fig. 8. $w = e^z$.

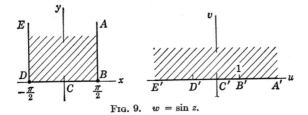

FIG. 9. $w = \sin z$.

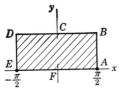
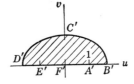

FIG. 10. $w = \sin z$.

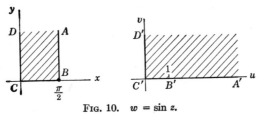

FIG. 11. $w = \sin z$; BCD: $y = k$, $B'C'D'$: $\left(\dfrac{u}{\cosh k}\right)^2 + \left(\dfrac{v}{\sinh k}\right)^2 = 1$.

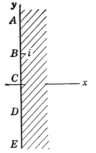
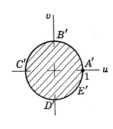

FIG. 12. $w = \dfrac{z-1}{z+1}$.

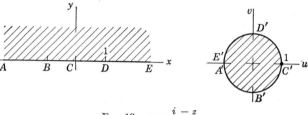

Fig. 13. $w = \dfrac{i - z}{i + z}$.

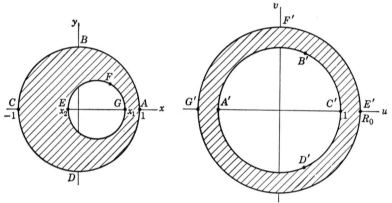

Fig. 14. $w = \dfrac{z - a}{az - 1}$; $a = \dfrac{1 + x_1 x_2 + \sqrt{(1 - x_1{}^2)(1 - x_2{}^2)}}{x_1 + x_2}$;

$R_0 = \dfrac{1 - x_1 x_2 + \sqrt{(1 - x_1{}^2)(1 - x_2{}^2)}}{x_1 - x_2}$, $(a > 1$ and $R_0 > 1$ when $-1 < x_2 < x_1 < 1)$.

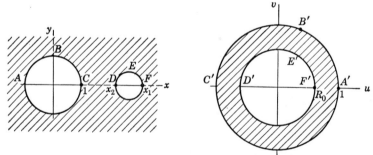

Fig. 15. $w = \dfrac{z - a}{az - 1}$; $a = \dfrac{1 + x_1 x_2 + \sqrt{(x_1{}^2 - 1)(x_2{}^2 - 1)}}{x_1 + x_2}$,

$R_0 = \dfrac{x_1 x_2 - 1 - \sqrt{(x_1{}^2 - 1)(x_2{}^2 - 1)}}{x_1 - x_2}$, $(x_2 < a < x_1$ and $0 < R_0 < 1$ when $1 < x_2 < x_1)$.

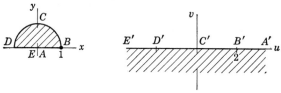

FIG. 16. $w = z + 1/z$.

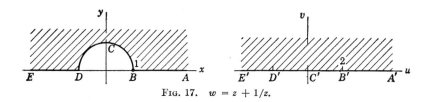

FIG. 17. $w = z + 1/z$.

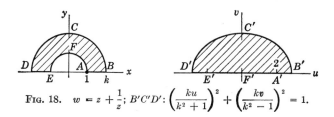

FIG. 18. $w = z + \dfrac{1}{z}$; $B'C'D'$: $\left(\dfrac{ku}{k^2 + 1}\right)^2 + \left(\dfrac{kv}{k^2 - 1}\right)^2 = 1$.

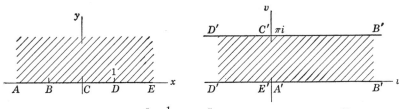

FIG. 19. $w = \operatorname{Log}\dfrac{z - 1}{z + 1} = \operatorname{Log}\dfrac{r_1}{r_2} + i(\theta_1 - \theta_2)$; $z = -\coth\dfrac{w}{2}$.

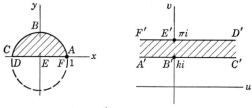

FIG. 20. $w = \operatorname{Log}\dfrac{z - 1}{z + 1}$; ABC: $x^2 + y^2 - 2y \cot k = 1$.

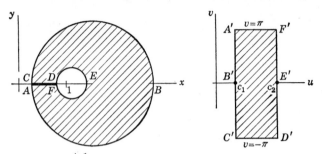

FIG. 21. $w = \operatorname{Log}\dfrac{z + 1}{z - 1}$; centers of circles at $z = \coth c_n$, radii: $\operatorname{csch} c_n\,(n = 1, 2)$.

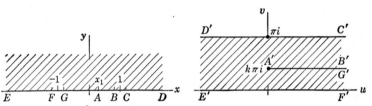

FIG. 22. $w = k\,\operatorname{Log}\dfrac{k}{1 - k} + \operatorname{Log} 2(1 - k) + i\pi - k\,\operatorname{Log}\,(z + 1) - (1 - k)\,\operatorname{Log}\,(z - 1)$;
$x_1 = 2k - 1$.

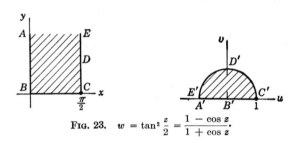

FIG. 23. $w = \tan^2\dfrac{z}{2} = \dfrac{1 - \cos z}{1 + \cos z}$.

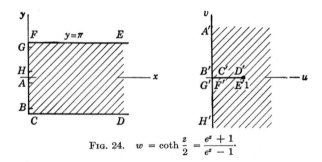

FIG. 24. $w = \coth\dfrac{z}{2} = \dfrac{e^z + 1}{e^z - 1}$.

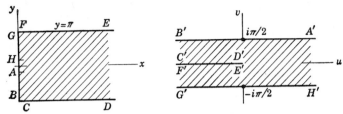

FIG. 25. $w = \text{Log coth} \dfrac{z}{2}$.

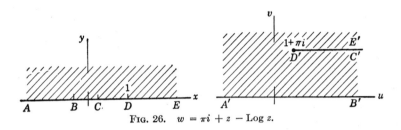

FIG. 26. $w = \pi i + z - \text{Log } z$.

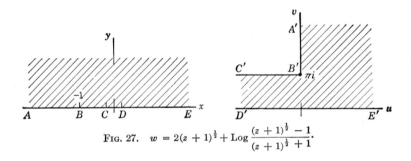

FIG. 27. $w = 2(z+1)^{\frac{1}{2}} + \text{Log} \dfrac{(z+1)^{\frac{1}{2}} - 1}{(z+1)^{\frac{1}{2}} + 1}$.

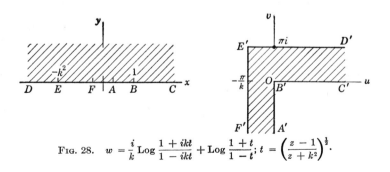

FIG. 28. $w = \dfrac{i}{k} \text{Log} \dfrac{1 + ikt}{1 - ikt} + \text{Log} \dfrac{1+t}{1-t}; \ t = \left(\dfrac{z-1}{z+k^2}\right)^{\frac{1}{2}}$.

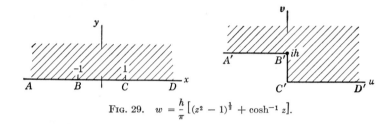

Fig. 29. $w = \dfrac{h}{\pi}\left[(z^2 - 1)^{\frac{1}{2}} + \cosh^{-1} z\right].$

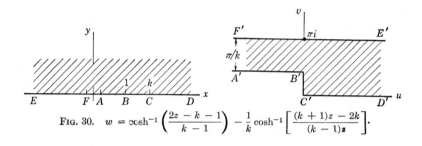

Fig. 30. $w = \cosh^{-1}\left(\dfrac{2z - k - 1}{k - 1}\right) - \dfrac{1}{k}\cosh^{-1}\left[\dfrac{(k + 1)z - 2k}{(k - 1)z}\right].$

INDEX